ELEMENTS OF
PLASMA PHYSICS

ELEMENTS OF
PLASMA PHYSICS

SOLOMON GARTENHAUS
Purdue University

HOLT, RINEHART AND WINSTON
NEW YORK · CHICAGO · SAN FRANCISCO · TORONTO · LONDON

PREFACE

The main purpose of this book is to provide to the research minded student an introduction to the theory of the physics of a fully ionized gas, and thereby to enable him to make the transition to and to profit from the rapidly expanding literature in this field. Primarily, it is intended that this volume be used as a text for a one-semester, graduate-level course. Although the book itself is relatively self-contained, it is assumed that the student has the "physics maturity" that is usually associated with second- to third-year graduate students and in particular has had some experience — at an advanced level — with subjects such as electromagnetic theory, classical mechanics, statistical mechanics, and kinetic theory.

Throughout the text much of the emphasis has been placed on deriving the working equations from first principles. For although one can find in the literature many applications of various forms of these equations, it is the author's feeling that most often the beginner is overwhelmed by the many seemingly different theoretical approaches that are possible and consequently needs guidance in making an intelligent choice among these for the particular application in mind. For purposes of developing the needed intuitive ideas, moreover, a substantial number of applications are included in the text and form the basis of some of the problems at the end of each chapter. In addition to expanding the text material, the purpose of these problems is also to enable the student to measure his comprehension and in some cases to be provoked into original thinking.

By and large, the first two chapters are a rather elementary review of electromagnetic theory and classical mechanics. In particular the motions of charged particles in various magnetic field configurations are examined and an introduction to orbit theory and the notion of an adiabatic invariant is also included. The third chapter then contains a discussion of Liouville's theorem for a collection of charged particles and develops the necessary statistical notions required to describe a plasma by means of distribution functions. After a heuristic derivation of the Boltzmann-Vlasov equation, Chapter 4 continues with the derivation of the BV equation by use of the method of Rostoker and Rosenbluth and the analysis is carried out sufficiently far so that explicit first-order corrections to this equation are produced. Chapter 5 then contains a discussion of magnetohydrodynamics with emphasis being placed on their derivation from the BV equation and the assumptions required to produce a closed system of equations. Also included in this chapter is a discussion of the method of Chew, Goldberger, and Low. Finally in Chapter 6 a more detailed analysis of plasma oscillations is presented.

Various references will be found at the end of each chapter. These are not intended as an exhaustive bibliography, nor has any effort been made to give the original sources. Rather, these references are ones that the author found particularly helpful in preparing this volume and ones that, in addition, will be most useful to beginners in the field.

This book is based upon a course in plasma physics that the author gave at Florida State University during the summers of 1960 and 1961 and subsequently at Purdue University. It is a pleasure to acknowledge the help of several people who have been helpful in the preparation of various parts of this manuscript and have otherwise aided in its preparation. In particular the author is indebted to Roger A. Holmes for the many suggestions made throughout the writing and to Richard L. Liboff for a critical reading of the final manuscript. For excellent secretarial help, an acknowledgement is due to Louisa Spencer for the typing of various parts of a preliminary version and to Bettye Hunter for the typing of the final manuscript. Finally, to my wife Johanna, I am grateful, not only for help in the typing, but also for her patience throughout the preparation of this volume.

JANUARY, 1964   S.G.
LAFAYETTE, INDIANA

CONTENTS

ELEMENTS OF
PLASMA PHYSICS

1

Maxwell's Equations

INTRODUCTION:
BASIC CONCEPTS AND DEFINITIONS

One very convenient and useful classification of matter in its various forms is on the basis of its interaction with electric and magnetic fields. For the present we are interested in the behavior of matter in electric fields; and for this case the more familiar categories are *electrets*, *dielectrics*, and *conductors*.

An *electret* is a solid material that has a permanent electric dipole moment per unit volume and, consequently, is always with an electric field. From the microscopic point of view, an electret consists of permanent electric dipoles that are oriented in some regular (not entirely random) way so that a macroscopic dipole moment is observed.

A *dielectric*, on the other hand, is a material that produces no electric field in its normal state. When it is placed into an external field, however, the molecules, of which the dielectric is composed, become polarized, and the resulting dipoles tend to line up with the field. In this way the external field becomes modified. The modifications that occur in a dielectric as a result of its being put into an electric field can usually be simply described in terms of an induced macroscopic electric dipole moment per unit volume which in turn depends upon the modified electric field. For many materials the induced dipole moment per unit volume is proportional to the modified field (the constant of proportionality is called the electric susceptibility) while for a few (for example, ferroelectric materials), the relationship is not as simple.

A *conductor* is a material that may be thought of as consisting of a fixed lattice of massive, positively charged particles (ions) and of relatively lighter, negatively charged electrons which are free to roam around in the lattice. The electrons will therefore respond almost instantaneously to any electric field and will attempt to nullify this field in the interior of the conductor. By making the conductor part of an electric circuit, however, the electric field may be sustained and thus it would seem at first that since the electrons are constantly being accelerated they could gain large amounts of energy. The fact that the electrons do not beome very energetic is due to the continual loss of energy to the lattice by collisions with it. This energy ultimately shows up as ohmic heating in the conductor. The phenomenon is characterized macroscopically by ascribing to the material a property called its *conductivity*; this may be defined as the flow of current per unit area per unit impressed electric field. Ohm's law is the statement of the empirical fact that for most materials the conductivity is independent of the field strength. With regard to the question of the number of free electrons in a conductor, the answer is that this number can vary between 1 electron for each ion in a very good conductor to 1 electron for each 10^{15} ions in a very poor one.

Perhaps not as familiar as the solid conductor just described is the liquid conductor—for example, mercury at room temperature. In this case the very massive ions are also free to move under the impressed electric field and thus we become involved in the bulk properties (mass motion) of the liquid as well as its electrical properties. In this connection it is important to realize that the ions are of the order of 10^5 times heavier than the electrons. For the case of a solid conductor inertial effects can usually be neglected since the electrons are so light; but this is not the case for a liquid conductor. For the latter, the description must be made not only in terms of its electrical behaviour, but must also be supplemented by the equations of motion for a fluid—that is, the equations of hydrodynamics. *Magnetohydrodynamics* may be defined as the study of this interaction between an electrically conducting fluid and the electromagnetic field. The fact that this subject is very complex is easily apparent. For when the liquid is in the presence of an electromagnetic field, currents are induced, and these not only modify the field but also experience forces due to this field, and, in turn, the resulting motions modify the current, and so forth.

A *plasma* may be defined as an electrically charged gas consisting of ions and electrons. It is therefore also a conductor. The distinction between a liquid conductor and a plasma is not very precise and can be made most easily in terms of particle densities. When speaking of a liquid conductor, we shall usually be talking in terms of the order of 10^{22} charged particles per cubic centimeter, while for plasmas this number is of order 10^{18} and lower. Thus, a plasma is to be thought of as a gaseous conductor.

Actually the idealization that has just been described as a plasma rarely occurs in nature. As a rule neutral atoms are always present, if for no other reason than because electrons are constantly being captured by ions with the emission of characteristic radiation. We shall assume, therefore, that the effects of these neutrals are negligible and play no important role. Further, in the presence of electromagnetic fields, charged particles are accelerated and, as a result, lose energy and momentum to the radiation field. These losses are often unimportant and will be essentially ignored. Similarly, we shall neglect all quantum effects; these turn out to be important only at very high densities and very low temperatures. Thus, for our purposes a plasma will be thought of as a gas consisting exclusively of (classical) ions and electrons that interact with each other by means of their mutual Coulomb and magnetic forces (and with any external electromagnetic fields) but not with the radiation field. These restrictions still leave open a wide variety of very interesting and physically observable phenomena, and our efforts will be directed at these.

While on this subject, let us also briefly examine the possible influence of relativistic effects. In most situations of interest, the velocities of the electrons are small compared to that of light, and thus relativistic effects can be safely ignored. In this connection, one often talks in terms of a particle temperature for which a useful conversion unit is that at room temperature (300 °K), $kT \sim 1/40$ ev, where k is Boltzmann's constant and 1 ev $\sim 1.6 \times 10^{-12}$ ergs. Since for a gas, $kT \simeq$ kinetic energy per particle, we see that a 1 kev electron corresponds to a temperature 10^7 °K, and the electron moves with velocity $\sim 1/30$ that of light. Relativistic corrections which are usually of the order of $(v/c)^2 \sim 10^{-3}$ are therefore indeed negligible. When the temperature becomes an order of magnitude or two above this value, however, the theory of relativity must be used. Our discussions will therefore be confined to these lower temperatures. Of course, there is rarely any problem with the ions since, for example, a proton becomes a relativistic particle only at temperatures of order 10^{13} °K.

One very important parameter often used in defining various domains of plasma physics is the collision frequency ω_c. For a solid conductor this is defined as the average number of times per second that an electron collides (in the kinetic theory sense) with the ions. The average distance traveled between collisions is called the *mean free path*. It is intuitively evident that the collision frequency varies inversely with the conductivity. A precise form of this relationship may be obtained by use of an argument originally due to Drude. As a given electron in the conductor starts to accelerate under the action of an electric field, it suffers repeated collisions with the ions and in this process loses energy. The actual trajectory of the electron is very complex and jagged. When looked at from a macroscopic point of view, however, the electron seems to drift in the direction of the electric field lines with a uniform velocity. Thus we can say that in addition to the electric field, the electron must experience a frictional force that just balances the electric field. Assuming that this frictional force is proportional to the product of the drift velocity and the collision frequency, we may write

$$m\omega_c \mathbf{v} = e\mathbf{E}_0 \tag{1.1}$$

where $\mathbf{E}_0$ is the impressed field, $\mathbf{v}$ is the drift velocity, e is the electronic charge, and m is the electronic mass whose presence is demanded at least by dimensional arguments. The current density $\mathbf{j}$ may be expressed in terms of the drift velocity by the formula

$$\mathbf{j} = ne\mathbf{v} \tag{1.2}$$

where n is the number of electrons per unit volume. Substituting eq. (1.2) into eq. (1.1) we find

$$\mathbf{j} = \frac{ne^2}{m\omega_c}\mathbf{E}_0$$

or what is the same thing

$$\sigma = \frac{ne^2}{m\omega_c} \tag{1.3}$$

This is the well-known and frequently used relationship between conductivity and collision frequency. Actually, of course, since ω_c is not itself directly measurable, this relationship, strictly speaking, should be interpreted as the definition of ω_c. In many cases, however, one can estimate ω_c for given physical systems and thereby make use of eq. (1.3) to predict the conductivity.

It is clear from this discussion that eq. (1.3) can be expected to be valid only when the frequency of the impressed field is very small compared to ω_c. For if the frequency of the electric field is of order ω_c, then the electrons accelerate and decelerate between collisions, and inertial effects must be taken into account. In the problems it is shown that if the electric field has a time dependence $e^{-i\omega t}$, then eq. (1.3) becomes modified to

$$\sigma = \frac{ne^2}{m(\omega_c - i\omega)} \tag{1.4}$$

which shows that in this case the current density and the field are not even in phase. It should be clear from the above derivation, moreover, that the concept of conductivity itself becomes obscure at frequencies much greater than ω_c.

As a final note, let us examine the concept of a "collision" somewhat critically. Because of the long-range nature of the Coulomb force, the notion of a collision in a plasma apparently means something different than it does in the kinetic theory of gases, where the collisions can usually be thought of as the "billiard ball" variety. In the case of a plasma it would appear that many particles are colliding with each other simultaneously, and the validity of the assumption of binary collisions that we have implicitly assumed above would be in doubt. We shall find later, however, that in a plasma there is an effective screening of the Coulomb field with a characteristic cutoff called the *Debye screening distance*. Numerically, it is given by

$$\lambda_D(cm) = 6.91 \left(\frac{T}{n}\right)^{\frac{1}{2}}$$

where T is the absolute temperature. For many situations of interest, this distance is very small compared to 1 centimeter but still sufficiently large to allow many particles to experience each other's forces simultaneously. Despite this difficulty, the notion of binary collisions is still very useful and, keeping in mind the above restrictions, we shall use the concept freely.

THE "SOLUTION"
OF MAXWELL'S EQUATIONS

For the sake of completeness and future reference, let us review here very briefly some of the basic features of Maxwell's equations. In rationalized mks units these are

$$\nabla \cdot \mathbf{B} = 0 \tag{1.5}$$

$$\nabla \cdot \mathbf{E} = \frac{\rho}{\varepsilon_0} \tag{1.6}$$

$$\nabla \times \mathbf{E} = -\frac{\partial B}{\partial t} \tag{1.7}$$

$$\nabla \times \mathbf{B} = \mu_0 \mathbf{j} + \frac{1}{c^2} \frac{\partial \mathbf{E}}{\partial t} \tag{1.8}$$

where $\mathbf{B}$ is the magnetic field, $\mathbf{E}$ the electric field, $\mathbf{j}$ is the current density— that is, the flow of charge per unit, per unit time—and ρ is the charge density—that is, the charge per unit volume. An immediate consequence of eqs. (1.6) and (1.8) is the continuity equation

$$\nabla \cdot \mathbf{j} + \frac{\partial \rho}{\partial t} = 0 \tag{1.9}$$

which is the statement of the conservation of charge. It is often very useful to discuss the electromagnetic fields in terms of the vector and scalar potentials, $\mathbf{A}$ and ϕ, respectively, and these are defined by the conditions

$$\mathbf{B} = \nabla \times \mathbf{A} \tag{1.10}$$

$$\mathbf{E} = -\nabla\phi - \frac{\partial \mathbf{A}}{\partial t} \tag{1.11}$$

Actually, these equations do not define $\mathbf{A}$ and ϕ uniquely, for it is easily verified that the (gauge) transformation

$$\mathbf{A} \to \mathbf{A} + \nabla\Lambda$$

$$\phi \to \phi = \frac{\partial \Lambda}{\partial t}$$

where Λ is an arbitrary function, leaves the fields $\mathbf{E}$ and $\mathbf{B}$ invariant according to eqs. (1.10) and (1.11). Some of this ambiguity may be eliminated by going into the Lorentz gauge where $\mathbf{A}$ and ϕ are restricted by the condition

$$\nabla \cdot \mathbf{A} + \frac{1}{c^2}\frac{\partial \phi}{\partial t} = 0 \tag{1.12}$$

The equations satisfied by $\mathbf{A}$ and ϕ may be obtained by substituting eqs. (1.10) and (1.11) into Maxwell's equations, and we find by use of eq. (1.12) the result

$$\nabla^2 \mathbf{A} - \frac{1}{c^2}\frac{\partial^2 \mathbf{A}}{\partial t^2} = -\mu_0 \mathbf{j} \tag{1.13}$$

$$\nabla^2 \phi = \frac{1}{c^2}\frac{\partial^2 \phi}{\partial t^2} = -\frac{\rho}{\varepsilon_0} \tag{1.14}$$

The simplest possible situation occurs if $\mathbf{j}(\mathbf{r},t)$ and $\rho(\mathbf{r},t)$ are completely known as functions of space and time, and for this case the solution of Maxwell's equations is

$$\mathbf{A}(\mathbf{r},t) = \frac{\mu_0}{4\pi}\int d\mathbf{r}' \frac{1}{|\mathbf{r}-\mathbf{r}'|}\mathbf{j}\left(\mathbf{r}',t - \frac{|\mathbf{r}-\mathbf{r}'|}{c}\right)$$

$$\Phi(\mathbf{r},t) = \frac{1}{4\pi\varepsilon_0}\int d\mathbf{r}' \frac{1}{|\mathbf{r}-\mathbf{r}'|}\rho\left(\mathbf{r}',t - \frac{|\mathbf{r}-\mathbf{r}'|}{c}\right) \tag{1.15}$$

which may be verified by substitution into eqs. (1.12), (1.13), and (1.14). Actually, eqs. (1.15) are the so-called *retarded solutions* which correspond to the physical requirement that the electromagnetic fields must vanish throughout all of space for all times prior to that when **j** and ρ became nonvanishing. The other solution (advanced) does not satisfy this requirement and has been discarded. The validity of eqs. (1.15) has been verified many times by its prediction, for example, of the radiation emitted from antennas and accelerated charged particles. Thus the electromagnetic fields generated by known charge and current densities may be obtained by substituting eqs. (1.15) into eqs. (1.10) and (1.11). Unfortunately, the cases for which eqs. (1.15) themselves are directly useful are very sparse.

In most interesting situations—namely, where matter in some form interacts with the electromagnetic field—the charge and current densities are not known *a priori* but must be codetermined with the solution of Maxwell's equations. The simplest situation occurs for those materials that have been sufficiently well studied to permit prediction of the induced macroscopic charge and current densities in terms of the fields existing inside the material. Included among these are, for example, dielectrics, various magnetic materials, and solid conductors. In other situations—for example, where plasmas and liquid conductors are present—complications arise because of the mass motion. This means, for example, that **P** (the electric dipole moment per unit volume) and **M** (the magnetic dipole moment per unit volume) must not only be known as functions of the fields but also as functions of the local fluid velocity. The "solutions" given by eqs. (1.15) are not transparently useful for these cases, but nevertheless we shall use the concept of a potential in later studies. One advantage of working with **A** and ϕ is that two of Maxwell's equations—namely eq. (1.5) and eq. (1.7)—are automatically satisfied according to eq. (1.10) and eq. (1.11).

The physical interpretation of the fields **E** and **B** can perhaps be obtained most easily by making Maxwell's equations plausible on the basis of well-known experimental facts. Let us therefore study these facts briefly.

THE ELECTROSTATIC FIELD

For the electrostatic field we start the discussion with Coulomb's law of force between two charged particles. It is found that the principle of superposition is valid; that is, the forces exerted on a test particle by a collection of charged particles are equal to the sum of the individual forces exerted if only one of these particles were present at a time. The electric field is defined as the force per unit charge exerted on a test particle in the limit as the charge on the test particle goes to zero. By using Coulomb's law and the principle of superposition, we can easily compute the divergence and curl of **E** to find

$$\nabla \cdot \mathbf{E} = \frac{\rho}{\varepsilon_0}$$

$$\nabla \times \mathbf{E} = 0 \tag{1.16}$$

where ρ is the charge density. Again, given ρ, the field may be computed directly from eqs. (1.15) and from the formula

$$\phi = \frac{1}{4\pi\varepsilon_0} \int d\mathbf{r}' \frac{1}{|\mathbf{r} - \mathbf{r}'|} \rho(\mathbf{r}')$$

to be $\mathbf{E} = -\nabla\phi$. Not unexpectedly, the interesting problems in electrostatics occur when matter is present and, in general, the charge density induced in dielectrics and conductors is not a given piece of data. Therefore, eqs. (1.16) must be supplemented by a knowledge of matter from which one may obtain the induced charge density as a function of the electric field. Once this functional dependence is known, we may substitute the result into eqs. (1.16) to obtain a mathematical problem that often is still fairly complex.

THE MAGNETOSTATIC FIELD

The definition of the magnetostatic field follows essentially the same pattern as for the electrostatic field with the charge density replaced by the current density. For a system consisting of various species of charged particles, by an obvious extension of eq. (1.2) we have for the current density, in general, the formula

$$\mathbf{j} = \sum_i e_i n_i \mathbf{v}_i \tag{1.17}$$

Experimentally it is found that there is a force between two currents, and this fact is called the *law of Biot and Savart*; and the principle of superposition holds here just as it does in electrostatics. The magnetic field **B** is defined as the force per unit current per unit volume on a "test current density" with direction such that the vector cross product of the test current density and the magnetic field points in the direction of the force. Using these experimental facts and definitions it is easy to derive the divergence and the curl of **B** to be

$$\nabla \cdot \mathbf{B} = 0$$

$$\nabla \times \mathbf{B} = \mu_0 \mathbf{j} \tag{1.18}$$

where $\mathbf{j}$ represents the current density that gives rise to $\mathbf{B}$. Again, for the case that $\mathbf{j}$ is a known function of space, the solution of eqs. (1.18) is given according to eq. (1.15) in terms of the vector potential $\mathbf{A}(\mathbf{r})$ by

$$\mathbf{A}(\mathbf{r}) = \frac{\mu_0}{4\pi} \int d\mathbf{r}' \, \frac{1}{|\mathbf{r} - \mathbf{r}'|} \, \mathbf{j}(\mathbf{r}') \tag{1.19}$$

and $\mathbf{B}$ is given by $\mathbf{B} = \nabla \times \mathbf{A}$. In most physically interesting situations, of course, $\mathbf{j}$ is not known *a priori* but must be codetermined with the magnetic field itself and very often this presents nonlinear problems.

This possibility of obtaining nonlinear equations will occur in most cases of interest in these studies. The reason for this is that in the presence of large magnetic fields there are correspondingly large induced currents and these, in turn, cause modifications in the field, and so forth, thus confronting us, usually, with very nonlinear phenomena. Although the equations for the magnetic field are essentially given by eqs. (1.18), the "solution" obtained in eq. (1.19) is not excessively helpful.

For materials that have a given magnetic-dipole moment per unit volume $\mathbf{M}$, the associated current density is given by $\mathbf{j} = \nabla \times \mathbf{M}$ and for this special case eqs. (1.18) may be rewritten into the form

$$\nabla \times \left(\frac{\mathbf{B}}{\mu_0} - \mathbf{M} \right) = 0$$

$$\nabla \cdot \left(\frac{\mathbf{B}}{\mu_0} - \mathbf{M} \right) = -\nabla \cdot \mathbf{M} \tag{1.20}$$

Therefore, the field $\left(\dfrac{\mathbf{B}}{\mu_0} - \mathbf{M} \right)$ is identical to an electrostatic field with charge density proportional to $-\nabla \cdot \mathbf{M}$. This result is often very useful.

Since the divergence of the curl of any vector field vanishes, it follows from the second of eqs. (1.18) that $\nabla \cdot \mathbf{j} = 0$. This is consistent with charge conservation since we have assumed that all phenomena are time independent and in particular

$$\frac{\partial \rho}{\partial t} = 0$$

It follows from the definitions of $\mathbf{E}$ and $\mathbf{B}$ as given above that if a charge density ρ and a current density $\mathbf{j}$ are in the electromagnetic fields $\mathbf{E}$ and $\mathbf{B}$, then the force per unit volume on these densities is given by

$$\mathbf{F}_v = \rho \mathbf{E} + \mathbf{j} \times \mathbf{B} \tag{1.21}$$

This relationship turns out to be valid also for time-dependent fields.

MAXWELL'S DISPLACEMENT CURRENT

If we now allow for the possibility that the sources of $\mathbf{E}$ and $\mathbf{B}$ vary in time, it becomes clear that eqs. (1.18) are no longer consistent, since in this case $\nabla \cdot \mathbf{j} \neq 0$ in general. Maxwell first noted this fact and proposed that another term be added to the right-hand side of the second of eqs. (1.18) in order to make it consistent with charge conservation. For the moment let us designate this added term by the vector $\mu_0 \mathbf{F}$. Since $\nabla \cdot (\nabla \times \mathbf{B}) = 0$, it follows that $\mathbf{F}$ satisfies the equation

$$\nabla \cdot \mathbf{F} + \nabla \cdot \mathbf{j} = 0$$

or by use of eq. (1.9)

$$\nabla \cdot \mathbf{F} = \frac{\partial \rho}{\partial t}$$

Comparing this with the time derivative of the first of eqs. (1.16) (which is experimentally verified to hold also for time dependent phenomena) the simplest choice for $\mathbf{F}$ is clearly

$$\mathbf{F} = \varepsilon_0 \frac{\partial \mathbf{E}}{\partial t} \tag{1.22}$$

This argument is not quite complete since it is obvious that the curl of an arbitrary vector function can be added to $\mathbf{F}$ without violating charge conservation. Fortunately this ambiguity may be resolved by various sorts of experiments—for example, radiation phenomena—that show that the choice in eq. (1.22) is the correct one.

As we shall see later, the displacement current is important only for very high frequencies and temperatures (that is, large thermal speeds) and therefore for many interesting physical situations it can be neglected.

FARADAY'S LAW

Faraday was the first to discover that in the presence of a time dependent field an emf is induced in a conductor with resulting current flow. For a closed loop—that is, one that can sustain a current—this induced emf may be expressed in terms of the line integral of the electric field around the loop—that is,

$$\oint_l \mathbf{E} \cdot d\mathbf{l} = -\frac{d}{dt} \int_s \mathbf{B} \cdot d\mathbf{S} \tag{1.23}$$

where $d\mathbf{l}$ is an element of arc length bounding the open surface S with area element $d\mathbf{S}$. This interpretation of the induced emf in terms of electric fields is correct and, for example, an isolated charged particle at rest in a time varying magnetic field experiences a force $e\mathbf{E}$. In a betatron, electrons are accelerated to velocities close to that of light by means of such electric fields. Thus, this electric field exists at every point of space regardless of whether or not a conductor is present and these fields, generated by time-dependent magnetic fields, are essentially the only electric fields important in our considerations. The other electric fields—namely, those generated by stationary or slowly moving charged particles—can often be neglected.

Returning now to eq. (1.23), if the limits of integration on the right-hand side do not depend on time—that is, the domain of integration is stationary —the time derivative may be taken under the integral, and simultaneously the left-hand side may be rewritten, by use of Stokes' Theorem, in terms of a surface integral of the normal component of $\nabla \times \mathbf{E}$. Finally, since the resulting equation is experimentally known to hold for arbitrary open surfaces, we obtain the equation

$$\nabla \times \mathbf{E} + \frac{\partial \mathbf{B}}{\partial t} = 0 \tag{1.7}$$

Let us briefly examine the important circumstance that arises if the surface in eq. (1.23) varies with time. In this connection, it is important to realize that Maxwell's equations (1.5)–(1.8) are valid in all inertial co-ordinate systems (systems moving with constant velocities relative to each other) according to the theory of relativity, provided we interpret the $\mathbf{E}$ and $\mathbf{B}$ in these equations as appropriate to the given system under consideration. As we transform from one moving system to another Maxwell's equations remain the same, but the fields must be interpreted as appropriate to the new system. According to the special theory of relativity, if $\mathbf{E}$ and $\mathbf{B}$ are the fields as observed in one system, then from the viewpoint of an observer moving with velocity $\mathbf{v}$ relative to this system there exist fields $\mathbf{E}'$, $\mathbf{B}'$ which are related to $\mathbf{E}$ and $\mathbf{B}$ via the relations

$$\mathbf{E}'_\perp = \gamma (\mathbf{E}_\perp + \mathbf{v} \times \mathbf{B})$$

$$\mathbf{B}'_\perp = \gamma \left(\mathbf{B}_\perp - \frac{\mathbf{v}}{c^2} \times \mathbf{E} \right) \tag{1.24}$$

$$\mathbf{E}'_{||} = \mathbf{E}_{||}$$

$$\mathbf{B}'_{||} = \mathbf{B}_{||} \tag{1.25}$$

where $\mathbf{E}_{||}$, $\mathbf{B}_{||}$; $\mathbf{E}_\perp$, $\mathbf{B}_\perp$ represent the components of the fields parallel and perpendicular to $\mathbf{v}$, respectively, and the factor $\gamma = (1 - v^2/c^2)^{-1/2}$. To terms linear in the velocity eqs. (1.24) and (1.25) may be written simply as

$$\mathbf{E}' = \mathbf{E} + \mathbf{v} \times \mathbf{B}$$

$$\mathbf{B}' = \mathbf{B} - \frac{\mathbf{v}}{c^2} \times \mathbf{E} \tag{1.26}$$

The physical interpretation of these equations is clear. We can consider, for example, a particle moving instantaneously with velocity **v** in the fields **E** and **B**. From the viewpoint of an observer moving relative to this system with velocity $+$**v**, the particle is at rest, and thus it experiences only forces of electric-field origins. The fact that the total force acting on the particle must be the same in both systems is assured by the first of eqs. (1.26). Similarly, the second of eqs. (1.26) is intuitively clear since from the viewpoint of the moving system, the charge—which generates the electric field in the old frame—appears as a current, and this gives rise to the magnetic field.

An immediate application of eqs. (1.26) is that if we consider a fluid moving with local velocity **v** in the presence of electromagnetic fields **E** and **B**, then Ohm's law is given by

$$\mathbf{j} = \sigma \left(\mathbf{E} + \mathbf{v} \times \mathbf{B} \right) \tag{1.27}$$

This reduces to the more familiar form for a fluid at rest. The justification for eq. (1.27) follows from the elementary considerations that were previously discussed when we equated the force on the charged particles comprising the current to an effective frictional drag due to collisions. In the present case the force is given by $\mathbf{E} + \mathbf{v} \times \mathbf{B}$, and thus we obtain eq. (1.27).

An alternate and somewhat more illuminating way of obtaining the first of eqs. (1.26) may be obtained by starting directly from eq. (1.23) and applying it to a rigid loop of wire that moves with velocity **v**. For this situation the limits of integration on the right-hand side of eq. (1.23) vary in time, and some care must be exercised in taking the time derivative. It is easiest to turn directly to the definition of a derivative. To this end we shall consider a time interval Δt during which the surface moves a distance $\mathbf{v}\,\Delta t$ (Fig. 1.1). We find in the limit as $\Delta t \to 0$, the result

$$\frac{d}{dt}\int \mathbf{B} \cdot d\mathbf{S} = \frac{1}{\Delta t}\left\{\int \mathbf{B}(t + \Delta t) \cdot d\mathbf{S}_2 - \int \mathbf{B}(t) \cdot d\mathbf{S}_1\right\}$$

$$= \frac{1}{\Delta t}\left\{\int \mathbf{B}(t) \cdot d\mathbf{S}_2 - \int \mathbf{B}(t) \cdot d\mathbf{S}_1\right\} + \int \frac{\partial \mathbf{B}}{\partial t} \cdot d\mathbf{S}_2 \tag{1.28}$$

In order to simplify the result, we consider the identity

$$0 = \int_V d\mathbf{r}\, \nabla \cdot \mathbf{B} = \int_S \mathbf{B}(t) \cdot d\mathbf{S}$$

where V is the volume contained between the two surfaces in Fig. 1.1, and

S is the closed, bounding surface of this volume. Carrying out the surface integral, we obtain

$$0 = \int \mathbf{B}(t) \cdot d\mathbf{S}_1 - \int \mathbf{B}(t) \cdot d\mathbf{S}_2 + \oint (v \nabla t \times dl) \cdot \mathbf{B}(t)$$

where the first two surface integrals go over the upper and lower open surfaces, respectively, and the last integral is a closed line integral about the

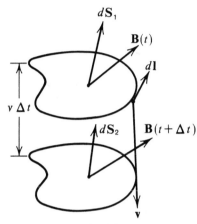

Fig. 1.1

bounding edge of the open surface. Now substituting this last result into eq. (1.28) and noting that we in the limit, $\Delta t \to 0$, $d\mathbf{S}_2 \to d\mathbf{S}_1 = d\mathbf{S}$, we obtain

$$\frac{d}{dt} \int \mathbf{B} \cdot d\mathbf{S} = \int \frac{\partial \mathbf{B}}{\partial t} \cdot d\mathbf{S} - \oint (\mathbf{v} \times \mathbf{B}) \cdot dl$$

which by use of Stokes' theorem may be transformed into

$$\frac{d}{dt} \int \mathbf{B} \cdot d\mathbf{S} = \int d\mathbf{S} \cdot \left[\frac{\partial \mathbf{B}}{\partial t} - \nabla \times (\mathbf{v} \times \mathbf{B}) \right]$$

Finally, combining this with eq. (1.23) we obtain, in the same way as before, the result

$$\nabla \times (\mathbf{E} - \mathbf{v} \times \mathbf{B}) = -\frac{\partial \mathbf{B}}{\partial t}$$

where now $\mathbf{E}$ is the electric field as observed in the rest frame of the loop that is the field previously called $\mathbf{E}'$. Thus we regain the first of eqs. (1.26). In this discussion we have, of course, assumed that $|\mathbf{v}| \ll c$ and have consistently neglected effects of order v^2/c^2; therefore the magnetic field is the same to the stationary observer as it is to the observer in the rest frame of the loop. For our purposes this approximation is always valid.

To summarize, Maxwell's equations are given by eqs. (1.5)–(1.8); and for the somewhat trivial case that **j** and ρ are known functions of space and time, the solution is given in eq. (1.15). For most physically interesting cases, **j** and ρ must be codetermined by combining Maxwell's equations with the physical properties of the plasma as well as its macroscopic state of motion.

FOURIER ANALYSIS OF MAXWELL'S EQUATIONS

As in many other branches of theoretical physics, we shall find it convenient to make use of the spectral distribution of the electromagnetic fields and for this purpose we shall need the Fourier integral theorem.

Let $f(t)$ be a function of time that is square integrable (and is reasonably well behaved in all other respects) and define its fourier transform f_ω by the relation

$$f_\omega = \frac{1}{2\pi} \int_{-\infty}^{\infty} f(t) e^{i\omega t} \, dt \tag{1.29}$$

Now considering this definition as an integral equation for the unknown function $f(t)$ given the function f_ω, Fourier's theorem states that the solution of eq. (1.29) is given by

$$f(t) = \int_{-\infty}^{\infty} f_\omega e^{-i\omega t} \, d\omega \tag{1.30}$$

This fact may be directly verified by substituting eq. (1.30) into eq. (1.29) interchanging the orders of integration, and making use of the fact

$$\int_{-\infty}^{\infty} e^{i(\omega-\omega')t} dt = 2\pi \delta(\omega-\omega') \tag{1.31}$$

where $\delta(\omega)$ is the *Dirac delta function*. This function simplifies so much of our work that it is worthwhile at this point to list its defining and more useful properties.

The delta function $\delta(x)$ is defined by the relation

$$\delta(x) = \begin{cases} 0 & x \neq 0 \\ \infty & x = 0 \end{cases} \tag{1.32}$$

and the infinity is fixed by the requirement

$$\int \delta(x) \, dx = 1$$

provided the range of integration includes the origin. Some properties of the delta function that follow directly from this definition are:

$$\int dx\, f(x)\, \delta\,(x-a) = f(a) \tag{1.33}$$

$$\int f(x)\, \frac{d}{dx}\, \delta\,(x-a)\, dx = -\frac{d}{da}\, f(a) \tag{1.34}$$

$$\delta\,\{f(x)\} = \sum_{i=1}^{N} \frac{\delta\,(x-x_i)}{|df/dx|_{x=x_i}}, \qquad f(x_i)=0, i=1,2,\cdots N \tag{1.35}$$

where in eqs. (1.33) and (1.34) the range of integration includes the point $x = a$, and in eq. (1.35) the numbers $\{x_i\}$ are the simple zeroes of the function $f(x)$. Needless to say, the delta function makes sense only when it appears under an integral and, for example, eq. (1.35) can be interpreted only in this way. For some purposes, we can think of the delta function as the limiting form of an ordinary function. For example, it is easily verified that we may write

$$\delta(x) = \lim_{\sigma\to 0} (2\pi\sigma^2)^{-\frac{1}{2}} \exp\left\{-\frac{x^2}{2\sigma^2}\right\}$$

and

$$\delta(x) = \lim_{\varepsilon\to 0_+} \frac{1}{\pi}\, \frac{\varepsilon}{x^2+\varepsilon^2}$$

The generalization of this definition of $\delta(x)$ to more than one dimension is straightforward. As a matter of notation, we shall use the shorthand $\delta(\mathbf{r})$ to mean

$$\delta(\mathbf{r}) = \delta(x)\, \delta(y)\, \delta(z) \tag{1.36}$$

and have the relation

$$\int_V d\mathbf{r}\, \delta(\mathbf{r}) = \left\{ \begin{matrix} 1 & \text{if } V \text{ contains the origin} \\ 0 & \text{if } V \text{ does not contain the origin} \end{matrix} \right\}$$

Returning to Fourier's theorem, we now see two interesting and useful properties that follow from eqs. (1.29) and (1.30). In most cases of interest, the function $f(t)$ is real and, therefore,

$$f_\omega^* = f_{-\omega} \tag{1.37}$$

The second useful relation is expressed by the formula

$$\int_{-\infty}^{\infty} f^2(t)\, dt = 4\pi \int_0^\infty d\omega |f_\omega|^2 \tag{1.38}$$

which also follows from the above definitions.

Let us now examine the Fourier transforms of Maxwell's equations. Let $\mathbf{E}_\omega(\mathbf{r})$, $\mathbf{B}_\omega(\mathbf{r})$, $\mathbf{j}_\omega(\mathbf{r})$, $\rho_\omega(\mathbf{r})$ be the Fourier transforms of $\mathbf{E}(\mathbf{r},t)$, $\mathbf{B}(\mathbf{r},t)$, $\mathbf{j}(\mathbf{r},t)$, $\rho(\mathbf{r},t)$ respectively. For physical reasons it is clear that each of these is square integrable, and thus the Fourier transforms exist. We can also see that if we take the transform of Maxwell's equations (1.5)–(1.8), the effect of the time differentiation is replaced by multiplication by $-i\omega$, and we obtain

$$\nabla \cdot \mathbf{B}_\omega = 0 \tag{1.39}$$

$$\nabla \cdot \mathbf{E}_\omega = \frac{\rho_\omega}{\varepsilon_0} \tag{1.40}$$

$$\nabla \times \mathbf{E}_\omega = i\omega \mathbf{B}_\omega \tag{1.41}$$

$$\nabla \times \mathbf{B}_\omega = \mu_0 \mathbf{j}_\omega - i\,\frac{\omega}{c^2}\,\mathbf{E}_\omega \tag{1.42}$$

In a similar way we may obtain the transforms of eqs. (1.10) and (1.11) to be

$$\mathbf{B}_\omega = \nabla \times \mathbf{A}_\omega$$

$$\mathbf{E}_\omega = -\nabla\phi_\omega + i\omega\mathbf{A}_\omega \tag{1.43}$$

while eq. (1.13) for example takes the form

$$\nabla^2 \mathbf{A}_\omega + \frac{\omega^2}{c^2}\,\mathbf{A}_\omega = -\mu_0 \mathbf{j}\omega \tag{1.44}$$

And this has solution

$$\mathbf{A}_\omega(\mathbf{r}) = \frac{\mu_0}{4\pi} \int d\mathbf{r}' \frac{1}{|\mathbf{r}-\mathbf{r}'|}\,\mathbf{j}_\omega(\mathbf{r}')\exp\left\{\frac{i\omega}{c}|\mathbf{r}-\mathbf{r}'|\right\} \tag{1.45}$$

The physical significance of these equations is, of course, unaltered by the transformations.

In addition to taking the Fourier transform with respect to the time variable, for some purposes (in situations for which surface effects are unimportant) we shall find it convenient to take the transform with respect to the three spatial variables. Thus, in analogy to the above, given a "well-behaved" function $f(\mathbf{r})$, we define a function $f(\mathbf{k})$ by the relation

$$f(\mathbf{k}) = \int d\mathbf{r}\, f(\mathbf{r})e^{-i\mathbf{k}\cdot\mathbf{r}} \tag{1.46}$$

which may be inverted to yield

$$f(\mathbf{r}) = \frac{1}{(2\pi)^3} \int d\mathbf{k}\, f(\mathbf{k}) e^{i\mathbf{k}\cdot\mathbf{r}} \tag{1.47}$$

In establishing the compatibility of eqs. (1.46) and (1.47) one uses the relation

$$\int d\mathbf{r} \exp\{i(\mathbf{k} - \mathbf{k}')\cdot\mathbf{r}\} = (2\pi)^3\, \delta(\mathbf{k} - \mathbf{k}')$$

where the delta function on the right-hand side is, of course, given by

$$\delta(\mathbf{k} - \mathbf{k}') = \delta(k_x - k_x')\, \delta(k_y - k_y')\, \delta(k_z - k_z')$$

Now let us take the Fourier transform of Maxwell's equations in both the time and spatial variables. Since the operation of taking the gradient becomes multiplication by $i\mathbf{k}$, we obtain easily

$$\mathbf{k}\cdot\mathbf{B}_\omega(\mathbf{k}) = 0 \tag{1.48}$$

$$\mathbf{k}\cdot\mathbf{E}_\omega(\mathbf{k}) = -\frac{i}{\varepsilon_0}\, \rho_\omega(\mathbf{k}) \tag{1.49}$$

$$\mathbf{k} \times \mathbf{E}_\omega(\mathbf{k}) = \omega\mathbf{B}_\omega(\mathbf{k}) \tag{1.50}$$

$$i\mathbf{k} \times \mathbf{B}_\omega(\mathbf{k}) = \mu_0\mathbf{j}_\omega(\mathbf{k}) - \frac{i\omega}{c^2}\mathbf{E}_\omega(\mathbf{k}) \tag{1.51}$$

Correspondingly, the vector and scalar potentials are given by

$$\mathbf{B}_\omega(\mathbf{k}) = i\mathbf{k} \times \mathbf{A}_\omega(\mathbf{k})$$

$$\mathbf{E}_\omega(\mathbf{k}) = -i\mathbf{k}\phi_\omega(\mathbf{k}) + i\omega\mathbf{A}_\omega(\mathbf{k})$$

and explicit solutions for $\mathbf{A}_\omega(\mathbf{k})$ and $\phi_\omega(\mathbf{k})$ can be given simply in terms of $\mathbf{j}_\omega(\mathbf{k})$ and $\rho_\omega(\mathbf{k})$; for example,

$$\mathbf{A}_\omega(\mathbf{k}) = \frac{\mu_0\mathbf{j}_\omega(\mathbf{k})}{k^2 - (1/c^2)(\omega + i\varepsilon)^2} \tag{1.52}$$

where ε is a small positive quantity that automatically selects the retarded solution provided we take the limit $\varepsilon \to 0^+$ after all integrations have been carried out.

Finally it is worth mentioning that the *longitudinal* and *transverse* components of $\mathbf{E}_\omega(\mathbf{k})$ and $\mathbf{B}_\omega(\mathbf{k})$ are defined to be the components of the fields *along* and *perpendicular* to $\mathbf{k}$, respectively. Using the subscripts l and t to distinguish the longitudinal from the transverse components, the following equalities are easily verified by use of eqs. (1.48)–(1.51):

$$\mathbf{B}_{\omega l}(\mathbf{k}) = 0$$

$$\mathbf{E}_{\omega l}(\mathbf{k}) = -i\,\frac{\mathbf{k}}{k^2}\,\frac{\rho_\omega(\mathbf{k})}{\varepsilon_0}$$

$$\mathbf{E}_{\omega t}(\mathbf{k}) = -\frac{\omega}{k^2}\mathbf{k} \times \mathbf{B}_{\omega t}(\mathbf{k})$$

$$\mathbf{B}_{\omega t}(\mathbf{k}) = \frac{i\mu_0}{k^2 - (\omega^2/c^2)}\mathbf{k} \times \mathbf{j}_\omega(\mathbf{k})$$

It is to be emphasized that the magnetic field is purely transverse while the charge density alone determines the longitudinal parts of the electric field. Thus, in the absence of a charge density, the electric as well as the magnetic fields are both purely transverse.

Suggested Reading and References

1. Electromagnetic Theory

J. D. Jackson, *Classical Electrodynamics*. New York: John Wiley & Sons, Inc., 1962.

K. H. Panofsky and M. Phillips, *Classical Electricity and Magnetism*. Reading, Mass: Addison-Wesley Publishing Company, Inc., 1955.

W. R. Smythe, *Static and Dynamic Electricity*. New York: McGraw-Hill Book Co., Inc. 1950

J. E. Stratton, *Electromagnetic Theory*. New York: McGraw-Hill Book Co., Inc., 1941.

2. Plasma Physics

S. Chandrasekhar, *Plasma Physics*. Chicago: University of Chicago Press, 1960.

F. Clauser (editor), *Plasma Dynamics*. Reading, Mass: Addison-Welsey Publishing Company, Inc., 1960.

T. G. Cowling, *Magnetohydrodynamics*. New York: John Wiley & Sons, Inc., 1957.

A. L. Simon, *An Introduction to Thermonuclear Research*. Oxford: Pergamon Press, Inc., 1960.

L. Spitzer, Jr., *Physics of Fully Ionized Gases*. New York: John Wiley & Sons, Inc., 1956.

Problems

1. Derive the frequency dependent formula for the conductivity —that is, eq. (1.4). Interpret physically the complex behavior of the conductivity by reference to a particular physical situation. In particular examine the case $\omega \gg \omega_c$.

2. (a) By use of the Fourier theorem derive eq. (1.31).

(b) By use of the definition of the delta function derive the properties given in eqs. (1.33)–(1.34).

3. Verify that eqs. (1.15) are a solution of eqs. (1.13) and (1.14) by direct substitution. *Hint*: A possible way of doing this is to establish the validity of the relation

$$\left(\nabla^2 - \frac{1}{c^2} \frac{\partial^2}{\partial t^2} \right) \frac{f(t - r/c)}{r} = -4\pi \delta(\mathbf{r}) f(t)$$

by first integrating both sides over a volume that does not contain the origin and a second time by integrating throughout a very small sphere centered at the origin.

4. Expand the solution given by eq. (1.15) in a power series in $1/c$, and show that if the charge and current densities are nonzero in a finite part of space then there are essentially no terms of order $1/c$. Calculate the terms of order $1/c^2$.

5. (a) By use of eqs. (1.24) and (1.25) show that $E^2 - B^2 c^2$ and $\mathbf{E} \cdot \mathbf{B}$ are both invariant under transformations to moving coordinate systems.

(b) Show that if $\mathbf{E}$ or $\mathbf{B}$ vanish in one coordinate system, they are orthogonal in all coordinate systems.

(c) Consider the uniform fields $\mathbf{E}_0$ and $\mathbf{B}_0$ that are at right angles to each other. Find the velocity of the coordinate system with respect to which one of these fields (depending on whether $E_0 \gtrless B_0 c$) vanishes.

(d) In part (c) suppose $E_0 = B_0 c$. Show that there are coordinate systems in which these electromagnetic fields can be arbitrarily small.

6. By inverting eq. (1.52) derive the first of eqs. (1.15). Show that the other choice of sign for ε in eq. (1.52) produces the advanced solution.

7. By use of eqs. (1.43)–(1.45) show that the energy radiated by a current distribution $\mathbf{j}(\mathbf{r},t)$ into a frequency range $d\omega$ into solid angle $d\Omega$ is given by

$$U_\omega \, d\omega \, d\Omega = \frac{1}{4\pi} \left(\frac{\mu_0}{\varepsilon_0} \right)^{1/2} \left| \int d\mathbf{r} \, \mathbf{j}_\omega(\mathbf{r}) \times \mathbf{k} e^{-i\mathbf{k}\cdot\mathbf{r}} \right|^2 d\omega \, d\Omega$$

where $\mathbf{k}$ is a vector that has magnitude ω/c and is oriented along the direction of observation.

8. (a) The "time-reversed" current density $\mathbf{j}^T(t)$ and charge $\rho^T(t)$ are defined by the relations

$$\mathbf{j}^T(t) = -\mathbf{j}(-t) \qquad \rho^T(t) = +\rho(-t)$$

Give a physical interpretation of these densities.

(b) Assuming the time reversed fields $\mathbf{E}^T(t)$, $\mathbf{B}^T(t)$ satisfy Maxwell's equations with the sources $\mathbf{j}^T$ and ρ^T, express $\mathbf{E}^T$, $\mathbf{B}^T$ in terms of the ordinary electromagnetic fields. Interpret these time reversed fields physically.

(c) Express ϕ^T and $\mathbf{A}^T$ in terms of the ordinary potentials.

(d) Is the "solution" in eq. (1.15) correct for the time reversed quantities? If not, what is the correct formula? Interpret this result physically.

9. (a) Suppose a charge density ρ_0 is placed in the interior of a very large conductor of conductivity σ. Show that

$$\rho(t) = \rho_0 \exp\left\{ -\frac{t\sigma}{\varepsilon_0} \right\}$$

(b) Obtain the numerical value of this time constant for copper and criticize the above formula on this basis.

10. (a) Given $\mathbf{E}$ and $\mathbf{B}$ at some fixed time t_0, and $\mathbf{j}$ and ρ for all time t, obtain the values for $\mathbf{E}$ and $\mathbf{B}$ a short time Δt later by use of Maxwell's equations. Calculate only through terms linear in Δt.

(b) Show that a knowledge of $\mathbf{A}$ and ϕ at a fixed time t_0 alone is not sufficient to fix them according to eqs. (1.13)–(1.14). What data, other than the requirement used in the text, would one need to obtain $\mathbf{A}$ and ϕ for all times?

(c) Contrast the results in parts (a) and (b) and justify the need for additional initial data for the potentials.

2

The Motion
of a Charged Particle
in Given
Electromagnetic Fields

INTRODUCTION

For many of the physically interesting situations that arise in a study of plasmas, even an approximate solution to the problem is often very difficult to obtain. The essential complications arise because the equations used to describe these phenomena are very nonlinear, and the customary methods based on the principle of superposition fail completely. In this state of affairs—for the present in any event—physical intuition and personal observation, both experimental and astrophysical, must be heavily relied on. Therefore, it is very necessary to attempt to obtain some intuitive grasp of what happens inside a plasma under various physical conditions. One convenient way of doing this is by means of the so-called *orbit theory*.

This method, which is applicable to plasmas of very low density and which we will study in some detail only for purposes of developing some physical intuition but not for purposes of solving practical problems, may be thought of in the following way. Given a plasma in some dynamical state, suppose one assumes a form for the internal electric and magnetic fields. Then we can check the consistency of this picture by solving Newton's laws of motion for the particles in these fields in order to discover if such motions will generate macroscopic charge and current densities, which in turn will reproduce the assumed electromagnetic fields. In principle, this method can be used to solve any given problem provided one makes the correct "guess" for the electromagnetic fields. For the present, this procedure\is useful for conceptual reasons since it enables us to see approximately effects that take place; and second, it provides us with a convenient language in terms of which various phenomena may be discussed.

Let us consider a particle of charge q and rest mass m in motion in given electromagnetic fields $\mathbf{E}$ and $\mathbf{B}$. Newton's law of motion may be written in the form

$$m \frac{d}{dt} \mathbf{v} = q \left(1 - \frac{v^2}{c^2}\right)^{\frac{1}{2}} \left(\mathbf{E} + \mathbf{v} \times \mathbf{B} - \frac{\mathbf{v}}{c^2} \mathbf{v} \cdot \mathbf{E}\right) \tag{2.1}$$

where c is the velocity of light in the vacuum. This form of the law is correct for arbitrarily large (that is, arbitrarily close to the speed of light) velocities, although its limiting form, when terms of order v^2/c^2 are neglected, that is

$$m \frac{d}{dt} \mathbf{v} = q \left(\mathbf{E} + \mathbf{v} \times \mathbf{B}\right)$$

is perhaps more familiar. Our present interests are for situations for which $\mathbf{E} \sim 0$, or equivalently $\mathbf{B}$ is very large; for these cases we may freely use the fully relativistic form in eq. (2.1) without generating complications. If the electric field vanishes, eq. (2.1) becomes

$$m \frac{d\mathbf{v}}{dt} = q \left(1 - \frac{v^2}{c^2}\right)^{\frac{1}{2}} \mathbf{v} \times \mathbf{B} \tag{2.2}$$

Upon taking the dot product of this equation of $\mathbf{v}$, we conclude immediately

$$\frac{d}{dt} v^2 = 0$$

that is, v^2 is a constant of the motion. Thus, the seemingly complex factor $(1 - v^2/c^2)^{\frac{1}{2}}$ is a constant (which may be expressed in terms of the initial velocity), and this factor may be combined with the particle's mass to yield the relativistic mass. With this understanding of the mass m, the motion of a charged particle in a magnetic field is the same for large and small velocities and is governed by the equation

$$\frac{d}{dt} = \frac{q}{m} \mathbf{v} \times \mathbf{B}$$

It is to be emphasized that this result will be valid regardless of how the magnetic field **B** varies in space. Of course, if **B** varies in time, then according to eq. (1.7) an electric field is also present, and this field does work on the particle, thus invalidating the above constancy of the particle's kinetic energy. In this case it is easiest to use the nonrelativistic form of eq. (2.1) with a corresponding limitation on applicability. Let us consider some special cases in detail.

MOTION IN A UNIFORM STATIC MAGNETIC FIELD

For the case of motion in a uniform static magnetic field, eq. (2.1) may be written

$$\frac{d\mathbf{v}}{dt} = \mathbf{v} \times \boldsymbol{\omega} \tag{2.3}$$

where $\boldsymbol{\omega}$ is a vector pointing along the direction of the magnetic field (for $q>0$). It has the magnitude

$$\omega = \frac{qB}{m} \tag{2.4}$$

and is called the Larmor or cyclotron frequency. For example, for an electron in a field of 1000 gauss ($= 10^{-1}$ weber/m^2) $\omega \sim 10^{10}$ sec^{-1}, while for a proton in the same field $\omega \sim 10^7$ sec^{-1}. A study of eq. (2.3) shows that the motion of the particle consists of uniform motion along the magnetic field with velocity $v_{\parallel}$ plus a circular motion with constant velocity $v_{\perp}$ about the magnetic field lines. The radius of this circular orbit about the magnetic field is given by

$$a = \frac{v_{\perp}}{\omega} = \frac{m}{q} \frac{v_{\perp}}{B} \tag{2.5}$$

For the cases considered above if $v \sim 10^5$ cm/sec, this radius $\sim 10^{-5}$ cm, 10^{-2} cm for electrons and protons, respectively. It is important to note that the Larmor frequency is proportional to the magnetic field and correspondingly that the radius of gyration is inversely proportional to the field. Thus, as the magnetic field gets larger, the particles spiral around more rapidly in smaller orbits.

Let us solve eq. (2.3) more quantitatively. Assuming that the magnetic field lies along the z direction, the components of eq. (2.3) become

$$\ddot{x} = \omega \dot{y}$$

$$\ddot{y} = -\omega \dot{x}$$

$$\ddot{z} = 0 \tag{2.6}$$

The last of these equations has the solution (assuming the particle is initially at the origin)

$$z = v_{||} t$$

where $v_{||}$ is the constant value of the velocity along **B**. In order to solve the first two of eqs. (2.6) in a convenient way, we define a complex variable $u = x + iy$, which satisfies the equation

$$\ddot{u} = -i\omega\dot{u} \tag{2.7}$$

The real and imaginary parts of u will yield $x(t)$ and $y(t)$, respectively. Since ω is not dependent on time, eq. (2.7) may be integrated once to yield

$$\dot{u} = \dot{u}_o e^{-i\omega t}$$

where $\dot{u}_o$ is the initial value for $\dot{u}$. Integrating again, we find

$$u = \frac{i\dot{u}_o}{\omega}(e^{-i\omega t} - 1)$$

where again the particle has been assumed to be at the origin initially. More specifically, if the particle moves originally along the negative y axis with velocity $v_\perp$ and along the z axis with velocity $v_{||}$, the trajectory for the particle is then explicitly given by

$$x = a(\cos \omega t - 1)$$

$$y = -a \sin \omega t \tag{2.8}$$

$$z = v_{||} t$$

where a is the radius of gyration. The path of the particle is evidently a helix with axis along **B** and located at $(-a, 0)$ and of pitch angle given by

$$\tan^{-1}\left(\frac{v_{||}}{v_\perp}\right)$$

MOTION IN STATIC AND UNIFORM
ELECTRIC AND MAGNETIC FIELDS

Motion in static and uniform electric and magnetic fields turns out to be very similar to the previous situation and requires little extra discussion.

First, if the electric field is parallel to **B**, the motion perpendicular to **B** is completely unaffected in that the particle again spirals around a magnetic line of force of appropriate radius. The motion along **B**, however, is changed somewhat since the particle will have a uniform acceleration qE/m instead of the uniform velocity as before.

Let us, therefore, turn to a second possibility for which the electric and magnetic fields are at right angles to each other. More specifically, for our purposes let us assume that the magnetic field is larger than the electric field which in our units is expressed by the inequality $|\mathbf{E}| < c|\mathbf{B}|$. This situation can again be reduced to the above case of a particle moving in a magnetic field alone by the use of the first of eqs. (1.24). The problem at hand is to find a transformation to a coordinate system where $\mathbf{E}'$ vanishes. Let us assume that $\mathbf{B}$ lies along the x direction and $\mathbf{E}$ along the z axis. It follows that if $\mathbf{v}$ in eqs. (1.24) lies along the positive y direction and has magnitude

$$|\mathbf{v}| = \frac{|\mathbf{E}|}{|\mathbf{B}|}$$

then the electric field in the new system $\mathbf{E}'$ vanishes identically, while the magnetic field $\mathbf{B}'$ has the value

$$\mathbf{B}' = \mathbf{B}\left(1 - \frac{E^2}{c^2 B^2}\right) \cong \mathbf{B}$$

since the second term represents a purely relativistic effect (that is, it is of order v^2/c^2) and is negligible for our purposes. The result of this discussion is, therefore, that for mutually perpendicular electric and magnetic fields, the particle's motion consists of a spiralling motion about the direction of the magnetic field plus a drifting motion of the *guiding center* with velocity $\mathbf{v}_D$ given by

$$\mathbf{v}_D = \frac{\mathbf{E} \times \mathbf{B}}{B^2} \tag{2.9}$$

This equation represents a way of stating the above results that is independent of the coordinate system used, and the drift velocity has the noteworthy property of being independent of the particle's charge and mass.

It is of some interest to re-examine this situation from a slightly more elementary point of view. Starting from Newton's law

$$\frac{d\mathbf{v}}{dt} = \frac{q}{m}(\mathbf{E} + \mathbf{v} \times \mathbf{B})$$

we define a velocity $\mathbf{v}'$ so that

$$\mathbf{v} = \mathbf{v}_D + \mathbf{v}' \tag{2.10}$$

where $\mathbf{v}_D$ is the *constant* drift velocity as defined in eq. (2.9). Substituting eq. (2.10) into Newton's law, we may derive for $\mathbf{v}'$ the result

$$\frac{d\mathbf{v}'}{dt} = \frac{q}{m}\left(\mathbf{E} + \frac{\mathbf{E} \times \mathbf{B}}{B^2} \times \mathbf{B} + \mathbf{v}' \times \mathbf{B}\right) = \frac{q}{m}\mathbf{v}' \times \mathbf{B} \tag{2.11}$$

which is the equation of motion of a charged particle in a pure magnetic field. The conclusions are, therefore, identical to those above in that the motion consists of the usual motion in a uniform magnetic field plus a drifting motion of the center of the Larmor orbit (guiding center) with velocity v_D as given in eq. (2.9). The situation is depicted for positive and negative particles in Fig. 2.1. Let us emphasize again that this analysis is

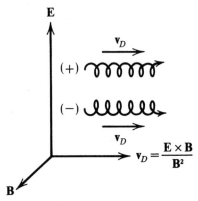

Fig. 2.1

applicable only if $|E| < c|B|$. The drift velocity is independent of the mass and the charge of the particles, and thus for the case of an electrically neutral plasma, no induced macroscopic currents will be generated in this way.

The arguments just presented are evidently also applicable for the case of motion in any constant external field (nonelectromagnetic) F, for example, a gravitational field. It is only necessary to make, in the above formulas, the replacement

$$E \to \frac{F}{q} \tag{2.12}$$

which leads to a drift velocity v_D given by

$$v_D = \frac{1}{q} \frac{F \times B}{B^2} \tag{2.13}$$

Significantly, this drift velocity is opposite for positive and negative carriers and therefore gives rise to a current

$$j = Nqv_D = N \frac{F \times B}{B^2} \tag{2.14}$$

where N is the total number of particles per unit volume.

MOTION IN A SPATIALLY UNIFORM
TIME-DEPENDENT MAGNETIC FIELD

It is easily verified that, in general, Maxwell's equations in the absence of charges and currents do not admit solutions that are spatially uniform but still time dependent and vice versa. Nevertheless, locally, such fields can exist to a fairly high degree of approximation, and for present purposes we shall assume that the trajectory of the charged particle under consideration is small enough so that it does not experience any spatial variations of **B**. In addition, according to eq. (1.7) a time-varying magnetic field must be accompanied by an electric field which in most cases of interest cannot be neglected. The basic effect of this electric field is to change the energy of the particle so that the orbits around the magnetic field lines are no longer closed. One expects, however, that if the magnetic field does not vary appreciably in one Larmor period, the motion will not differ greatly from that in a static uniform field. This notion leads to the concept of an *adiabatic invariant*. Let us explore the matter further, although somewhat qualitatively at first.

Consider the motion of a particle of charge q, mass m, and kinetic energy $w_\perp$ associated with the velocity perpendicular to the slowly varying magnetic field **B**. The electric field **E** associated with this time-varying magnetic field does work on the particle and in one Larmor period changes $w_\perp$ by an amount, say, $\delta w_\perp$. This work may be expressed by the relations

$$\delta w_\perp = q \oint \mathbf{E} \cdot d\mathbf{l} = q \int (\nabla \times \mathbf{E}) \cdot d\mathbf{S} \tag{2.15}$$

$$= -q \int \frac{\partial \mathbf{B}}{\partial t} \cdot d\mathbf{S} \cong -q\pi a^2 \left| \frac{\partial \mathbf{B}}{\partial t} \right|$$

where the first integral is over the approximately closed orbit of the particle about the field line and a is the (approximately constant) Larmor radius of the particle. By assumption, **B** does not vary appreciably during a Larmor period, and if we let δB be its variation in one period, then the time derivative of B may be written approximately

$$\left| \frac{\partial \mathbf{B}}{\partial t} \right| \cong \frac{\delta B}{2\pi/\omega}$$

Inserting this into eq. (2.15), and adjusting the sign there by using the fact that if $\delta B > 0$, then the energy of the particle increases, we find

$$\delta w_\perp = q\pi a^2 \frac{\delta B}{\partial \pi/\omega} = w_\perp \frac{\delta B}{B} \tag{2.16}$$

or

$$\delta(\ln w_\perp) = \delta(\ln B) \tag{2.17}$$

which states the fact that the quantity $w_\perp/B$ is an approximate constant of the motion. It is not a true constant of the motion since, in general, the orbit will not close on itself thus invalidating the above discussion. However, for the case that the field varies slowly in time intervals of order $1/\omega$, this expression is approximately a constant and is called an *adiabatic invariant*.[*]

The approximate constancy of the quantity $w_\perp/B$ may also be looked at in terms of the magnetic moment associated with the particle's motion. As the particle spirals around the magnetic field line one may think of its trajectory as a small circular current loop of radius a and carrying a current

$$i = \frac{q\omega}{2\pi} = \frac{q^2 B}{2\pi m} \tag{2.18}$$

For both positively and negatively charged particles, this current is counterclockwise when viewed along the direction of the field. The associated magnetic moment μ is given by the product of the current and the area of the loop and thus we find

$$\mu = -\frac{\mathbf{B}}{B}\frac{q\omega}{2\pi}\pi a^2 = -\frac{\mathbf{B}}{B}\frac{w_\perp}{B} \tag{2.19}$$

where the second equality follows by use of eq. (2.5). Thus, the content of eq. (2.17) is often referred to as the approximate constancy of the magnetic moment.

Let us now examine this motion somewhat more quantitatively. For this purpose, we shall assume that the magnetic field may be written

$$\mathbf{B} = \mathbf{B}_o h(t) \tag{2.20}$$

where $\mathbf{B}_o$ is a constant vector that points in, say, the z direction, and $h(t)$ is some function of time that for the present need be specified no further. In order to obtain the electric field, it is convenient to make use of a vector potential $\mathbf{A}$ so that eq. (1.7) is always automatically satisfied, and a convenient choice is

$$\mathbf{A} = \frac{1}{2}(\mathbf{B}_o \times \mathbf{r})h(t) \tag{2.21}$$

It is easily verified that $\nabla \times \mathbf{A}$ reproduces eq. (2.20) and that the electric field becomes

$$\mathbf{E} = -\frac{\partial \mathbf{A}}{\partial t} = -\frac{1}{2}(\mathbf{B}_o \times \mathbf{r})\,h'(t) \tag{2.22}$$

---

[*] For a more precise and complete discussion of this concept see, for example, L. D. Landau and E. M. Lifshitz, *Mechanics*, Reading, Mass: Addison Wesley Publishing Company Inc., 1960, pp. 155–62.

where the prime denotes differentiation with respect to time. The equation of motion of the particle thus becomes

$$m\ddot{\mathbf{r}} = q\left[\dot{\mathbf{r}} \times \mathbf{B}_o h(t) - \frac{1}{2}(\mathbf{B}_o \times \mathbf{r})h'(t)\right] \qquad (2.23)$$

from which it is clear that the motion along the magnetic field—that is, the z direction—is completely unaffected by the field and the particle moves along $\mathbf{B}_o$ with its initial velocity $\mathbf{v}_{||}$. The motion at right angles to $\mathbf{B}_o$, however, is more complicated and the components of eq. (2.23) become

$$\ddot{x} = \omega\left[\dot{y}h(t) + \frac{1}{2}yh'(t)\right]$$

$$\ddot{y} = -\omega\left[\dot{x}h(t) + \frac{1}{2}xh'(t)\right] \qquad (2.24)$$

where ω is the Larmor frequency, qB_o/m. In a manner analogous to the static case, we define a complex variable $u = x+iy$, so that eq. (2.24) may be rewritten (h is a real function)

$$\ddot{u} + i\omega h(t)\dot{u} + \frac{i}{2}\omega h'(t)u = 0 \qquad (2.25)$$

The solution of eq. (2.25) may be put into more convenient form by defining a new function $\zeta(t)$ by the relation

$$u = e^{-i\Omega\phi(t)}\zeta \qquad (2.26)$$

where $\Omega = \omega/2$, and $\phi(t)$ is given by

$$\phi(t) = \int_0^t h(t')\, dt' \qquad (2.27)$$

We note that $\phi(t)$ is real and $\phi(0) = 0$. Substituting the assumed form eq. (2.26) into eq. (2.27) we find for the equation satisfied by $\zeta(t)$ the result

$$\ddot{\zeta} + \Omega^2 h^2(t)\zeta = 0 \qquad (2.28)$$

which shows that $\zeta(t)$ may be selected to be real. Still without specifying the precise form of $h(t)$ any further, eq. (2.28) shows that in general ζ will be an oscillatory function (since its curvature, which is proportional to $\ddot{\zeta}/\zeta$, is always towards the t axis), that a constant times a solution is still a solution, and that there are exactly two linearly independent solutions, call them $\zeta_1(t)$ and $\zeta_2(t)$. These two solutions will be uniquely defined in terms of initial conditions by the formulas

$$\zeta_1(0) = 0 \qquad \zeta_1'(0) = 1$$

$$\zeta_2(0) = 1 \qquad \zeta_2'(0) = 0 \qquad (2.29)$$

Putting all of these results together, we find that the solution of eq. (2.25) may be written

$$u = e^{-i\Omega\phi(t)}[u_0\zeta_2 + \zeta_1\{\dot{u}_0 + i\Omega h(0)u_0\}] \tag{2.30}$$

where u_0 and $\dot{u}_0$ represent the initial position and velocity, respectively. Finally, without loss of generality, let us assume that the particle is initially at the origin and moving with velocity v_0 in the direction of the negative y axis, so that

$$u_0 = 0 \qquad \dot{u}_0 = -iv_0$$

Eq. (2.30) may be then written in the final form

$$u = e^{-i\Omega\phi(t)}(-iv_0\zeta_1) \tag{2.31}$$

and consequently we find

$$x = v_0\zeta_1(t) \sin[\Omega\phi(t)]$$
$$y = -v_0\zeta_1(t) \cos[\Omega\phi(t)] \tag{2.32}$$

In the special case for which the field is not time dependent and $h(t) = 1$, we find $\phi(t) = t$ and $\zeta_0(t) = (1/\Omega) \sin \Omega t$, and therefore eqs. (2.32) reproduce our previous results.

As a matter of practicality, we see that the motion of a particle in a spatially uniform magnetic field is readily solved; this is basically due to the fact that the equation of motion, eq. (2.23), is a linear equation. For a given $h(t)$, therefore, all of the mathematical problems are thus reduced to that of finding the solution of eq. (2.28) satisfying appropriate initial conditions.* For some forms of $h(t)$, eq. (2.28) may be brought into the form of well-studied equations. For example, with the choice $h(t) = \sin \omega_o t$, eq. (2.28) becomes a Mathieu equation, while the choice $h(t) = e^{-\alpha t}$, and the substitution $\tau = e^{-\alpha t}$ in eq. (2.28) produces Bessel's equation. Of most interest is the form $h(t) = 1 - \alpha t$ for which one solves eq. (2.28) in a power series in α. In the problems it is shown that if we calculate the ratio $(\dot{x}^2 + \dot{y}^2)/B(t)$ by use of this solution, we find that there are no terms of order α. This is consistent with the above discussion on the constancy of the magnetic moment.

MOTION IN A STATIC

SPATIALLY VARYING MAGNETIC FIELD

In many applications—for example, astrophysics—there exist magnetic

---

* In practice, this solution may be obtained by numerical means by taking the first net point to have the value zero at the origin and the second such that the solution starts out with unit slope.

fields that are almost uniform over distances of many Larmor radii, but nevertheless have some very small nonuniformities. In general the motions of charged particles in such fields are not analytically solvable since the equations of motion are, of course, nonlinear. As a result we shall be content with problems where the deviations from uniformity are very slight and solve for the trajectories, only in first order. It is to be expected in these cases that the motion of the particle can be described in terms of the motion in a uniform field, plus a slight drifting motion of the guiding center due to these perturbations.

Let us first consider the situation in which there is a very large uniform field $\mathbf{B}_0$ in, say, the z direction, but we shall suppose that the magnetic field has small spatial gradients at right angles to $\mathbf{B}_0$, say, in the x direction. The magnetic field may be written

$$\mathbf{B} = \mathbf{B}_0\{0,0,h(x)\} \tag{2.33}$$

where $h(x)$ is a function of the form

$$h(x) \cong 1 - \alpha x$$

with the coefficient α having the property $\alpha a \ll 1$, where a is a Larmor radius. We note that eq. (2.33) is consistent with Maxwell's equations for any choice of the function $h(x)$.

It follows from eq. (2.33) and Newton's law that the motion in the z direction is not disturbed at all, and that the particle will, therefore, continue to travel along z with its initial uniform velocity $v_{\parallel}$. The equations of motion in the x and y directions become for this case

$$\ddot{x} = \omega \dot{y} h(x)$$

$$\ddot{y} = - \omega \dot{x} h(x) \tag{2.34}$$

where ω is, again, $\omega = qB_0/m$. The second of eqs. (2.34) may be integrated once to yield

$$\dot{y} = - \omega H(x) \tag{2.35}$$

where $H(x)$ is given by

$$H(x) = \int_0^x h(x)\, dx \tag{2.36}$$

and we have assumed that initially the particle is at the origin and moving in the x direction. Substituting eq. (2.35) into the first of eqs. (2.34), the latter may also be integrated once to yield

$$\dot{x}^2 = v_0^2 - \omega^2 H^2(x) \tag{2.37}$$

where v_o is the initial velocity in the x direction. We see, therefore, that for this particular case, regardless of the form of $h(x)$, the orbit may be completely determined, for we find from eq. (2.37) the result

$$\omega t = \int_0^x dx [a^2 - H^2(x)]^{-\frac{1}{2}} \tag{2.38}$$

where a is the Larmor radius. Finally, $y = y(t)$ may be obtained by integrating eq. (2.35) using the result given in eq. (2.38). Unfortunately, these solutions are fairly complex and are not useful for aiding one's physical intuition. For the latter purpose, let us turn to solving this problem by perturbation theory, the validity of whose results may be checked by use of the analytic solutions just described.

To this end, Newton's laws may be written

$$\ddot{x} = \omega \dot{y} - \omega \dot{y} \alpha x$$

$$\ddot{y} = -\omega \dot{x} + \omega \dot{x} \alpha x \tag{2.39}$$

where α is a parameter of smallness, and we are interested in keeping only terms linear in α. As a consequence, the factor x in the second term of both of eqs. (2.39) may be expressed in terms of its zero order value, namely,

$$x^0(t) = -a \sin \omega t \tag{2.40}$$

and thus eqs. (2.39) may be written approximately as

$$\ddot{x} = \omega \dot{y} + \omega \dot{y} \alpha a \sin \omega t$$

$$\ddot{y} = -\omega \dot{x} - \omega \dot{x} \alpha a \sin \omega t \tag{2.41}$$

In a manner identical to that used for a time-dependent magnetic field, we define a complex variable $u = x + iy$ whose time development is governed by the equation

$$\ddot{u} = -i\omega \dot{u} (1 + \alpha a \sin \omega t)$$

which can be immediately integrated to yield

$$\dot{u} = \dot{u}_0 \exp \left\{ -i\omega \left[t + \frac{\alpha a}{\omega} - \frac{\alpha a}{\omega} \cos \omega t \right] \right\}$$

$$\cong \dot{u}_0 [1 + i\alpha a(\cos \omega t - 1)] e^{-i\omega t} \tag{2.42}$$

correct to terms linear in α. It is clear that this velocity consists of two types of terms: one set that oscillates with the frequency ω and the second set that does not. Only the latter are of immediate interest and in order to obtain these we average $\dot{u}$ as given in eq. (2.42) over a period $2\pi/\omega$. We find in this way

$$\bar{\dot{u}} = \frac{\omega}{2\pi}\int_0^{2\pi/\omega} dt \; \dot{u}(t) = \frac{\dot{u}_0\omega}{2\pi}\int_0^{2\pi/\omega} dt \left[e^{-i\omega t} - i\alpha a e^{-i\omega t} + \frac{i\alpha a}{2} + \frac{i\alpha a}{2} e^{-2i\omega t} \right]$$

of which only the third term fails to vanish. Thus, we obtain

$$\bar{\dot{u}} = \dot{u}_0 \frac{i\alpha a}{2} \tag{2.43}$$

According to eq. (2.40) the particle is initially at the origin and moving with velocity v_o in the negative x direction, and therefore, $\dot{u}_o = -v_o$, and consequently, we find from eq. (2.43) the result

$$\bar{\dot{x}} = 0$$

$$\bar{\dot{y}} = -\frac{\alpha a}{2} v_o \tag{2.44}$$

This states that the particle, in addition to its circular motion about the field lines, has a drift velocity in a direction at right angles to both the

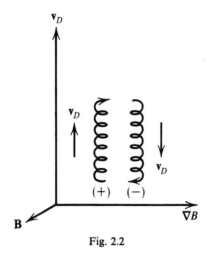

Fig. 2.2

magnetic field and its spatial derivative. This result may be stated: the drift velocity $\mathbf{v}_D$ is given (in language independent of coordinate system) by the formula

$$\frac{\mathbf{v}_D}{v_0} = \frac{a}{2B_0^2} (\mathbf{B}_0 \times \nabla B) \tag{2.45}$$

since for the present case $\nabla B \cong B_o(-\alpha, 0, 0)$. Let us emphasize again, that eq. (2.45) is valid provided $\alpha a \ll 1$, a fact equivalent to the statement that the drift velocity is very small compared to v_o. A second point worthy of notice is that the drift velocity is opposite for particles of opposite signs of charge, since a is given by $a = mv_o/qB_o$. The situation is depicted in Fig. 2.2. It is clear that spatial variations of this type produce macroscopic currents $\mathbf{j} = Nq\mathbf{v}_D$ as before.

MOTION IN A MAGNETIC FIELD
WITH CURVATURE

A second class of spatial variations in the magnetic field lines which are of interest are those field configurations that are essentially uniform over a Larmor radius, but from a macroscopic point of view have some sort of curvature. An example of this situation is the motion of a charged particle with Larmor radius $\lesssim 1$ cm in the magnetic field of the earth. In order to describe this conveniently, let us assume that the magnetic field lines are circles in the x-y plane and have magnitude $\mathbf{B}_o$. We have already con-

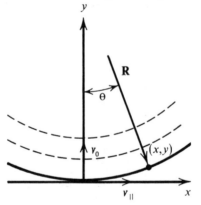

Fig. 2.3

sidered gradients at right angles to the magnetic field, and since the condition $\nabla \cdot \mathbf{B} = 0$ does not allow variations along the $\mathbf{B}$ lines, it follows that we may consider the magnitude of the magnetic field to be constant throughout all of space. For purposes of making a perturbation expansion, however, it is necessary to assume that the field lines have radius R that is much larger than the Larmor radius a; and as we shall see, for this case, the particle moves as if it were attached to a field line. The picture to keep in mind in the following, therefore, is that the particle spirals around a magnetic field line that is essentially straight over many Larmor orbits. The field is shown schematically in Fig. 2.3.

The equations of motion of a particle in this magnetic field, assuming there is no component of the field in the z direction, are

$$\ddot{x} = -\omega \dot{z} \sin \theta \cong -\omega \dot{z} \theta$$

$$\ddot{y} = \omega \dot{z} \cos \theta \cong \omega \dot{z}$$

$$\ddot{z} = \omega (\dot{x} \sin \theta - \dot{y} \cos \theta) \cong \omega (\theta \dot{x} - \dot{y}) \tag{2.46}$$

where we have assumed that the particle is near the origin, and hence the angle θ is very small and given approximately by

$$\theta \cong \frac{x}{R}$$

Eqs. (2.46) may, therefore, be written to order $1/R$ in the form

$$\ddot{x} = -\omega \dot{z} \frac{x}{R}$$

$$\ddot{y} = \omega \dot{z}$$

$$\ddot{z} = \omega \left(\frac{x}{R} \dot{x} - \dot{y} \right) \tag{2.47}$$

which may be solved in a power series of a/R by assuming

$$x = x^{(0)} + \frac{1}{R} x^{(1)} + \cdots,$$

and similarly for y and z. The unperturbed solutions, that is, with $1/R = 0$, are easily solved. One finds, assuming the particle is initially at the origin and moving with velocity $v_{||}$ in the x direction and with velocity v_0 in the positive y direction, the result

$$x^{(0)} = v_{||} t$$

$$y^{(0)} = a \sin \omega t$$

$$z^{(0)} = a(\cos \omega t - 1) \tag{2.48}$$

which is, of course, equivalent to eq. (2.8). Substituting this back into eqs. (2.47), we obtain correct to first order in $1/R$ the result

$$\ddot{x} = \frac{\omega}{R} (v_{||} t) v_0 \sin \omega t$$

$$\ddot{y} = \omega \dot{z}$$

$$\ddot{z} = \omega \left(\frac{v_{||}^2 t}{R} - \dot{y} \right) \tag{2.49}$$

where x stands for $x^{(0)} + (1/R)x^{(1)}$ and similarly for y and z. The first of these equations can easily be integrated once, and there are no secular terms, that is, $\bar{\dot{x}} = 0$; thus there is no net drift velocity in addition to $v_{||}$. The second of eqs. (2.49) may also be integrated once to yield

$$\dot{y} = \omega z + v_o$$

which when substituted into the third of eqs. (2.49) yields

$$\ddot{z} + \omega^2 z = \frac{\omega}{R} v_{||}^2 t - \omega v_o \tag{2.50}$$

In addition to oscillatory terms (which are of no interest here) this equation has the particular integral

$$z = \frac{v_{||}^2 t}{\omega R} - \frac{v_o}{\omega} \tag{2.51}$$

which leads to a drift velocity in the z direction

$$\mathbf{v}_D = \mathbf{e}_z \frac{v_{||}^2}{\omega R} \tag{2.52}$$

We note on substituting eq. (2.51) into the above $\ddot{y}$ equation that there is no drift velocity in the y direction. There is an acceleration $\ddot{y} = v_{||}^2/R$, however, which constrains the particle to follow along the arc of the circle. The result as given in eq. (2.52) may upon examination of Fig. 2.3 be put into the coordinate independent form,

$$\mathbf{v}_D = \frac{v_{||}^2}{\omega R} \left(\frac{\mathbf{R} \times \mathbf{B}}{RB} \right) \tag{2.53}$$

As before, this drift is in opposite directions for opposite signs of charge because of the ω factor and thus gives rise to a macroscopic current.

For certain applications, this drift velocity due to curvature causes great difficulties. We may consider, for example, a toroidal tube containing a strong axial magnetic field due to currents flowing in wires wrapped around the torus. More specifically, let us suppose $R \sim 10^2$ cm, $B \sim 10^3$ gauss and the particles are protons at 10^4 °K. We find that the drift velocity, according to eq. (2.53), is $\sim 10^3$ cm/sec, and thus the particles strike the walls of the tube and are lost to the plasma in a small fraction of a second. Of course, at these conditions the particles make many circuits around the tube before they strike the walls. This effect may be overcome as in the Stellarator by constructing a torus in the shape of a figure eight. Then during the first half of its circuit around the tube the particle drifts in one direction, while for the second half it drifts in the opposite direction. The net effect is to nullify this drift velocity, thus "confining" the plasma.

MOTION IN REGIONS
OF CONVERGING FIELD LINES

The third type of spatial variations in the magnetic field lines of interest are fields that have a rotationally symmetric angular divergence that is, fields that are directed mostly in, say, the z direction, but have in addition a very weak dependence on z. Again, it is sufficient to consider these z variations to take place in dimensions very large compared to the appropriate Larmor radii. The situation is depicted in Fig. 2.4.

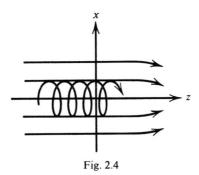

Fig. 2.4

By use of eq. (1.5), it follows that such a field is impossible unless, in addition to the z component, a small radial component also exists. For example, if e_r, e_z are unit vectors along r and z (cylindrical coordinates), then a possible choice for **B** may be taken to be

$$\mathbf{B} = B_0 \left[-\frac{\alpha}{2} r e_r + e_z(1 + \alpha z) \right] \tag{2.54}$$

which is easily shown to be consistent with the equation $\nabla \cdot \mathbf{B} = 0$. The parameter α will be assumed to satisfy the condition $\alpha a \ll 1$, where a is a Larmor radius. The effect of the field in the z direction is to produce a force tending to slow down the particle assuming it was originally traveling to the right about the central line in Fig. 2.4. This means that since v^2 is conserved, the kinetic energy of the particle at right angles to the field must increase, which in turn implies that according to eq. (2.5) the particle gyrates more rapidly around a smaller circle. This process will continue until the z component of the particle's velocity $v_{||}$ vanishes. Then the guiding center of the particle turns around and will move along the negative z direction until something else happens to change this. In effect, we see that the particle has been *reflected* by the magnetic field.

Fields of this type are very easily generated in the laboratory. It is only necessary to wrap wire, carrying a steady current, about a long cylinder and vary the density of the windings. For example, a *magnetic bottle* consists of a long cylinder with essentially a uniform density of windings in the center and a very high density at the ends. Particles, once they have been introduced into the bottle, are reflected at both ends and are thus trapped in its interior. This effect has also been used by Fermi in an attempt to explain the high energies of cosmic-ray particles. Fermi assumed that there exist very large clouds of particles in intergalactic space that have magnetic fields associated with them. If there are two clouds moving toward each other with some, albeit slight, velocity, a particle trapped between two such clouds will suffer repeated collisions with them and slowly increase its velocity $v_{||}$ due to their relative motions. After many such collisions, the particle will eventually have enough energy so that it can *leak* out of this bottle and ultimately arrive at the earth with a very large energy.

The quantitative understanding of this phenomenon may be easily obtained by use of eq. (2.54) and use of the fact $\alpha a \ll 1$. The equations of motion are

$$\ddot{x} = \omega \left[\dot{y} + \alpha \left(z\dot{y} + \frac{1}{2} y\dot{z} \right) \right]$$

$$\ddot{y} = -\omega \left[\dot{x} + \alpha \left(z\dot{x} + \frac{1}{2} x\dot{z} \right) \right]$$

$$\ddot{z} = \frac{\omega\alpha}{2} (x\dot{y} - y\dot{x}) \tag{2.55}$$

of which the last is of most interest to us. Since we are concerned only with the solution correct to terms linear in α, the z equation may be solved by using the unperturbed solution on the right-hand side of this equation. Assuming the particle is originally at the point $(a, 0, 0)$ and moving with velocity $(0, -v_o, v_{||})$, the unperturbed solutions of eqs (2.55) are

$$x^0 = a \cos \omega t$$

$$y^0 = -a \sin \omega t$$

$$z^0 = v_{||}t \tag{2.56}$$

which when substituted into the last of eqs (2.55) yields

$$\ddot{z} = -\frac{1}{2}(\omega a)^2 \alpha = -\frac{1}{2} v_0^2 \alpha \tag{2.57}$$

This shows that to this order of magnitude there is a constant deceleration acting in the negative z direction. This equation for the motion in the z direction may be explicitly integrated to yield

$$z = -\frac{1}{4} v_0^2 \alpha t^2 + v_{||}^0 t$$

where $v_{||}^0$ is the initial velocity along the positive z direction. Needless to say, the approximation $\alpha a \ll 1$ will be valid for the macroscopic bottles of the sort described above, provided the Larmor radii are no longer than fractions of a millimeter.

An alternate and somewhat more intuitive derivation of this reflection phenomenon may be obtained by turning back to the concept of an adiabatic invariant. It will be recalled that for the case for which the magnetic field varied very slowly in time the quantity $w_\perp/B$ is approximately a constant of the motion. It is clear that a spatially varying magnetic field is equivalent—in lowest order, in any event—from the particle's point of view to a time-varying magnetic field and thus the quantity $w_\perp/B$ is a constant as the particle follows its trajectory. More quantitatively, if we let $v_{||}$ and $v_\perp$ be the velocities along and perpendicular to the magnetic field, we find, since $v_{||}^2 + v_\perp^2$ is a true constant, the result

$$d(v_{||}^2) = -d(v_\perp^2) = -d\left(v_\perp^2 \frac{B}{B}\right) = -\frac{v_\perp^2}{B} dB$$

The last equality follows, since $v_\perp/B$ is assumed to be constant during the time interval dt when all of the above small changes take place. By use of this result we can now easily compute the acceleration $dv_{||}/dt$ along the magnetic field to be

$$\frac{dv_{||}}{dt} = -\frac{v_\perp^2}{2B} \frac{1}{v_{||}} \frac{dB}{dt} \cong -\frac{v_\perp^2}{2B} \frac{dB}{dz} = -\frac{v_\perp^2}{2}\alpha$$

where use has been made of eq. (2.54). We see, therefore, that the result embodied in eq. (2.57) follows directly and simply by use of the notion of an adiabatic invariant.

COLLAPSE OF AN INFINITE, CYLINDRICAL PINCH

Before we turn to the more formal aspects of the dynamics of a plasma, let us consider a very simple but physically interesting application of orbit theory. It will be recalled that this theory is useful if some means are available for obtaining approximate values for the electromagnetic fields inside a plasma. In the following, we shall not bother to carry out a consistency check very thoroughly, since the correctness of choice will depend upon the conditions existing inside the plasma under consideration, and the results thus will be applicable only to such restricted cases. Nevertheless, the situations for which it works are interesting from both a practical and physical point of view.

Let us consider a very long cylinder (long enough so that end effects can be neglected) of a plasma having a circular cross section of initial radius R_o. At the ends of the cylinder there are two electrodes that form part of a closed circuit consisting of a power source and other circuit components. The situation is depicted schematically in Fig. 2.5. Let us assume that the mass density ρ_o of the plasma is sufficiently small, that the conductivity is essentially infinite, and therefore there are no electric or magnetic fields existing anywhere inside the plasma. Nevertheless, there is a current flow

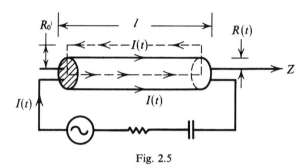

Fig. 2.5

$I(t)$ through the circuit, and because of the infinite conductivity of the plasma, it follows that this current must be confined to a very thin layer on the surface of the plasma and flows along the z direction. Since parallel current elements attract each other, it is physically reasonable that this surface will collapse under these magnetic stresses, and the speed of the collapse will increase with the current. For reasons of simplicity, let us assume that the current is so large that this collapse takes place with velocity much larger than the original thermal velocities of the particles comprising the plasma. This situation was first proposed and considered in detail by Rosenbluth, and our discussion is based on this work.

In order to describe this collapse, it is necessary to specify the fields in some detail. As we have already noted, the fields inside the plasma vanish, while outside the plasma the magnetic field lines are circles concentric with the axis of the cylinder and of magnitude

$$B = \frac{\mu_o}{2\pi} \frac{I(t)}{r} \tag{2.58}$$

for $r > R(t)$ where $R(t)$ is the radius of the cylinder at time t. $I(t)$ is the current that flows through the circuit and is thus the current on the surface of the plasma at time t. To proceed with the analysis—that is, in order to find $R(t)$ and $I(t)$—we need two more equations; one of these is the circuit equation and the second describes the interaction of the plasma with the magnetic field itself.

The circuit equation follows directly from first principles and entails no ambiguities. We take eq. (1.7) and integrate over the area denoted by the rectangle in Fig. 2.5. The line integral of **E** through the center of the plasma vanishes, the contributions along the edges are also negligible, while the contribution from the outer path yields $\phi(t)$ where $\phi(t)$ is the potential drop that includes the power source in the external circuit as well as any capacitors, resistors, inductances that may be there. We find, therefore, the circuit equation

$$\phi(t) = -\frac{d}{dt}\int \mathbf{B}\cdot d\mathbf{S} \tag{2.59}$$

which by substitution from eq. (2.58) may be written

$$\phi(t) = -\frac{d}{dt}\int_{-1/2}^{1/2} dz \int_{R(t)}^{R_0} \frac{\mu_0}{2\pi}\frac{I(t)}{r}\, dr$$

The integrals are easily carried out and we obtain finally

$$\phi(t) = \frac{\mu_0 l}{2\pi}\frac{d}{dt}\left[I(t)\ln\frac{R_o}{R(t)}\right] \tag{2.60}$$

We note the interesting fact that on carrying out the time differentiations in eq. (2.60) two distinct terms are produced; one of these is proportional to the current itself, and the second is proportional to the time derivative of the current. The former has the effect of modifying the original resistance in the circuit and thus corresponds, from the circuit point of view, to a dissipation of power. Of course, this power is not dissipated in the usual sense of this term, since the energy goes directly into the plasma and increases the kinetic energies of the particles. The second term—namely, the one proportional to dI/dt—corresponds to energy being stored in the magnetic field and can be understood in the same way as an ordinary inductance. Let us finally note that if the plasma temperature is high enough so that the cylinder expands instead of contracting—that is, $R(t) > R_o$ rather than $R(t) < R_o$ as we have implicitly assumed above—then power might be taken out of the plasma and converted directly to electric energy for usage elsewhere.

In order to obtain the third equation, we need to look at the details of the plasma to some extent. We have already assumed that the particles in the plasma are essentially at rest when they are struck by the rapidly collapsing current surface. Let us follow a particular particle in the process of being hit by this "wall." It is convenient to discuss this situation from the viewpoint of the instantaneous rest frame of the wall in which the particle approaches the surface current with a very large velocity. Initially, the particle moves in a region of space that is essentially free of all electromagnetic fields, and then it enters a region in which the magnetic field rises very rapidly. The particle will be turned around by this field and re-enter the plasma with roughly the same velocity. In addition, while the particle makes a Larmor orbit inside the surface, it also makes a contribution to the current. Since the Larmor radii of ions are larger than those of electrons, one expects that there is also in this surface a large electric field directed radially inward due to this charge separation. The electrons, because of their relatively smaller mass, never penetrate enough into the surface to experience this field, but the ions do. In any event, we see that this current surface is of a fairly complex nature, but its net effect is to turn around the particles it strikes. As far as the motions of the particles are concerned, we may say, therefore, that a given particle that starts out from rest is struck by a "piston" moving with velocity $\dot{R}(t)$ and flies into the plasma with velocity $2\dot{R}$. By this process, energy and momentum are added to the plasma, and this energy, as we have already seen, comes from the circuit that drives the system.

Once we have established this picture of the particles being elastically reflected by the wall, a further assumption (whose consistency can easily be checked later) must be made. One possibility is that the surface is accelerating so rapidly that the wall catches up with all of the particles it has previously struck. This may be thought of as a sort of a snow plow on which all particles stick to the wall once they have been struck by it. This model is called the *snow-plow model* and has been discussed in the literature. A second possibility is that the surface does not accelerate very much, and thus the particles once they have been struck by the wall, readily re-enter the plasma. This point of view is called the *independent particle model*, and we shall consider only this model in detail. Care must be exercised in using this model, however, since the struck particles will move with a large velocity and eventually strike the other side of the cylinder and be reflected a second time, but *not* from rest. Because of the infinite conductivity assumption the struck particle re-enters the plasma and does not suffer any collisions with the other particles in it. We expect this assumption to be valid at sufficiently low densities. Again we shall not concern ourselves with this point but be content with a "one-bounce" formulation.

Let us consider a small element of area ΔA of the current surface that moves radially inward with a velocity $\dot{R}$ so that in a time Δt it travels a distance $\dot{R} \Delta t$. The impulse given to the plasma in this time interval is given by the product of $\Delta A \Delta t$ and the magnetic stress:

$$\frac{B^2}{2\mu_0} \Delta A \Delta t \tag{2.61}$$

where B is the magnetic field at the current surface and is given explicitly by

$$B = \frac{\mu_o}{2\pi} \frac{I(t)}{R(t)} \tag{2.62}$$

On the other hand, assuming that the mass density of the plasma is given by ρ_o (which can be taken to be that of the ions exclusively since the electrons have negligible mass by comparison) a mass of gas $\rho_o(\dot{R} \Delta t) \Delta A$ changes its velocity from zero to $2\dot{R}$ and thus gains momentum in the amount

$$2\rho_o \dot{R}^2 \Delta t \Delta A \tag{2.63}$$

Equating eqs. (2.61) and (2.63) and making use of eq. (2.62), we obtain for the equation governing the momentum balance the result

$$R^2(t)\dot{R}^2(t) = \frac{\mu_o}{(4\pi)^2} \frac{1}{\rho_o} I^2(t) \tag{2.64}$$

This equation, together with eq. (2.60) and the specification of $\phi(t)$ comprise, in this approximation, a "complete" description of the plasma as far as its macroscopic radial motion is concerned.

The radial motion as expressed in eq. (2.64) may be put into a somewhat simpler form by defining a new variable τ by the relation

$$\tau = \frac{1}{4\pi} \left(\frac{\mu_o}{\rho_o}\right)^{\frac{1}{2}} \int_0^t |I(t)| \, dt$$

which makes evident the fact that τ is a monotonic increasing function of time. Making this substitution we find $R(\tau)$ satisfies the simpler equation

$$R(\tau) \frac{d}{d\tau} R(\tau) = -1 \tag{2.65}$$

where the minus sign in front of the square root has been chosen in order that the surface contracts as time (or equivalently as τ) increases. Eq. (2.65) may be integrated immediately to yield

$$2\tau = R_0^2 - R^2(\tau) \tag{2.66}$$

where R_0 is the initial value for R. Of course, in order to find R as a function of time, we need to solve the circuit equation eq. (2.60) as well and substitute into eq. (2.66). For conceptual reasons, however, we note that the details of the circuit will only affect the time scale and thus eq. (2.66) is adequate. It is clear that the present analysis is not applicable all the way down to a vanishingly small radius, a fact that can easily be understood if we recall that many particles will strike the wall more than once and will certainly slow it down this way. Further, detailed considerations by Rosenbluth have shown that the surface can even expand as a result of such repeated collisions.

THE NONCYLINDRICAL CASE

The extension of these ideas to plasmas that have noncylindrical shapes is sometimes possible. Consider, for example, the situation depicted in Fig. 2.6, for which the surface is still symmetric under rotations about the

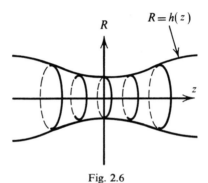

Fig. 2.6

z axis, but the surface originally has the form $R = h(z)$ where h is some given function. Under the same assumptions as made above, the analysis may be repeated step by step. Brief reflection shows that the result in eq. (2.58) is still applicable, while the circuit equation (2.60) must be modified slightly by allowing for z variations in carrying out the surface integral. Finally, the momentum balance equation appears in the same form,

$$2\rho_o v^2 = \frac{\mu_o}{8\pi^2} \frac{I^2(t)}{R^2} \tag{2.67}$$

however, $\mathbf{v}$ is now the velocity normal to the surface and is not generally directed along R. The remaining problem, therefore, is to express this normal velocity in terms of parameters that specify the surface.

Let the equation of the current surface at time t be given by

$$f(R,z,t) = 0 \tag{2.68}$$

our problem now being to find the function f. In order to obtain this function, let δR, δz be small changes in R and z such that if R and z lie on the surface at time t, then so does the point $R + \delta R$ and $z + \delta z$. Also, let ΔR and Δz be small changes in R and z so that if this point lies on the surface at time t, then the point $R + \Delta R$ and $z + \Delta z$ lies on the surface at time $t + \Delta t$. Since these increments are related by the condition

$$\Delta R\, \delta R + \Delta z\, \delta z = 0 \tag{2.69}$$

the square of the local normal velocity is given by

$$v^2 = \lim_{\Delta t \to 0} \frac{(\Delta R)^2 + (\Delta z)^2}{(\Delta t)^2} \tag{2.70}$$

Using the definitions of δR, Δz, and so on, given above, we find that they are related to each other by the conditions

$$\delta R\, \frac{\partial f}{\partial R} + \delta z\, \frac{\partial f}{\partial z} = 0 \tag{2.71}$$

and

$$\Delta R\, \frac{\partial f}{\partial R} + \Delta z\, \frac{\partial f}{\partial z} + \Delta t\, \frac{\partial f}{\partial t} = 0 \tag{2.72}$$

Solving now the ratios $\Delta R/\Delta t$, $\Delta z/\Delta t$ by use of eqs. (2.69), (2.71), (2.72), and substituting these into eq. (2.70) we find

$$v^2 = \left(\frac{\partial f}{\partial t}\right)^2 \left[\left(\frac{\partial f}{\partial R}\right)^2 + \left(\frac{\partial f}{\partial z}\right)^2\right]^{-1} \tag{2.73}$$

which may be substituted into eq. (2.67) to yield the final equation expressing momentum blance for this case in the form

$$\left(\frac{\partial f}{\partial t}\right)^2 \left[\left(\frac{\partial f}{\partial R}\right)^2 + \left(\frac{\partial f}{\partial z}\right)^2\right]^{-1} = \frac{\mu_0}{16\pi^2}\, \frac{1}{\rho_o R^2}\, I^2(t) \tag{2.74}$$

This is a partial differential equation whose solution will describe in detail the motion of the current surface in the present case. We note that this is a particularly simple equation in that it involves only first derivatives and thus, once $I(t)$ is known, it is readily solvable. Also in the special case for which there is no z dependence, that is, $(\partial f/\partial z) = 0$, eq. (2.74) becomes identical to the previous result as given in eq. (2.64).

As in that case, it is convenient to change the variable from t to τ, which is defined by

$$\tau = \frac{1}{4\pi} \left(\frac{\mu_o}{\rho_o}\right)^{1/2} \int_0^t |I(t)|\, dt \tag{2.75}$$

Changing variables, eq. (2.74) takes on the simpler form

$$\left(\frac{\partial f}{\partial \tau}\right)^2 = \frac{1}{R^2}\left[\left(\frac{\partial f}{\partial R}\right)^2 + \left(\frac{\partial f}{\partial z}\right)^2\right] \tag{2.76}$$

in which all the dependence on the details of the circuit have been lumped into the variable τ.

Using the initial condition that at $\tau = 0$, the current surface has the form

$$f(R,z,0) = R - h(z) = 0$$

eq. (2.76) may be integrated analytically*, to yield

$$z - \lambda = \frac{hh'}{[1+(h')^2]^{\frac{1}{2}}}\ln\frac{h[1+1/\{1+(h')^2\}^{\frac{1}{2}}]}{R+[R^2 - h^2(h')^2/\{1+(h')^2\}]^{\frac{1}{2}}}$$

$$2\tau = \frac{h^2}{[1+(h')^2]^{\frac{1}{2}}} - R\left[R^2 - \frac{h^2(h')^2}{1+(h')^2}\right]^{\frac{1}{2}} + \frac{hh'}{[1+(h')^2]^{\frac{1}{2}}}(z-\lambda) \tag{2.77}$$

where λ is a parameter which is to be eliminated between these two equations and where $h = h(\lambda)$ and $h' = dh/d\lambda$. This solution of eq. (2.76) involves no surprises, and physically the collapse of the plasma occurs in just the way one would expect. That is, the parts of the current surface which are closest to the axis collapse most rapidly since the magnetic pressure goes as $1/R^2$. In the limit when the surface becomes smooth, i.e., $h(z) = $ constant, the previous result, eq. (2.65) is reproduced. There are many applications of orbit theory besides those considered above and some of these will be found in the references and problems.

Suggested Readings and References

1. Particle Dynamics: Adiabatic Invariants

M. Alfven, *Cosmological Electrodynamics*, Chap. II. New York: Oxford University Press, 1950.

M. Born, *The Mechanics of the Atom*. London: G. Bell & Sons, Ltd., 1927.

S. Chandrasekhar, "Adiabatic Invariants in the Motions of Charged Particles," *The Plasma in a Magnetic Field*, K. M. Landshoff (editor). Stanford, Calif: Stanford University Press, 1958.

S. Chandrasekhar, *Plasma Physics*. Chicago: University of Chicago Press, 1960.

J. D. Jackson, *Classical Electrodynamics*, Chap. 12. New York: John Wiley & Sons, Inc., 1962.

---

* See, for example, Courant, and Hilbert, *Methods of Mathematical Physics*, Volume II. New York: Interscience Publishers, Inc., 1962, pp. 62–69.

M. N. Rosenbluth and C. L. Longmire, "Stability of Plasmas Confined by Magnetic Fields," *Ann. Phys.* **1**, 120 (1957).

L. Spitzer, Jr., *Physics of Fully Ionized Gases*, Chap. I. New York: Interscience Publishers, Inc., 1956.

2. Collapse of a Pinch

J. D. Jackson, *Classical Electrodynamics*, Chap. 10. New York: John Wiley & Sons, Inc., 1962.

M. N. Rosenbluth, "Dynamics of a Pinched Gas," *Magnetohydrodynamics*, K. M. Landshoff (editor). Stanford, Calif: Stanford University Press, 1957.

H. W. Wyld, Jr., "Dynamic Stability of a Self-Pinched Discharge," *J. Appl. Phys.*, **29**, 1460 (1958).

Problems

1. (a) Assuming that $h(t)$ in eq. (2.28) has the form $e^{-\alpha t}$, show that the substitution $\tau = (\Omega/\alpha)e^{-\alpha t}$, transforms eq. (2.28) into

$$\frac{d^2\zeta}{d\tau^2} + \frac{1}{\tau}\frac{d\zeta}{d\tau} + \zeta(\tau) = 0$$

which is Bessel's equation of order zero.

(b) Find the two solutions that satisfy the boundary condition in eq. (2.29).

(c) Give a physical interpretation of the parts of this solution that grow linearly with time; examine both possibilities of α positive and negative.

2. Consider the motion of a charged particle in a time-dependent magnetic field with $h(t)$ given by $h(t) = 1 - \alpha t$. Find the trajectory to order α, and verify explicitly the fact that there are no terms linear in α in the adiabatic invariant.

3. Solve completely for the trajectory of a charged particle in the field of a monopole. This magnetic field is given by

$$\mathbf{B} = \lambda \frac{\mathbf{r}}{r^3}$$

where λ is a constant.

4. Study the equation of motion for a charged particle in the

field of a dipole. Obtain two constants of the motion and interpret them physically. (See, C. Störmer, *The Polar Aurora*, University Oxford Press, 1955).

5. (a) The magnetic field of the earth (outside of the earth) may be approximately represented by a dipole placed at the center. Using the fact that at a magnetic pole, the earth's field is approximately $\frac{1}{2}$ gauss, calculate the strength of the dipole.

(b) Consider the motion of an electron of energy 1 Mev, at an altitude of 2 earth radii. Calculate the Larmor frequency and the radius of gyration.

(c) Assuming that this electron is confined to motion in the equatorial plane, calculate the direction and the time it takes to drift once around the earth.

(d) Assuming now that $w_\perp = w_{||}$, calculate the time it takes to be reflected between the congested magnetic field lines, between the magnetic poles. At what altitude does reflection occur?

(e) Repeat (b), (c), (d) leaving as parameters the energy and altitude of the particle (but still assume that the earth's radius is much larger than the radius of gyration of the particle) and examine these formulas in the light of known values for the Van Allen belts.

6. Assuming $h(x)$ has the form $e^{-\alpha x}$, integrate eq. (2.38) explicitly and thus obtain the trajectory. Expand the result in a power series in α and thus verify eqs. (2.44).

7. Consider the motion of a charged particle in a region of converging field lines.

(a) Show that if θ is the angle that the velocity makes with the direction of the magnetic field at a point where it has strength B, then

$$\frac{\sin^2 \theta}{B} = \text{constant}$$

along the particle's guiding center.

(b) Consider a plasma with an isotropic velocity distribution which is trapped in a mirror geometry. Show that the fraction of the particles that are reflected at a given mirror point is given by

$$1 - \frac{B_o}{B_m}$$

where B_m is the maximum value of the field (at the reflection point) and B_o is the field far away.

8. Consider a plasma containing N particles per cubic centimeter and suppose that the equilibrium shape of this plasma is that of a very long cylinder of radius b and that there is a uniform external magnetic field B_o oriented along the axis of the cylinder.

(a) Assuming that the induced field is small compared to the external field, show that the magnetic moment per unit volume is given by

$$\mathbf{M} = -N\frac{B_o}{B_o^2} w_\perp$$

(b) Calculate the currents produced by $\mathbf{M}$ and show that the total magnetic field inside the plasma is smaller than B_o (diamagnetism) and is given by

$$\mathbf{B} = \mathbf{B}_o\left[1 - \frac{Nw_\perp}{B_o^2/2\mu_o}\right]$$

provided that the kinetic energy density in the plasma is very small compared to the magnetic energy density.

(c) Calculate the magnetic field outside of the cylinder.

(d) By use of the results in (b), calculate the magnetic susceptibility in terms of $\mathbf{B}_o$. Is the concept of $\mathbf{H}$ very useful here? Discuss briefly.

(e) Justify the result obtained in (b) in the light of the theorem that classically there is no diamagnetism.

9. Consider the motion of a charged particle in a uniform time independent magnetic field $\mathbf{B}_o$ and in a spatially uniform but time-dependent electric field $\mathbf{E}(t)$ at right angles to $\mathbf{B}_o$.

(a) Show that if $\mathbf{v}$ is the actual velocity of the particle and $\mathbf{v}_D$ the drift velocity as given in eq. (2.9), then the equation of motion for $\mathbf{v}'$, which is defined by

$$\mathbf{v} = \mathbf{v}_D + \mathbf{v}' + \mathbf{v}_p$$

is expressible as

$$m\dot{\mathbf{v}}' + m\dot{\mathbf{v}}_p = q\mathbf{v}' \times \mathbf{B}$$

where $\mathbf{v}_p$ is given by

$$\mathbf{v}_p = \frac{m}{qB_0^2}\frac{\partial \mathbf{E}}{\partial t}$$

(b) Show that if the electric field does not change appreciably during a Larmor period, then the $\dot{\mathbf{v}}_p$ term may be neglected, and the resulting equation for $\mathbf{v}'$ is that of a particle moving in a simple magnetic field.

(c) Show that no current is associated with $\mathbf{v}_D$ in a neutral plasma; but that with $\mathbf{v}_p$ there is associated a "polarization" current $\mathbf{j}_p$ and this is given by

$$\mathbf{j}_p = \frac{\rho}{B^2}\frac{\partial \mathbf{E}}{\partial t}$$

where ρ is the mass density of the plasma.

(d) Show by use of the appropriately modified forms of eqs. (1.6) and (1.8) in terms of $\mathbf{D} = \kappa\varepsilon_o\mathbf{E}$ rather than $\mathbf{E}$, that the dielectric constant is given by

$$\kappa = 1 + \frac{\rho}{\varepsilon_o B^2}$$

(e) Calculate the magnitude of κ for a hydrogen plasma of density 10^{12} particles/cc in the earth's magnetic field.

(f) Account for the source of energy in the electric field $(1/2\mathbf{E}\cdot\mathbf{D})$ which is above and beyond $1/2\,\varepsilon_o E^2$.

10. An alternative description for the collapse of the cylindrical pinch is in terms of the so-called snow-plow model. In this case the acceleration of the collapsing surface is assumed to be so large that every struck particle is carried along by the surface.

(a) Show that for the snow-plow model, the equation that is analogous to (2.64) is

$$\frac{d}{dt}[M(R)R] = \frac{\mu_o}{4\pi}\frac{I^2}{R}$$

where

$$M(R) = \pi\rho_o[R_o^2 - R^2]$$

(b) Show that during the early part of the collapse, the snow-plow model and the independent-particle model give qualitatively the same results.

(c) Assuming that $\phi(t)$ in eq. (2.60) is given by the constant electric field E_o, determine the order of magnitude of the time required for the pinch to collapse for the snow-plow model and for the independent-particle model.

(d) Using the same $\phi(t)$ as in (c) set up the differential equation for the snow-plow model and obtain its solution.

11. Consider the collapse of the current surface surrounding a plasma as in Fig. 2.6 and assume that there is an opening into a vacuum on the right-hand side of this surface. Assuming that each particle is hit only once by the surface and thereafter it escapes through this opening, show that the momentum in the z direction imparted to the plasma in a time dt is given by

$$dP_z = 4\pi \ dt \int_{R_<}^{R_>} R \ dR \ \rho v^2$$

where $R_<(t)$ $(R_>(t))$ are the minimum (maximum) values of R at time t. Show also that this result may be written in the form

$$\frac{dP_z}{dt} = \frac{\mu_o}{4\pi} I^2(t) \ln \frac{R_>(t)}{R_<(t)}$$

and make a numerical estimate of this thrust for $I = 10^5$ amps. Justify qualitatively the fact that the density of the plasma does not appear explicitly in this relation.

3

The Dynamics of Many-particle Systems

INTRODUCTION

A possible—albeit impractical—description of the dynamics of a plasma may be obtained by solving for the trajectory of a typical particle as it moves under the combined influence of external electromagnetic fields as well as the fields generated by the other particles in the plasma. The latter fields give rise to the Coulomb forces as well as to interparticle magnetic forces. For situations of present interest we shall be involved, therefore, not only with the problem of solving of the order of 10^{22} coupled differential equations of motion but also of interpreting these generally complex motions in terms of a few macroscopic observables. It is clear that not all of a given particle's trajectory is significant on a macroscopic scale, and thus the obtaining of exact individual particle orbits is a very inefficient way of making predictions. In addition, of course, in order to solve these equations of motion we shall need as input data the initial positions and momenta of all of the particles; in general, these are not available, and can, as a matter of practicality, be specified only in a statistical way. Therefore, any results obtained in this way will not be exact, but will have fluctuations; these fluctuations, however, turn out to be quite small for systems with large numbers of degrees of freedom. A formal way of describing the method of solution just outlined is to say that one solves *Liouville's equation* subject to some given initial distribution function. If this initial distribution is an exact constant of the motion (for example, any function of the total energy of an isolated system would satisfy this condition), this solution of Liouville's equation is independent of time and the study of the resulting equilibrium behaviour of a many-particle system is called *statistical mechanics*.

A second and much more useful but approximate way of describing the dynamics of a plasma may be obtained in the following way. It is physically reasonable to expect that the motion of a given particle in the plasma may be obtained by assuming that the forces experienced by this particle are due to the external fields plus the macroscopically smoothed (in space and time) fields due to the motions of all of the other nearby particles in the plasma. This means that instead of having to solve for the precise orbits of all of the particles in each other's fluctuating force fields, we need to solve only for the motion of a typical particle in the macroscopically smoothed electromagnetic fields. The simplifications available by use of this method are obviously enormous. However, the problem of obtaining the fields themselves is still very complex. In fact, what is involved is the writing down of a partial differential equation (the Boltzmann-Vlasov equation) that describes the evolution of the distribution function of a typical particle in time and that directly involves the smoothed fields. This distribution function is then formally used to compute the macroscopic charge and current desnsities present in the plasma. These charge and current densities (which are already functionals of the electromagnetic fields) are then inserted into Maxwell's equation to yield a "self-consistent" solution. The resulting mathematical problem is clearly very nonlinear and very approximate methods of solving even this approximation must be used.

This method of finding a self-consistent solution to this system of equations may seem to be unnecessarily complicated, since the method necessitates our finding an explicit form for the single-particle distribution function. In general, the latter can be expected to be very complicated since it contains all possible information about the system, the physically interesting macroscopic variables, as well as an infinity of others. Such a scheme, therefore, may not appear as a very efficient method of solving the problem. This argument leads to the attempt to write down differential equations that directly involve only macroscopic observables and whose solution will yield directly all quantities of physical interest. These differential equations may be obtained from the Boltzmann-Vlasov equation by taking those moments of the latter that will yield the variables of interest. Not unexpectedly, a closed set of equations is not obtained in this way. For if we take a certain moment of the BV equation in order to find out how a given quantity develops in time, we find invariably that this evolution in time depends on another higher moment. If we attempt to find the temporal behaviour of this second moment, we find that it depends on a third moment, and so on. The customary practice in using this scheme has been to close this sequence of equations somewhat arbitrarily in order to see if at some stage contact cannot be made with the physical world by usage of such a finite set. Unfortunately, some further assumptions are still required beyond these; for example, the introduction of a set of transport coefficients will give a set of equations called the *equations of magnetohydrodynamics*, which are still not too easy to solve in most cases of interest.

In this chapter we shall first make a study of Liouville's equation itself and then turn to the Boltzmann-Vlasov equation and to the equations of magnetohydrodynamics at a later stage. The reason for this order is that the latter two descriptions of a plasma can be obtained from the former by use of particular assumptions, and in this sense Liouville's equation is more fundamental. In addition, as we shall see, Liouville's equation is equivalent to Newton's laws of motion and thus we shall have the advantage of familiarity in the early stages of our studies. More importantly considerations of features such as two particle correlations, quantum effects, and so on, involves corrections to the Boltzmann-Vlasov equation, and such corrections can only be obtained by an appeal to something more basic such as Liouville's equation.

HAMILTONIAN MECHANICS
FOR A SINGLE PARTICLE

The equations of motion for a charged particle, which is acted upon by the electromagnetic fields $\mathbf{E}$ and $\mathbf{B}$, are given by eqs. (2.1). In the nonrelativistic limit (that is, when terms of order v^2/c^2 are neglected) this equation has the well-known form

$$m \frac{d\mathbf{v}}{dt} = q(\mathbf{E} + \mathbf{v} \times \mathbf{B}) \tag{3.1}$$

and is to be interpreted as the means of calculating the unique trajectory of the particle in terms of its (presumed given) initial position and velocity. Thus eq. (3.1) may be looked upon as a complete specification for the dynamics of a charged particle.

An alternate but completely equivalent way for describing the motion of a particle is by use of the Hamiltonian formulation of mechanics. As is well known, this formulation is very convenient for purposes of predicting the dynamical behavior of a many-particle system, and has been used as a descriptive basis for various fields of physics including, for example, equilibrium statistical mechanics and transport theory. Indeed, in the present chapter we shall use the Hamiltonian formulation as a basis for the dynamical description of a classical plasma. Let us at this point, review briefly some of the more important results in this field.

The Hamiltonian for a nonrelativistic charged particle is given by

$$H = \frac{1}{2m}[\mathbf{p} - q\mathbf{A}(\mathbf{r},t)]^2 + q\phi(\mathbf{r},t) \tag{3.2}$$

where $\mathbf{A}$ and ϕ are the potentials in terms of which the external fields $\mathbf{E}$ and $\mathbf{B}$ are given by eqs. (1.10)–(1.11), and $\mathbf{p}$ is the momentum canonically conjugate to $\mathbf{r}$, the position of the particle. Hamilton's equations of motion are given in terms of the Hamiltonian in eq. (3.2) by the formulas

$$\dot{\mathbf{r}} = \mathbf{H}_p, \qquad \dot{\mathbf{p}} = -\mathbf{H}_r \tag{3.3}$$

where $\mathbf{H}_r$, $\mathbf{H}_p$ are *known* vector functions of $\mathbf{r}$, $\mathbf{p}$, and t and are defined by

$$\mathbf{H}_p = \frac{\partial}{\partial \mathbf{p}} H \qquad \mathbf{H}_r = \frac{\partial}{\partial \mathbf{r}} H \tag{3.4}$$

and H is given by eq. (3.2). Let us verify that eqs. (3.2)–(3.3) are indeed equivalent to Newton's law of motion—that is, eq. (3.1).

On making use of eq. (3.2), the first of eqs. (3.3) becomes

$$\dot{\mathbf{r}} = \frac{1}{m}(\mathbf{p} - q\mathbf{A}) \tag{3.5}$$

and the second may be written in the forms

$$\dot{\mathbf{p}} = -q\,\nabla\phi - \frac{1}{m}\{(\mathbf{p} - q\mathbf{A}) \times [\nabla \times (\mathbf{p} - q\mathbf{A})] + [(\mathbf{p} - q\mathbf{A}) \cdot \nabla](\mathbf{p} - q\mathbf{A})\}$$

$$= -q\,\nabla\phi + q\dot{\mathbf{r}} \times \mathbf{B} + q(\dot{\mathbf{r}} \cdot \nabla)\mathbf{A} \tag{3.6}$$

In this equation, the first equality follows by use of the vector identity

$$\tfrac{1}{2}\nabla(F^2) = \mathbf{F} \times (\nabla \times \mathbf{F}) + (\mathbf{F} \cdot \nabla)\mathbf{F}$$

and the second then follows by use of eqs. (1.10) and (3.5). Finally, the time derivative of eq. (3.5) may be written in the form

$$\dot{\mathbf{p}} = m\ddot{\mathbf{r}} + q\left(\frac{\partial \mathbf{A}}{\partial t} + (\dot{\mathbf{r}} \cdot \nabla)\mathbf{A}\right) \tag{3.7}$$

and then substituted into eq. (3.6) to yield the relation

$$m\ddot{\mathbf{r}} + q\left(\frac{\partial \mathbf{A}}{\partial t} + (\dot{\mathbf{r}} \cdot \nabla)\mathbf{A}\right) = -q\nabla\phi + q\dot{\mathbf{r}} \times \mathbf{B} + q(\dot{\mathbf{r}} \cdot \nabla)\mathbf{A}$$

This equation is clearly identical to eq. (3.1) because of the relationship between the electric field and the potentials as given in eq. (1.11). Thus, we have verified that the motion of a single charged particle can be described equally well by Newton's laws and in terms of the Hamiltonian equations of motion.

LIOUVILLE'S THEOREM
FOR A SINGLE PARTICLE

A further interesting, and for our purposes useful, formulation for the dynamics of a single particle may be obtained in the following way. A function $f(\mathbf{r},\mathbf{p},t)$ depends on the seven variables $\mathbf{r}$, $\mathbf{p}$, t and satisfies the equation

$$\frac{\partial f}{\partial t} + \mathbf{H}_p \cdot \frac{\partial}{\partial \mathbf{r}} f - \mathbf{H}_r \cdot \frac{\partial}{\partial \mathbf{p}} f = 0 \tag{3.8}$$

where $\mathbf{H}_r$ and $\mathbf{H}_p$ are those functions of $\mathbf{r}$, $\mathbf{p}$, and t that are defined by eq. (3.4). This equation—in the present context of a single charged particle moving in the given external fields $\mathbf{E}$ and $\mathbf{B}$—is known as Liouville's theorem for a single particle if one interprets the function f as a density of points in phase space. It is also known as the Boltzmann-Vlasov equation, provided the particle under consideration is thought of as a typical one in a plasma that is described by the single-particle distribution function f, and provided the electromagnetic fields, which are explicitly contained in $\mathbf{H}_r$ and $\mathbf{H}_p$, are interpreted to represent the sum of the external fields and the fields generated (in a self-consistent way) by the other particles in the plasma. We shall return to the latter point of view further in our studies; for the moment we shall refer to eq. (3.8) as Liouville's theorem.

The equivalence of Liouville's theorem—that is, eq. (3.8)—and the Hamiltonian equations of motion is easily established. We note that eq. (3.8) is a partial differential equation in seven independent variables and that it has the very important feature of involving only first-order derivatives. Any equation with this latter property is reducible to a coupled system of ordinary differential equations and is thus "solved." More specifically, the most general solution of eq. (3.8) is an arbitrary function of the six independent integrals of the system of coupled equations

$$dt = \frac{dx}{(\mathbf{H}_p)_x} = \frac{dy}{(\mathbf{H}_p)_y} = \frac{dz}{(\mathbf{H}_p)_z} = \frac{dp_x}{-(\mathbf{H}_r)_x} = \frac{dp_y}{-(\mathbf{H}_r)_y} = \frac{dp_z}{-(\mathbf{H}_p)_z} \tag{3.9}$$

and these are, of course, the Hamiltonian equations of motion themselves. Thus, a knowledge of the solutions of Hamilton's equation is equivalent to having available the most general solution of Liouville's equation.

Let us assume, in particular, that an integral of eq. (3.9) has the form

$$h(\mathbf{r},\mathbf{p},t) = C \tag{3.10}$$

where C is a constant. For example, h may be the Hamiltonian for a harmonic oscillator and C its energy. At any fixed time t, eq. (3.10) may be thought of as representing a surface in the six-dimensional $\mathbf{r}$, $\mathbf{p}$ space (phase space), and in the course of time this surface evolves in the manner specified by eq. (3.9). In other words, if the point $\mathbf{r}$, $\mathbf{p}$ lies on the surface at time t, then the point $\mathbf{r} + \mathbf{H}_p \, \Delta t$, $\mathbf{p} - \mathbf{H}_r \, \Delta t$ must lie on the surface at time $t + \Delta t$; that is, we have

$$C = h(\mathbf{r},\mathbf{p},t) = h(\mathbf{r} + \mathbf{H}_p \Delta t, \mathbf{p} - \mathbf{H}_r \Delta t, t + \Delta t) \tag{3.11}$$

Furthermore, this relation must be valid for all time intervals Δt; and in particular if we take Δt to be sufficiently small so that terms of order $(\Delta t)^2$ are negligible, then by use of Taylor's theorem eq. (3.11) becomes

$$\frac{\partial h}{\partial t} + \mathbf{H}_p \cdot \frac{\partial}{\partial \mathbf{r}} h - \mathbf{H}_r \cdot \frac{\partial}{\partial \mathbf{p}} h = 0 \tag{3.12}$$

That is to say, the function h, which is an integral of Hamilton's equation, satisfies Liouville's eq. (3.8).

In general one expects to find six integrals of eqs. (3.9); call them $h_i(\mathbf{r},\mathbf{p},t)$, $i = 1, 2, \cdots 6$. Since it is evident and easily verified that any function of a solution of eq. (3.8) is itself a solution of this same equation, the most general solution of Liouville's equation is an arbitrary function of these six integrals of the Hamiltonian equations of motion. That is to say, the function $f(\mathbf{r},\mathbf{p},t)$, which is given by the formula

$$f(\mathbf{r},\mathbf{p},t) = F\{h_1(\mathbf{r},\mathbf{p},t), h_2(\mathbf{r},\mathbf{p},t), \cdots h_6(\mathbf{r},\mathbf{p},t)\} \tag{3.13}$$

is the most general solution of eq. (3 8) for F an arbitrary function of the six variables $h_1, h_2, \cdots h_6$.

In order to obtain a particular example of functions $\{h_i\}$ let us suppose that one has solved the Hamiltonian equations of motion subject to the initial conditions $\mathbf{r} = \mathbf{r}_o$, $\mathbf{p} = \mathbf{p}_o$ at $t = 0$, and has obtained the solution in the form

$$\mathbf{r} = \mathbf{f}_1(\mathbf{r}_o, \mathbf{p}_o, t)$$

$$\mathbf{p} = \mathbf{f}_2(\mathbf{r}_o, \mathbf{p}_o, t) \tag{3.14}$$

where $\mathbf{f}_1$ and $\mathbf{f}_2$ are known vector functions of the time as well as the indicated parameters. Since the trajectory of a point in phase space is unique, it follows that these equations may be solved backwards in order to obtain

$\mathbf{r}_o$, $\mathbf{p}_o$ as functions of $\mathbf{r}$, $\mathbf{p}$, t. Let these solutions be expressed in the form

$$\mathbf{r}_o = \mathbf{g}_1(\mathbf{r},\mathbf{p},t)$$
$$\mathbf{p}_o = \mathbf{g}_2(\mathbf{r},\mathbf{p},t) \tag{3.15}$$

where again $\mathbf{g}_1$ and $\mathbf{g}_2$ are presumed to be known vector functions of all the variables. Now it is clear that each of these six relations in eq. (3.15) has the form specified in eq. (3.10), and consequently these functions $\mathbf{g}_1$, $\mathbf{g}_2$ comprise a possible set of functions $\{h_i\}$. Therefore, the most general solution of eq. (3.8) for this case is given by

$$f(\mathbf{r},\mathbf{p},t) = F\{\mathbf{g}_1(\mathbf{r},\mathbf{p},t),\mathbf{g}_2(\mathbf{r},\mathbf{p},t)\} \tag{3.16}$$

where $\mathbf{g}_1$ and $\mathbf{g}_2$ are given by eq. (3.15) and F is, of course, an arbitrary function.

One immediate application of this result deals with the following problem. Given the initial value for $f(\mathbf{r},\mathbf{p},t)$, call it $f_o(\mathbf{r},\mathbf{p})$, calculate that solution of eq. (3.8) which equals f_o at $t = 0$. By use of eq. (3.15), we first "calculate" the function F in terms of f_o by the formula

$$F\{\mathbf{g}_1(\mathbf{r},\mathbf{p},0), \mathbf{g}_2(\mathbf{r},\mathbf{p},0)\} = f_o(\mathbf{r},\mathbf{p})$$

and the solution of eq. (3.8) which coincides with f_o at $t = 0$ is therefore given by eq. (3.16). Needless to say, even when it is possible to obtain F, the practical usage of this result would require a knowledge of $\mathbf{g}_1$ and $\mathbf{g}_2$ and except for the simplest cases this is generally not available. A simple application of this result will be found in Problem 12.

For later usage, let us rewrite eq. (3.8) into a slightly different but more convenient and conventional form. On substituting from eqs. (3.2) and (3.4), Liouville's equation becomes

$$\frac{\partial}{\partial t}f+\frac{1}{m}(\mathbf{p}-q\mathbf{A})\cdot\frac{\partial}{\partial \mathbf{r}}f-q(\nabla\phi)\cdot\frac{\partial}{\partial \mathbf{p}}f -\frac{1}{m}\Big\{(\mathbf{p}-q\mathbf{A})\times[\nabla\times(\mathbf{p}-q\mathbf{A})]$$

$$+\Big[(\mathbf{p}-q\mathbf{A})\cdot\frac{\partial}{\partial \mathbf{r}}\Big](\mathbf{p}-q\mathbf{A})\Big\}\cdot\frac{\partial}{\partial \mathbf{p}}f=0 \tag{3.17}$$

This equation may be considerably simplified by changing variables from $\mathbf{r}$, $\mathbf{p}$, t to $\mathbf{r}$, $\mathbf{v}$, t where $\mathbf{v}$ is the velocity and is defined by

$$\mathbf{v} = \frac{1}{m}(\mathbf{p}-q\mathbf{A}) \tag{3.18}$$

The function f is now to be thought of as depending on $\mathbf{r}$, $\mathbf{v}$, and t. For this change of variables, we find on using the familiar rules for transforming partial derivatives that the differential operators in eq. (3.17) become replaced according to the prescription

$$\frac{\partial}{\partial t} \to \frac{\partial}{\partial t} - \frac{q}{m} \frac{\partial \mathbf{A}}{\partial t} \cdot \frac{\partial}{\partial \mathbf{v}}$$

$$\mathbf{v} \cdot \frac{\partial}{\partial \mathbf{r}} \to \mathbf{v} \cdot \frac{\partial}{\partial \mathbf{r}} - \frac{q}{m} \left[\left(\mathbf{v} \cdot \frac{\partial}{\partial \mathbf{r}} \right) \mathbf{A} \right] \cdot \frac{\partial}{\partial \mathbf{v}} \qquad (3.19)$$

$$\frac{\partial}{\partial \mathbf{p}} \to \frac{1}{m} \frac{\partial}{\partial \mathbf{v}}$$

where each differential operator is to differentiate only the factor standing immediately to its right. On making the substitutions indicated in eq. (3.19) and on using eqs. (1.10)–(1.11), eq. (3.17) may be cast into the more suggestive and familiar form

$$\frac{\partial}{\partial t} f + \mathbf{v} \cdot \frac{\partial}{\partial \mathbf{r}} f + \frac{q}{m} (\mathbf{E} + \mathbf{v} \times \mathbf{B}) \cdot \frac{\partial}{\partial \mathbf{v}} f = 0 \qquad (3.20)$$

and it is this form that will usually be referred to as Liouville's equation for a single particle.

It is to be re-emphasized that Liouville's equation itself is not very useful for obtaining the trajectory of a particle that has well-specified initial conditions. However, there are cases of interest (for example, a scattering event) for which eq. (3.8) is useful and for which the initial conditions are not precisely known and can only be specified in a probabilistic way. For example, in the problem of two-particle scattering, even though the initial momentum and position of the incident particle may be exactly known, the location of the target particle is not. The conventional description is that the target particle (in the barycentric system) is fixed at the origin while the incident particle is "distributed" with uniform probability over a small disk of appropriate radius and this disk approaches the target with the given speed. Let us suppose that at $t = 0$, the probability that the particle be located at $\mathbf{r}$ in the range $d\mathbf{r}$ and with momentum $\mathbf{p}$ in the range $d\mathbf{p}$ is given by

$$f_o(\mathbf{r},\mathbf{p}) \, d\mathbf{r} \, d\mathbf{p}$$

Then according to the discussion following eq. (3.14), the probability of finding the particle at $\mathbf{r}$, $\mathbf{p}$ at time t is given by the solution of Liouville's equation subject to the given initial distribution f_o—that is, eq. (3.16). In effect this means that we must solve the Hamiltonian equations of motion for all initial conditions that have appreciable probabilities. Of course, all predictions made by use of eq. (3.16) in this way can only be used in a statistical way.

HAMILTON'S EQUATIONS
FOR A MANY-PARTICLE SYSTEM

The generalization of the above ideas to the more interesting case of a many-particle system is straightforward and involves essentially no new ideas, but only slightly more complicated mathematics. In particular, we shall analyze only a system of identical particles; the inclusion of different species only serves to complicate the notation and may therefore be left for the problems.

The Hamiltonian for a system of charged particles that interact with each other and with external fields represented by $A(r,t)$ and $\phi(r,t)$ is given to order $1/c^2$ by the formula*

$$H = \frac{1}{2m} \sum_{i=1}^{N} \left(\mathbf{p}_i - \frac{e}{c} \mathbf{A}(\mathbf{r}_i t) \right)^2 + e \sum_{i=1}^{N} \phi(\mathbf{r}_i,t)$$

$$+ \frac{e^2}{2} \sum_{\substack{i,j=1 \\ i \neq j}}^{N} \frac{1}{r_{ij}} - \frac{e^2}{4m^2 c^2} \sum_{\substack{i,j=1 \\ i \neq j}}^{N} \left\{ \frac{\mathbf{p}_i \cdot \mathbf{p}_j}{r_{ij}} + \frac{\mathbf{p}_i \cdot \mathbf{r}_{ij} \, \mathbf{p}_i \cdot \mathbf{r}_{ij}}{r_{ij}^3} \right\} \quad (3.21)$$

where $\mathbf{p}_i$, $\mathbf{r}_i$ are the momenta and coordinates of the ith particle and $\mathbf{r}_{ij} = \mathbf{r}_i - \mathbf{r}_j$. This formula was first derived by Darwin.† Actually, Darwin's result also contains $1/c^2$ corrections to the first or kinetic energy term in eq. (3.21), but these have been omitted for reasons of simplicity. The interactions between the charged particles and the external fields are contained in the first two terms of eq. (3.21) and should be familiar since they are only obvious extensions of the one-particle interactions. Equally familiar is the third term, which represents the Coulomb repulsion between the particles. The fourth term, which is of order v^2/c^2 compared to the other three terms, represents the magnetic interactions between the particles. At first, we might think that for cases of interest to us in the nonrelativistic region, this term is negligible and should therefore be omitted. However, the effects produced by this term may actually be quite appreciable if the particles behave in a collective way so that, for example, large induced magnetic fields are produced. In this case the quantity v^2/c^2 is not

---

* In making use of a $1/c$ expansion, cgs units are mandatory and we shall make use of them in the following discussion. All final results, of course, will be rewritten in MKS units. The symbol e stands for the unit charge in the cgs system, while q represents this quantity in MKS units.

† C. G. Darwin, *Proc. Cambridge Phil. Soc.*, **20**, 56 (1920).

actually the expansion parameter but rather this quantity multiplied by the number of particles. Therefore, for many systems of interest the fourth term in eq. (3.21) may play a much more important role than the term that represents the Coulomb repulsions. This would happen, for example, if the particles are distributed with uniform density so that on the average the Coulomb repulsions cancel each other out.

Hamilton's equations for this many-particle system are obvious extensions of the single-particle equations and are explicitly given by the formulas

$$\dot{\mathbf{r}}_i = \mathbf{H}_{p_i} \qquad \dot{\mathbf{p}}_i = -\mathbf{H}_{r_i} \qquad i = 1, 2, \cdots N \qquad (3.22)$$

where $\mathbf{H}_{r_i}$ and $\mathbf{H}_{p_i}$ are given by

$$\mathbf{H}_{p_i} = \frac{\partial}{\partial \mathbf{p}_i} H \qquad \mathbf{H}_{r_i} = \frac{\partial}{\partial \mathbf{r}_i} H \qquad (3.23)$$

and H is given in eq. (3.21). By following essentially the same argument as used in eqs. (3.5)–(3.7) and by making use of eq. (3.21) and consistently dropping terms of order $(v/c)^3$, in mks units, eqs. (3.22) may be cast into the form

$$m\ddot{\mathbf{r}}_i = q[\mathbf{E} + \mathbf{E}_i + \mathbf{v}_i \times (\mathbf{B} + \mathbf{B}_i)] \qquad i = 1, 2, \cdots, N \qquad (3.24)$$

where $\mathbf{E}$ and $\mathbf{B}$ are the given external fields, and $\mathbf{E}_i$ and $\mathbf{B}_i$ the fields produced by all particles (except the ith). That is, $\mathbf{E}_i(r,t)$ and $\mathbf{B}_i(r,t)$ are the solutions of Maxwell's equation with charge and current densities given by the formulas*

$$\rho_i(\mathbf{r},t) = q \sum_{j=1}^{N}{}' \delta(\mathbf{r} - \mathbf{r}_j)$$

$$\mathbf{j}_i(\mathbf{r},t) = q \sum_{j=1}^{N}{}' \mathbf{v}_j \delta(\mathbf{r} - \mathbf{r}_j) \qquad (3.25)$$

and therefore $\mathbf{E}_i$ and $\mathbf{B}_i$ are very complicated functions of the positions and velocities of all the particles except the ith one. The simple-looking—but actually very complicated—result contained in eq. (3.24) is, of course, expected, but its detailed derivation from eq. (3.22) involves a considerable amount of uninstructive algebra. In carrying out this derivation it is very important to recall that all terms of order $(v/c)^3$ must be consistently neglected.

LIOUVILLE'S THEOREM
FOR A MANY-PARTICLE SYSTEM

A complete discussion of Liouville's theorem for a system containing many

---

* As usual, the prime on the sum means that the term $j = i$ is to be omitted.

particles would essentially parallel the arguments presented above for the case of a single particle and thus only a few brief remarks are needed. This theorem is of paramount importance to us since our entire discussion of the dynamical behavior of an ionized gas is essentially based on it.

Liouville's theorem for the system which is governed by the Hamiltonian in eq. (3.21) is given by

$$\frac{\partial F^{(N)}(t)}{\partial t} + \sum_{j=1}^{N} \mathbf{H}_{p_j} \cdot \frac{\partial}{\partial \mathbf{r}_j} F^{(N)}(t) - \sum_{j=1}^{N} \mathbf{H}_{r_j} \cdot \frac{\partial}{\partial \mathbf{p}_j} F^{(N)}(t) = 0 \quad (3.26)$$

where $\mathbf{H}_{p_i}$ and $\mathbf{H}_{r_i}$ are defined in terms of H by eqs. (3.22) and where we have put a superscript N on the distribution function $F^{(N)}(t)$ to denote the fact that $F^{(N)}(t)$ is a function of the coordinates and momenta $\mathbf{r}_1, \mathbf{r}_2 \cdots \mathbf{r}_N$, $\mathbf{p}_1, \mathbf{p}_2 \cdots \mathbf{p}_N$ of all N particles as well as a function of time. The proof of the equivalence of eq. (3.26) to the Hamiltonian equations of motion is identical to one given above for the case of a single particle. Thus, if $\mathbf{R}_1', \mathbf{R}_2' \cdots$ $\mathbf{R}_N', \mathbf{P}_1', \mathbf{P}_2' \cdots \mathbf{P}_N'$ represent the solutions of the Hamiltonian equations of motion subject to the initial conditions $\mathbf{r}_{o1}, \mathbf{r}_{o2} \cdots \mathbf{r}_{oN}, \mathbf{p}_{o1}, \mathbf{p}_{o2} \cdots \mathbf{p}_{oN}$ (that is, the $\{\mathbf{R}_i'\}$ and $\{\mathbf{P}_i'\}$ are functions of $\mathbf{r}_{o1}, \mathbf{r}_{o2} \cdots \mathbf{p}_{oN}$, and t), and these solutions are inverted as in eq. (3.15) to obtain

$$\mathbf{r}_{o1} = \mathbf{R}_1^{(N)}(\mathbf{r}_1, \mathbf{r}_2, \cdots \mathbf{p}_N, t)$$

$$\mathbf{r}_{o2} = \mathbf{R}_2^{(N)}(\mathbf{r}_1, \mathbf{r}_2, \cdots \mathbf{p}_N, t)$$

$$\cdot$$
$$\cdot$$
$$\cdot$$

$$\mathbf{p}_{oN} = \mathbf{P}_N^{(N)}(\mathbf{r}_1, \mathbf{r}_2, \cdots \mathbf{p}_N, t) \quad (3.27)$$

then the most general solution of eq. (3.26) is given by

$$F^{(N)}(t) = \phi\{\mathbf{R}_1^{(N)}(t), \mathbf{R}_2^{(N)}(t), \cdots \mathbf{P}_N^{(N)}(t)\} \quad (3.28)$$

for ϕ an arbitrary function of the $6N$ variables. Of course, these $6N$ variables are themselves integrals of the Hamiltonian equations of motion and in order to obtain these we must solve eqs. (3.22). With the possible exception of the case $N = 1$, the latter is generally impossible.

Therefore, for a many-particle system, the result contained in eq. (3.28) is of no practical interest except perhaps for establishing facts such as the following:

> If $F^{(N)}(t)$ is nonnegative throughout all of phase space at any instant of time, then it is nonnegative for all times.

On the other hand, for the more practical objective of predicting the dynamical behaviour of a plasma, we must still discuss two points; the first of these deals with a probabilistic interpretation of $F^{(N)}(t)$ (which is made possible by the above mentioned nonnegativeness of $F^{(N)}(t)$ for all t) and the second deals with the problem of finding methods for obtaining approximate solutions for eq. (3.26). The former will be examined in the next section while the latter is considerably more complicated and will be studied later.

From a mathematical point of view, Liouville's equation may be thought of as follows. Given the distribution function $F^{(N)}$ throughout all of phase space, at $t = 0$ eq. (3.26) determines $F^{(N)}$ at a slightly later time Δt. For we have by use of Taylor's theorem and eq. (3.26) the result

$$F^{(N)}(\Delta t) \cong F^{(N)}(0) + \Delta t \left. \frac{\partial F^{(N)}}{\partial t} \right|_{t=0}$$

$$= F^{(N)}(0) + \Delta t \sum_{j=1}^{N} \left[\mathbf{H}_{p_j} \cdot \frac{\partial}{\partial \mathbf{r}_j} - \mathbf{H}_{r_j} \cdot \frac{\partial}{\partial \mathbf{p}_j} \right] F^{(N)}(0) \qquad (3.29)$$

which fixes $F^{(N)}(\Delta t)$ in terms of $F^{(N)}(0)$. It is clear that in principle—in any event—repeated application of this method determines $F^{(N)}$ at any time t. Thus, even without having available the solution of the Hamiltonian equations of motion, we can think of eq. (3.26) as determining $F^{(N)}(t)$ in terms of $F^{(N)}(0)$. For this purpose, of course, $F^{(N)}(0)$ must be completely specified at $t = 0$ throughout all of phase space—that is, for all values of the coordinates and momenta of all of the particles.

STATISTICAL INTERPRETATION OF $F^{(N)}(t)$

In general, even without regard to the mathematical problems involved, it makes no sense whatsoever to attempt to solve eqs. (3.22) since this would require the specification of a vast number of initial conditions and these are not obtainable. Thus, as in the discussion below eq. (3.20), it is necessary to treat these initial conditions statistically; and, consequently, the predictions of the theory at all subsequent times are expected to be in the form of statements involving probabilities such as averages and fluctuations.

From now on, therefore, we shall interpret the function $F^{(N)}(t)$ by the following definition:

The quantity

$$F^{(N)}(t)\, d\mathbf{r}_1\, d\mathbf{r}_2 \cdots d\mathbf{r}_N\, d\mathbf{p}_1\, d\mathbf{p}_2 \cdots d\mathbf{p}_N$$

is the joint probability at time t that particle number 1 is located at $\mathbf{r}_1$ in the range $d\mathbf{r}_1$ and with momentum $\mathbf{p}_1$ in the range $d\mathbf{p}_1$ and that particle number 2 is located at $\mathbf{r}_2$ in the range $d\mathbf{r}_2 \cdots$, and that particle number N is located at $\mathbf{r}_N$ in the range $d\mathbf{r}_N$ and with momentum $\mathbf{p}_N$ in the range $d\mathbf{p}_N$.

This definition is obviously self-consistent for, as we have seen, if $F^{(N)}(0) \geqslant 0$, then $F^{(N)}(t) \geqslant 0$ for all times t; thus if $F^{(N)}(0)$ is the initial probability, and therefore nonnegative, so is $F^{(N)}(t)$ for all subsequent times.

In more intuitive language $F^{(N)}(t)$ may be thought of in terms of the trajectories of points in phase space. If the initial conditions were precisely known (that is, $F^{(N)}(0)$ were represented by products of delta functions), the initial state of the system could be represented by a single point in the $6N$-dimensional phase space, and in the course of time this point would move along a path that would be completely specified by the Hamiltonian equations of motion. As a matter of practicality, however, we have previously noted that the initial conditions cannot be precisely known, and therefore we must think of the initial state of the system as being represented by a collection, or an *ensemble*, of phase points each of which represents a possible state of the system and each of which is compatible—in a probability sense—with the factual knowledge that is actually available about the system. In the course of time each of these phase points moves along a trajectory that is again uniquely determined by the Hamiltonian equations of motion. That is, the entire collection of phase points moves about in a manner that can be calculated, in principle, by use of eqs. (3.22) or equivalently by use of Liouville's theorem. Furthermore, at any time t the actual system has certain macroscopic properties of interest and these can only be calculated by averaging these properties over all members of the ensemble. Thus, for example, if at time t most of the phase points had the property that they were associated with the physical system's being in the form of a gas and distributed uniformly throughout a certain container, then clearly we would predict a corresponding uniform density for the actual system. At this point, we might well wonder if it is not possible to make incorrect predictions in this way if, for example, half of the members of the ensemble had a different value of a certain property than the other half did. The answer is that such an incorrect prediction is possible but not very probable. The reason being that if we make statistical predictions for a system containing a large number of particles, we will find that these predictions (actually average values) have fluctuations, but these fluctuations are very small in that they are inversely proportional to the square root of the number of particles. Thus for our present purposes, since we shall be dealing with systems that contain of the order of 10^{20} particles, these fluctuations are negligible and the predictions of the theory may be thought of as being relatively precise. If further assurance is required, we need only think of the agreement with experiment obtained by the predictions of statistical mechanics where this same problem arises.

As we have noted above, the predictions of the theory are exclusively in terms of averages over the distribution function $F^{(N)}(t)$. It is convenient to normalize this function to unity and therefore we write

$$\int d\Omega \, F^{(N)}(t) = 1 \tag{3.30}$$

where the $d\Omega$ is defined by

$$d\Omega = \prod_{i=1}^{N} d\mathbf{r}_i \, d\mathbf{p}_i$$

and it is always understood that the limits on the $6N$ integral are all from $-\infty$ to $+\infty$. Since Liouville's equation is homogeneous in $F^{(N)}$, the normalization in (3.30) is somewhat arbitrary and some authors normalize $F^{(N)}$ to the total number of particles. The fact that we can normalize $F^{(N)}(t)$ as in eq. (3.30) without having a function of the time on the right-hand side is again a consequence of eq. (3.28). Or equivalently, we can show that the integral of $F^{(N)}$ over all of phase space is independent of time by integrating Liouville's equation directly.

By making use of the above definition of $F^{(N)}(t)$ in terms of a probability, we can now calculate the average values of various macroscopic quantities of interest. These include, for example, the particle density $n(\mathbf{x},t)$, the local velocity field $\mathbf{u}(\mathbf{x},t)$, the local temperature $T(\mathbf{x},t)$, and the pressure tensor $p_{\alpha\beta}(\mathbf{x},t)$. For a system consisting of a single species, these quantities are given by:

$$n(\mathbf{x},t) = \int d\Omega \sum_{i=1}^{N} \delta(\mathbf{r}_i - \mathbf{x}) F^{(N)}(t) \tag{3.31}$$

$$\mathbf{u}(\mathbf{x},t) = \frac{1}{n(\mathbf{x},t)} \int d\Omega \sum_{i=1}^{N} \delta(\mathbf{r}_i - \mathbf{x}) \mathbf{H}_{p_i} F^{(N)}(t) \tag{3.32}$$

$$p_{\alpha\beta}(\mathbf{x},t) = m \int d\Omega \sum_{i=1}^{N} \delta(\mathbf{r}_i - \mathbf{x}) \{\mathbf{H}_{p_i} - \mathbf{u}(\mathbf{x},t)\}_\alpha \{\mathbf{H}_{p_i} - \mathbf{u}(\mathbf{x},t)\}_\beta F^{(N)}(t) \tag{3.33}$$

$$\frac{3}{2} k T(\mathbf{x},t) = \frac{1}{2n(\mathbf{x},t)} \sum_{\alpha=1}^{3} p_{\alpha\alpha}(\mathbf{x},t) \tag{3.34}$$

where for purposes of simplifying the notation we have made use of the 3-dimensional delta function $\delta(\mathbf{r}_i - \mathbf{x})$ and where k is Boltzmann's constant. For the case of more than a single species, obvious generalizations of these formulas would apply. The physical interpretation and significance of $n(\mathbf{x},t)$, the number of particles per unit volume, are clear from its form in eq. (3.31) while the physical significance of the velocity can be obtained by noting that $\mathbf{u}(\mathbf{x},t)n(\mathbf{x},t)$ represents the flux of particles—that is, the number of particles that cross unit area at the point $\mathbf{x}$ in unit time. In the same way the α, β element of the pressure tensor $p_{\alpha\beta}$ represents the flux of momentum along the direction α that crosses in unit time a unit area whose normal is along the direction β. Physically, this means that if there is a net transport of momentum across the surface by the particles, then this corresponds to a pressure or a force per unit area on this surface element. Finally, eq. (3.34) is the definition of temperature in terms of the thermal motions of the particles. We shall examine all of these macroscopic quantities in more detail later on.

Other physical quantities of interest, such as mass density, $\rho(\mathbf{x},t)$, charge density $\rho_q(\mathbf{x},t)$, current density $\mathbf{j}(\mathbf{x},t)$, and so on, may be expressed in terms of the above formulas by relations such as

$$\rho(\mathbf{x},t) = mn(\mathbf{x},t)$$

$$\rho_q(\mathbf{x},t) = qn(\mathbf{x},t)$$

$$\mathbf{j}(\mathbf{x},t) = qn(\mathbf{x},t)\mathbf{u}(\mathbf{x},t) \tag{3.35}$$

where m is the mass of a particle that has charge q.

Let us briefly summarize the situation up to this point. The quantities that can be related directly to experiments are certain macroscopic variables, and these may be calculated by formulas such as those given by eqs. (3.31)–(3.35), provided, of course, the distribution function $F^{(N)}(t)$ is available. In turn, the latter is to be calculated from Liouville's theorem— or some approximation thereto—and as we have seen this can only be done in terms of the initial distribution function $F^{(N)}(0)$. Therefore, it is now necessary to turn to this important problem of the specification of $F^{(N)}(0)$ in terms of partial and incomplete initial data.

THE SPECIFICATION
OF THE INITIAL DISTRIBUTION FUNCTION

Let us suppose that we have a given physical system and that at $t = 0$ we have measured several macroscopic properties such as $n(\mathbf{x},0)$ and $T(\mathbf{x},0)$. The problem now becomes what form of $F^{(N)}(0)$ should we select in order to make predictions of these and other macroscopic variables at subsequent times? On examination of eqs. (3.31) and (3.34) it becomes clear that there are infinitely many choices for $F^{(N)}(0)$ that will reproduce the given $n(\mathbf{x},0)$ and $T(\mathbf{x},0)$, and therefore the problem may also be stated: which of these choices is the correct one? Or even, is there a unique and correct choice? The answers to these and related questions obviously require much more subtle and elaborate considerations than are appropriate for our present interests in plasmas. Therefore, in order to have some method for selecting $F^{(N)}(0)$, we shall at this point make a digression to the information-theoretical arguments that were originally proposed by Jaynes.* For a very readable introductory exposition of this subject the interested reader is referred to the book by Tribus.† It would be very much out of place to make an extensive study of information theory right here; however, a few ideas and results of this theory can be simply stated and easily utilized, and since we shall, in this way, be able to settle the problem of obtaining a unique form for $F^{(N)}(0)$, let us examine the matter briefly.

A certain quantity y is capable of taking on a finite (for the sake of simplicity) number of discrete values $y_i (i = 1, 2 \ldots n)$. The quantities y_i, for example, may represent the number of spots on the various sides of a die. Let the symbol $p_i (i = 1, 2, \ldots n)$ stand for the probability that the quantity y takes on the value y_i; and thus in the above example, p_i would represent the probability that i spots would come up on a given throw. The problem confronting us may now be stated as follows:

> Let us assume we are given some partial data, say the average value of a function $f(y)$—that is, the number $\bar{f}$ that is defined by
>
> $$\bar{f} = \sum_{i=1}^{n} p_i f(y_i) \tag{3.36}$$
>
> (compare eqs. (3.32)–(3.34)) as well as the usual condition
>
> $$1 = \sum_{i=1}^{n} p_i \tag{3.37}$$
>
> How shall we select the probabilities p_i such that the constraints in eqs. (3.36) and (3.37) are satisfied and we are maximally unbiased‡ with regard to the prediction of the averages of other quantities such as
>
> $$\bar{h} = \sum_{i=1}^{n} p_i h(y_i)$$

In the above illustration of the die, for example, we might know that the

---

* E. T. Jaynes, "Information Theory and Statistical Mechanics", *Phys. Rev.* 106, 620 (1957) and 108, 171 (1957).
† Myron Tribus, *Thermostatics and Thermodynamics*, Chaps. 2–4. Princeton, N.J.: D. Van Nostrand Company, Inc., 1961.
‡ That is, maximally noncommittal with regard to all unavailable information.

mean number of spots which turn up on a given throw of the die is 2—an honest die would give

$$\sum_{i=1}^{6} i p_i = \frac{1}{6} \sum_{i=1}^{6} i = 3.5$$

The problem would then be what probabilities shall we assign to the various sides of the die in the light of this partial data? Information theory supplies the following answer:

> The least biased choice would be to find that collection of the probabilities $\{p_i\}$ which maximizes the quantity
>
> $$I = -\sum_i p_i \ln p_i \qquad (3.38)$$
>
> and is consistent with all constraints such as those given in eqs. (3.37)–(3.38).

For the above mentioned particular case—that is, when the constraints consist only of eqs. (3.37)–(3.38)—we can apply this principle in a straightforward way. By making use of LaGrange multipliers $(\lambda - 1)$ and μ we obtain

$$0 = \delta \sum_{i=1}^{n} p_i[\ln p_i + (\lambda - 1) + \mu f(y_i)]$$

$$= \sum_{i=1}^{n} [\ln p_i + \lambda + \mu f(y_i)]\delta p_i$$

which is immediately reduced to

$$p_i = \exp\{-\lambda - \mu f(y_i)\} \qquad (3.39)$$

The parameters λ and μ are fixed by eqs. (3.36)–(3.37) and are explicitly given by

$$\lambda = \ln Z(\mu)$$

$$\bar{f} = -\frac{\partial}{\partial \mu} \ln Z(\mu) \qquad (3.40)$$

where the partition function $Z(\mu)$ is given by

$$Z(\mu) = \sum_{i=1}^{n} \exp\{-\mu f(y_i)\} \qquad (3.41)$$

Thus, the distribution in eq. (3.40) is uniquely specified and information theory assures us that this distribution is maximally noncommittal with regard to all missing information.

As a particular case let us apply these results to the above used illustration of the loaded die for which the mean number of spots that show up on a given throw is 2. The partition function is given by

$$Z(\mu) = \sum_{i=1}^{6} e^{-\mu i} = \frac{e^{-\mu}(1 - e^{-6\mu})}{1 - e^{-\mu}} \cong \frac{1}{e^{\mu} - 1}$$

On substituting this result back into the second of eqs. (3.41), we find for the present case for which $\bar{j} = 2$, the result

$$2 = \frac{e^{\mu}}{(e^{\mu} - 1)}$$

and therefore μ is approximately $\ln 2$. Consequently, the probability that j spots will come up on a given throw is approximately given by

$$p_j = \frac{e^{-j\mu}}{e^{\mu} - 1} = \left(\frac{1}{2}\right)^j$$

and as expected this sharply favors the smallest values of j.

Let us apply these ideas directly to our more immediate problem of fixing $F^{(N)}(0)$ given say $n(\mathbf{x},0)$ and $T(\mathbf{x},0)$. The analogues of eqs. (3.36)–(3.38) are given by

$$n(\mathbf{x},0) = \int d\Omega \sum_{j=1}^{N} \delta(\mathbf{r}_j - \mathbf{x}) F^{(N)}(0) \tag{3.42}$$

$$T(\mathbf{x},0) = \frac{m}{3kn(\mathbf{x},0)} \int d\Omega \sum_{j=1}^{N} \delta(\mathbf{r}_j - \mathbf{x}) H_{p_j}^2 F^{(N)}(0) \tag{3.43}$$

$$1 = \int d\Omega \, F^{(N)}(0) \tag{3.44}$$

$$I = -\int d\Omega \, F^{(N)}(0) \ln F^{(N)}(0) \tag{3.45}$$

where for reasons of simplicity the mean velocity $\mathbf{u}$ has been assumed to be negligible. The distinction between these formulas and eqs. (3.36)–(3.38) are first that it is now necessary to sum over a continuous index—that is, to integrate over all of phase space instead of summing over the discrete index i—and second, that there are now an infinite number of constraints in that eqs. (3.42) and (3.43) must be satisfied for every point of physical space $\mathbf{x}$. This latter complication means that eqs. (3.42) and (3.43) must be multiplied by LaGrange multipliers—say $u(x)$ and $v(x)$—and integrated over all x in order to obtain the variational expression. On making use of these facts we find in a manner essentially identical to that used in deriving eq. (3.39) the result

$$
0 = \delta \int d\Omega \left\{ \ln F^{(N)}(0) + \lambda - 1 + \int dx\, u(x) \sum_{j=1}^{N} \delta(\mathbf{r}_j - x) \right.
$$

$$
\left. + \int dx \sum_{j=1}^{N} \delta(\mathbf{r}_j - x)v(x)\mathbf{H}_{p_j}^2 \right\} F^{(N)}(0)
$$

$$
= \int d\Omega \left\{ \ln F^{(N)}(0) + \lambda + \sum_{j=1}^{N} [u(\mathbf{r}_j) + v(\mathbf{r}_j)\mathbf{H}_{p_j}^2] \right\} \delta F^{(N)}(0) \quad (3.46)
$$

and therefore $F^{(N)}(0)$ is given by

$$
F^{(N)}(0) = \exp\left\{ -\lambda - \sum_{j=1}^{N} [u(\mathbf{r}_j) + v(\mathbf{r}_j)\mathbf{H}_{p_j}^2] \right\} \quad (3.47)
$$

The constant λ is to be fixed by eq. (3.45) while u and v are fixed by eqs. (3.43) and (3.44). Therefore, in terms of the partition function

$$
Z = \int d\Omega \, \exp\left\{ -\sum_{j=1}^{N} [u(\mathbf{r}_j) + v(\mathbf{r}_j)\mathbf{H}_{p_j}^2] \right\}
$$

we obtain

$$
\lambda = \ln Z \quad (3.48)
$$

$$
n(x,0) = \frac{1}{Z} \int d\Omega \sum_{j=1}^{N} \delta(\mathbf{r}_j - x) \exp\left\{ -\sum_{i=1}^{N} [u(\mathbf{r}_i) + v(\mathbf{r}_i)\mathbf{H}_{p_i}^2] \right\} \quad (3.49)
$$

$$
kT(x,0) = \frac{1}{3n(x,0)} \frac{1}{Z} \int d\Omega \sum_{j=1}^{N} \delta(\mathbf{r}_j - x)\mathbf{H}_{p_j}^2
$$

$$
\exp\left\{ -\sum_{i=1}^{N} [u(\mathbf{r}_i) + v(\mathbf{r}_i)\mathbf{H}_{p_i}^2] \right\} \quad (3.50)
$$

and these three relations fix the constant λ and the two unknown functions u, v in terms of the given function $n(x,0)$ and $T(x,0)$. Actually the solution of eqs. (3.49) and (3.50) for u and v in terms of n and T may be carried out explicitly and it is left as an exercise to show that eq. (3.47) may be written in the final form

$$F^{(N)}(0) = \prod_{j=1}^{N} \left\{ \frac{n(\mathbf{r}_j)}{N} \left[\frac{1}{2\pi k T(\mathbf{r}_j,0)} \right]^{3/2} \exp\left[-\frac{m\mathbf{H}_{pj}^2}{2k T(\mathbf{r}_j,0)} \right] \right\} \quad (3.51)$$

This result, which is not really very surprising, is the solution produced by information theory, for the present case. That is, the form of $F^{(N)}(0)$ in eq. (3.51) is consistent with the given constraints $n(x,0)$ and $T(x,0)$ and it is maximally noncommittal with regard to all other macroscopic variables. Thus, now that we have $F^{(N)}(0)$ in eq. (3.51), we may use this result as input data into Liouville's equation and, in principle, calculate the distribution function at any subsequent time t. The result in eq. (3.51) is not completely satisfactory from all points of view in that, for example, in statistical mechanics it does not explain why predictions made by its usage are very precise. It is useful, however, since it allows the usage of Liouville's equations with little possibility of injecting bias and in this way it has practical value.

In closing this section it is perhaps reasonable to make a few remarks on a very much related subject. This problem is easily much more difficult from a conceptual point of view than that involved in selecting $F^{(N)}(0)$ and comes about because of the invariance under time reversal of Newton's laws of motion and therefore also of Liouville's equation. It is an easily verifiable fact that if in the equations of motion we formally reverse the time—that is, we make the transformation $t \to -t$, $\mathbf{r} \to \mathbf{r}$, $\mathbf{p} \to -\mathbf{p}$—then the equations of motion are completed unaltered. This implies that if we make the substitution $t \to -t$ in the solution of the equations of motion, then another solution of these same equations is obtained. Stated in more physical language one may say that if we take a motion picture of an event, then a person viewing this film cannot tell on the basis of Newton's laws alone whether the film is being shown forward or backward. Thus, the portrayal of a waterfall on a motion picture represents just as much a solution of Newton's laws when played backward as it does when played forward. On the basis of intuition, however, we would argue that the actual event corresponds to water falling downward. If we take the trouble to analyze the source of this intuition we ultimately conclude that the initial conditions required in order for the water to go up the waterfall are so improbable that this event never happens. Thus, the difficulty does not involve Newton's laws themselves but rather deals with the choice of initial conditions. Since our approach to the study of a many-particle system is equivalent to that obtained via Newton's laws, it would seem that we are also faced with this problem of initial conditions. In view of the "maximally noncommittal" nature of our method for selecting $F^{(N)}(0)$, however, it is very plausible to expect that we shall rarely obtain a very improbable distribution in this way. In any event we shall, of course, assume this to be the case.

Historically, this problem first arose when it was experimentally observed that all many-particle systems, if left alone, always approached equilibrium regardless of their initial states. A paradox was therefore created since it was believed that this approach to equilibrium should be a consequence of Newton's laws and at the same time it was known that there could be no such consequence since these laws are invariant under time reversal. Thus, if Newton's laws would predict the approach to equilibrium, then they would equally well predict the departure from equilibrium; and the latter was never observed. The answer, of course, is that the overwhelming majority of initial states correspond to the system's approaching equilibrium, and thus to find a system in an initial state from which it will not approach equilibrium is so improbable that it is, for practical purposes, never observed. Therefore, it is the peculiarities of the occurrence of certain initial conditions that create this temporal asymmetry. It is not a property of Newton's laws.

THE REDUCTION
OF LIOUVILLE'S EQUATION

The N-particle distribution function $F^{(N)}(t)$ is evidently very complicated both from a mathematical as well as from a conceptual point of view. Conceptual difficulties arise primarily because normally we do not think in terms of distribution functions for large numbers of particles but rather in terms of distribution functions that involve one or possibly two particles. In addition, the many-particle distribution function contains a great deal of information including, for example, interparticle correlations of various orders. For most physical situations of interest one expects only a very small number of these correlations to play an important role. Thus, it is convenient and practically mandatory that $F^{(N)}(t)$ be reduced to distribution functions involving only small numbers of particles by averaging out the coordinates and momenta of the remaining large collection of particles. Needless to say, one hopes as a by-product to obtain a mathematical simplification as well.

Again, let us restrict our attention to a gas consisting of only one species and therefore the distribution function $F^{(N)}(t)$ will be symmetrical with respect to exchange of the coordinates and momenta of any two particles. The s-particle distribution function $F^{(s)}(t)(s \ll N)$ is obtained by averaging over the coordinates and momenta of the remaining N-s particles. Explicitly it is given by

$$F^{(s)}(t) = \int F^{(N)}(t) \prod_{j=s+1}^{N} (d\mathbf{r}_j \, d\mathbf{p}_j) \tag{3.52}$$

and has the interpretation that the quantity

$$F^{(s)}(t) \prod_{i=1}^{s} (d\mathbf{r}_i \, d\mathbf{p}_i)$$

is the joint probability at time t that a particular collection of s particles will be located at the points $\mathbf{r}_1$, $\mathbf{r}_2 \cdot \cdot \cdot \mathbf{r}_s$ in the ranges $d\mathbf{r}_1$, $d\mathbf{r}_2 \ldots d\mathbf{r}_s$, respectively, and with momenta $\mathbf{p}_1$, $\mathbf{p}_2 \cdot \cdot \cdot \mathbf{p}_s$ in the respective ranges $d\mathbf{p}_1 \cdot \cdot \cdot d\mathbf{p}_s$, regardless of the locations and the states of motion of the remaining N-s particles. Thus, for example, $NF^{(1)}(t) \, d\mathbf{r} \, d\mathbf{p}$ is the probability of finding a single particle at time t at the point $\mathbf{r}$, in the range $d\mathbf{r}$, and with momentum $\mathbf{p}$ in the range $d\mathbf{p}$. Clearly, $F^{(1)}(t)$ has a much more direct and simple interpretation than does $F^{(N)}(t)$.

Many macroscopic quantities of interest are often in the form of phase-space integrals that involve, of course, $F^{(N)}(t)$ and in addition only sums of terms each of which depends on the coordinates momenta of a *single* particle only. For example, if the magnetic-magnetic interactions in eq. (3.21) (that is, the fourth term) is neglected, so that $\mathbf{H}_{p_i}$ depends only on the coordinates and momenta of the ith particle, then according to eqs. (3.32)–(3.35), $n(\mathbf{x},t)$, $\mathbf{u}(\mathbf{x},t)$, $p_{\alpha\beta}(\mathbf{x},t)$, $T(\mathbf{x},t)$ are all of this form. And in such a case, we may carry out most of the phase-space integrations and thereby obtain formulas for macroscopic quantities exclusively in terms of the single-particle distribution function. Thus, on making use of the symmetry property of $F^{(N)}(t)$ and eq. (3.52), we may rewrite eq. (3.31) into the forms

$$n(\mathbf{x},t) = \int d\Omega \sum_{i=1}^{N} \delta(\mathbf{r}_i - \mathbf{x}) F^{(N)}(t)$$

$$= N \int d\Omega \, \delta(\mathbf{r}_1 - \mathbf{x}) F^{(N)}(t)$$

$$= N \int d\mathbf{p} \, F^{(1)}(\mathbf{x},\mathbf{p},t) \tag{3.53}$$

In a similar way we obtain for eqs. (3.33) and (3.34) the results

$$\mathbf{u}(\mathbf{x},t) = \frac{N}{n(\mathbf{x},t)} \int d\mathbf{p}_1 \ \mathbf{H}_{p_1}(\mathbf{x},\mathbf{p}_1,t) F^{(1)}(\mathbf{x},\mathbf{p}_1,t) \tag{3.54}$$

$$p_{\alpha\beta}(\mathbf{x},t) = Nm \int d\mathbf{p}_1 \ [\mathbf{H}_{p_1}(\mathbf{x},\mathbf{p}_1,t) - \mathbf{u}(\mathbf{x},t)]_\alpha$$

$$[\mathbf{H}_{p_1}(\mathbf{x},\mathbf{p}_1,t) - \mathbf{u}(\mathbf{x},t)]_\beta \, F^{(1)}(\mathbf{x},\mathbf{p}_1,t) \tag{3.55}$$

and therefore a knowledge of $F^{(1)}$ alone is sufficient for obtaining these macroscopic quantities. If the fourth term of the Hamiltonian in eq. (3.21) is not negligible, then $\mathbf{H}_{p_i}$ will involve sums of terms each of which depends on the coordinates of two particles; for this case the analogues of eqs. (3.54)–(3.55) will involve the two-particle distribution function $F^{(2)}(\mathbf{r}_1,\mathbf{p}_1,\mathbf{r}_2,\mathbf{p}_2,t)$. Consequently, almost all macroscopic quantities of interest can be expressed exclusively in terms of $F^{(1)}$ and $F^{(2)}$. Since these two distribution functions are so much simpler both from a mathematical as well as from a physical point of view, it would seem worthwhile to make an effort to get around working with Liouville's equation by attempting to derive equations that will determine $F^{(1)}$ and $F^{(2)}$ directly. Not unexpectedly, this attempt turns out to be unsuccessful, but the effort itself is worthwhile since it leads to results that suggest several practical approximation schemes.

In order to simplify the following reduction of Liouville's equation, let us continue to assume that $F^{(N)}(t)$ is symmetric and that the magnetic-magnetic interactions are negligible; and that therefore $\mathbf{H}_{p_i}$ is explicitly given by

$$\mathbf{H}_{p_i} = \frac{1}{m} \left\{ \mathbf{p}_i - \frac{e}{c} \mathbf{A}(\mathbf{r}_i,t) \right\} \tag{3.56}$$

We now take Liouville's equation and integrate over the coordinate and momenta of all of the particles except those for, say, particle number 1. Considerable simplification is obtained by noting the identity

$$\mathbf{H}_{p_i} \cdot \frac{\partial}{\partial \mathbf{r}_i} F^{(N)} - \mathbf{H}_{r_i} \cdot \frac{\partial}{\partial \mathbf{p}_i} F^{(N)} = \frac{\partial}{\partial \mathbf{r}_i} \cdot [\mathbf{H}_{p_i} F^{(N)}] - \frac{\partial}{\partial \mathbf{p}_i} \cdot [\mathbf{H}_{r_i} F^{(N)}] \tag{3.57}$$

and therefore since $F^{(N)}$ must vanish for infinite values of all coordinates and momenta, the integrals over the second and third term in eq. (3.26) will vanish except for those terms in the sums that involve $\partial/\partial \mathbf{r}_i$ and $\partial/\partial \mathbf{p}_i$. Thus on making use of this fact and eq. (3.52), the integration of eq. (3.26) over the entire phase space except for that of particle 1 may be written

$$\frac{\partial}{\partial t}F^{(1)} + \frac{1}{m}\left[\mathbf{p}_1 - \frac{e}{c}\mathbf{A}(\mathbf{r}_1,t)\right] \cdot \frac{\partial}{\partial \mathbf{r}_1}F^{(1)} - e\frac{\partial \phi(\mathbf{r}_1,t)}{\partial \mathbf{r}_1} \cdot \frac{\partial}{\partial \mathbf{p}_1}F^{(1)}$$

$$- \frac{1}{m}\left\{\left(\mathbf{p}_1 - \frac{e}{c}\mathbf{A}\right) \times \left[\nabla \times \left(-\frac{e}{c}\mathbf{A}\right)\right]\right.$$

$$\left. + \left[\left(\mathbf{p}_1 - \frac{e}{c}\mathbf{A}\right) \cdot \frac{\partial}{\partial \mathbf{r}_1}\right]\left(-\frac{e}{c}\mathbf{A}\right)\right\} \cdot \frac{\partial}{\partial \mathbf{p}_1}F^{(1)}$$

$$= e^2 \int \prod_{i=2}^{N}(d\mathbf{r}_i\, d\mathbf{p}_i)\left\{\frac{\partial}{\partial \mathbf{r}_1}\sum_{j=2}^{N}\frac{1}{|\mathbf{r}_1 - \mathbf{r}_j|}\right\} \cdot \frac{\partial}{\partial \mathbf{p}_1}F^{(N)}(t) \qquad (3.58)$$

On making use of the symmetry in $F^{(N)}$, and the fact that $N-1 \approx N$, the last term in this equation becomes

$$Ne^2 \int d\mathbf{r}_2\, d\mathbf{p}_2\left(\frac{\partial}{\partial \mathbf{r}_1}\frac{1}{|\mathbf{r}_1 - \mathbf{r}_2|}\right) \cdot \frac{\partial}{\partial \mathbf{p}_1}F^{(2)}(\mathbf{r}_1,\mathbf{r}_2,\mathbf{p}_1,\mathbf{p}_2,t)$$

where again the derivatives operate only on the factors standing immediately to the right. Thus, we see that by integrating over the above described portion of phase space, Liouville's equation is reduced to one that involves only $F^{(1)}$ and $F^{(2)}$. As in the derivation of eq. (3.20) from eq. (3.17), the above result may be considerably simplified by changing variables from $\mathbf{r}_1,\mathbf{p}_1,t$ into $\mathbf{r}_1,\mathbf{v}_1,t$, where $\mathbf{v}_1$ is given by the formula

$$\mathbf{v}_1 = \frac{1}{m}\left\{\mathbf{p}_1 - \frac{e}{c}\mathbf{A}(\mathbf{r}_1,t)\right\} \qquad (3.18)$$

Under this substitution the derivatives become replaced according to eq. (3.19) (with $q \to e/c$ since we are now in the cgs system) and eq. (3.58) now becomes

$$\frac{\partial}{\partial t}F^{(1)}(\mathbf{r},\mathbf{v},t) + \mathbf{v} \cdot \frac{\partial}{\partial \mathbf{r}}F^{(1)} + \frac{e}{m}\left[\mathbf{E} + \frac{\mathbf{v}}{c} \times \mathbf{B}\right] \cdot \frac{\partial}{\partial \mathbf{v}}F^{(1)}$$

$$- \frac{Ne^2}{m}\int d\mathbf{r}_2\, d\mathbf{p}_2\left[\frac{\partial}{\partial \mathbf{r}}\frac{1}{|\mathbf{r} - \mathbf{r}_2|}\right] \cdot \frac{\partial}{\partial \mathbf{v}}F^{(2)}(\mathbf{r},\mathbf{v},\mathbf{r}_2,\mathbf{v}_2,t) = 0 \qquad (3.59)$$

This is the final result obtained by the reduction of Liouville's equation.

The first and perhaps most important feature about eq. (3.59) is that it is incomplete. That is to say, in the sense used in the discussion following eq. (3.29), the reduced equation (3.59) does not by itself produce $F^{(1)}(t)$ given $F^{(1)}(0)$ and $F^{(2)}(0)$. It is, of course, possible to calculate $F^{(1)}(\Delta t)$ for sufficiently small Δt in terms of $F^{(1)}(0)$ and $F^{(2)}(0)$; however, this process cannot be repeated without a knowledge of $F^{(2)}(\Delta t)$. And the time dependence of

$F^{(2)}$ is not determined at all by eq. (3.59). In order to obtain an equation that involves $\partial F^{(2)}/\partial t$, we can, of course, integrate Liouville's equation again but this time over all of phase space except for that of particles 1 and 2. It should be evident from the above derivation that such an equation will involve $F^{(3)}$. And to be sure, a similarly derived equation for $\partial F^{(3)}/\partial t$ will involve $F^{(4)}$. Proceeding in this way we will eventually get back to Liouville's equation itself. This hierarchy of equations, of which eq. (3.59) is the first member and Liouville's equation is the last, has been derived independently by various authors and is sometimes referred to as the BBGKY (Bogoliubov, Born, Green, Kirkwood, and Yvon) hierarchy. In many cases this set of equations is truncated at some stage by assuming that for some integer $s(1 < s \ll N)$ $F^{(s)}$ may be expressed in terms of distribution functions that involve no more than $s-1$ particles, and in this way a closed set of equations may be obtained. For example, the assumption expressed by the relation

$$F^{(2)}(\mathbf{r}_1,\mathbf{p}_1,\mathbf{r}_2,\mathbf{p}_2,t) \cong F^{(1)}(\mathbf{r}_1,\mathbf{p}_1,t)F^{(1)}(\mathbf{r}_2,\mathbf{p}_2,t) \qquad (3.60)$$

when combined with eq. (3.59) reduces the latter to a "solvable" equation. Indeed, it is in precisely this way that we can obtain the Boltzmann-Vlasov equation which we shall study in some detail in the next chapter.

Finally, let us note that eq. (3.59) has an easily understandable form. For if there were no interparticle forces, then the last term which involves $F^{(2)}(t)$ would not be present and eq. (3.59) would become simply Liouville's equation for a single particle. That is, in the absence of interparticle forces, there are, of course, no correlations between particles, and this statistical independence is expressed by the fact that $F^{(N)}(t)$ for this case has the form

$$F^{(N)}(t) = \prod_{i=1}^{N} F^{(1)}(\mathbf{r}_i,\mathbf{p}_i,t)$$

or in other words, the joint probability breaks up into a product of individual-particle probabilities. Thus, the presence of the two-particle distribution function in eq. (3.59) is a reflection of the fact that there are correlations between the particles because of their Coulomb forces, and only if these forces are negligible are the particles statistically independent.

Suggested Readings and References

1. Liouville's Theorem.

H. Goldstein, *Classical Mechanics*, Chap. 8. Reading, Mass.: Addison-Wesley Publishing Company, Inc., 1951.

R. C. Tolman, *The Principles of Statistical Mechanics*, Chap. 3. New York: Oxford University Press, 1938.

2. Reduction of Liouville's Equation

N. N. Bogoliubov, "Problems of a Dynamical Theory in Statistical Physics," Part A of *Studies in Statistical Mechanics*, J. D. Boer and G. E. Uhlenbeck (editors). Amsterdam: North Holland Co., 1962.

H. Grad, "Principles of the Kinetic Theory of Gases," *Handbuch der Physik*, B. **XII**. Berlin: Springer-Verlag, 1958.

A. N. Kaufman, "Plasma Transport Theory", contained in *La theorie des gaz neutres et ionises*, C. DeWitt and J. F. Detoeuf (editors). New York: John Wiley & Sons, Inc., 1960.

J. G. Kirkwood and J. Ross, "The Statistical Mechanical Basis of the Boltzmann Equation"; contained in *Transport Processes in Statistical Mechanics*, I. Prigogine (editor). New York: Interscience Publishers, Inc., 1958.

N. Rostoker and M. N. Rosenbluth, "Test Particles in a Completely Ionized Plasma," *Phys. of Fluids*, 3, 1 (1960).

3. Information Theory

L. Brillouin, *Science and Information Theory*. New York: Academic Press, Inc., 1962.

M. Tribus, *Thermostatics and Thermodynamics*. Princeton, N.J.: D. Van Nostrand Company, Inc., 1961.

Problems

1. Show that the single-particle Hamiltonian

$$H = c\left[m^2c^2 + (\mathbf{p} - q\mathbf{A})^2\right]^{\frac{1}{2}} + q\phi$$

when used with the Hamiltonian equations of motion will reproduce the relativistic form of Newton's laws of motion—that is, eq. (2.1).

2. Derive the relativistic form of Liouville's equation for a single particle by making use of the Hamiltonian in Problem 1. Show that by an appropriate change of variables this equation may be written

$$\frac{\partial f}{\partial t} + \mathbf{v} \cdot \frac{\partial}{\partial \mathbf{r}} f + \frac{q}{m}\left(1 - \frac{v^2}{c^2}\right)^{\frac{1}{2}}\left[\mathbf{E} + \mathbf{v} \times \mathbf{B} - \frac{1}{c^2}\mathbf{v}\mathbf{v} \cdot E\right] \cdot \frac{\partial}{\partial \mathbf{v}} f = 0$$

3. Formulate the problem of scattering by a central potential by use of Liouville's Theorem. Consider that at $t = 0$, the nonvanishing incident particles are distributed with uniform density throughout a very long cylinder of radius a and whose axis defines the z axis and that the particles move with incident velocity v_o which is also parallel to the z axis. The target particle is assumed to be located at the origin.

(a) Write down the initial distribution function and by use of the equivalence between Newton's laws of motion and Liouville's theorem calculate the distribution function at any time t.

(b) By use of (a), calculate the flux of particles that crosses a unit element of area very far away from the scattering centre.

(c) Divide the result of (b) by the incident flux and thus show that the differential cross section $\sigma(\theta)$ is given by

$$\sigma(\theta) = -\frac{b(\theta)}{\sin\theta}\frac{db}{d\theta}$$

where $b(\theta)$ is the impact parameter that is associated with the scattering angle θ and is derivable in terms of the given central potential.

4. Show that the vector functions $\mathbf{g}_1$ and $\mathbf{g}_2$ in eq. (3.15) are expressible in terms of $\mathbf{f}_1$ and $\mathbf{f}_2$ in eq. (3.14) by the formulas

$$\mathbf{g}_1(\mathbf{r},\mathbf{p},t) = \mathbf{f}_1(\mathbf{r},\mathbf{p}-t) \qquad \mathbf{g}_2(\mathbf{r},\mathbf{p},t) = \mathbf{f}_2(\mathbf{r},\mathbf{p},-t)$$

Hint: Follow the trajectory of a point in phase space forward and then backward in time.

5. Show that sums, products, quotients, and arbitrary differentiable functions of solutions of Liouville's equation are still solutions of this same equation by direct substitution into eq. (3.26).

6. Give a qualitative argument why the $(v/c)^3$ corrections to eq. (3.21) have a form different from the terms that are of order $(v/c)^2$. State the basic distinction between these $(v/c)^3$ terms and the ones given in eq. (3.21).

7. Derive a simplified version of eq. (3.24) that is obtained by neglecting the magnetic-magnetic interactions in the Hamiltonian.

8. By integrating Liouville's equation over all of phase space show that

$$\int F^{(N)}(t)\, d\Omega$$

is independent of time. In a similar way, show that the integral of an arbitrary function of $F^{(N)}(t)$ is also independent of time.

9. Multiply Liouville's equation by $\sum_{i=1}^{N} \delta(\mathbf{r}_i - \mathbf{x})$ and then integrate over all of phase space and thus show

$$\frac{\partial}{\partial t} n(\mathbf{x},t) + \nabla \cdot [\mathbf{u}(\mathbf{x},t)n(\mathbf{x},t)] = 0$$

Interpret this result: first as it stands; second, by first multiplying it by the mass of a particle; and third, by multiplying it by the charge of a particle.

10. Multiply Liouville's equation by $\sum_{i=1}^{N} \delta(\mathbf{r}_i - \mathbf{x}) \, \mathbf{H}_{p_i}$ and again integrate over all of phase space. Neglect the magnetic-magnetic inter-actions. Interpret the various terms physically, and thus give a physical description of the entire equation.

11. Show by use of information-theoretical arguments that for a physical system, which is governed by the time independent Hamiltonian H and for which one knows only its average energy $\bar{E}$, that the most un-biased distribution in phase space is given by

$$F^{(N)} = \frac{e^{-\beta H}}{\int d\Omega \, e^{-\beta H}}$$

where β is a LaGrange multiplier and is explicitly given by

$$\bar{E} = -\frac{\partial}{\partial \beta} \ln \left\{ \int d\Omega \, e^{-\beta H} \right\}$$

Show that this distribution does not change in the course of time by direct substitution into Liouville's equation.

12. Consider a collection of N uncoupled harmonic oscillators, each one of which is governed by the Hamiltonian

$$H = \frac{1}{2m}\mathbf{p}^2 + \frac{1}{2}m\omega^2 \mathbf{r}^2$$

(a) Show that the solution of the Hamiltonian equation subject to the initial conditions $\mathbf{r}_o$, $\mathbf{p}_o$ is given by

$$\mathbf{r} = \mathbf{r}_o \cos \omega t + \frac{1}{\omega}\mathbf{p}_o \sin \omega t$$

$$\mathbf{p} = \mathbf{p}_o \cos \omega t - m\omega \mathbf{r}_o \sin \omega t$$

and thus verify the result in problem 4 for this special case.

(b) Assuming that at $t = 0$, these particles are distributed with uniform density throughout the interior of a sphere of radius a, and that they have a mean energy $\bar{E}$, write down the initial distribution function.

(c) Calculate the distribution function at any time t, by use of the equivalence between Liouville's theorem and the Hamiltonian equations of motion.

(d) Calculate the density, temperature, and pressure tensor at any time t and interpret these formulas in physical terms.

13. Consider a cube of matter at absolute zero that is placed in thermal contact with a horizontal surface at temperature T. According to Newton's laws, is it possible for this cube to rise up against the force of gravity after it has come to equilibrium? Explain the situation from a microscopic point of view and examine the source of energy and momentum that the cube has if it can indeed rise.

14. A worn-out roulette wheel has slots for the numbers 0, 1, 2, $\cdots$ 35 and the house pays 35:1 odds on any of these 36 numbers. If the mean number that comes up on any spin is 15, find the "least biased" distribution; and from this, calculate for which numbers (if any) one would have a positive mathematical expectation. Make a plot of the partition function and use this plot to estimate the La Grange multiplier.

15. Modify the derivation of eq. (3.59) by integrating Liouville's equation over the coordinates and momenta of all particles except for numbers 1, 2, $\cdots$ s, where $s \ll N$. Show that $F^{(S)}$ satisfies the equation

$$\frac{\partial}{\partial t} F^{(s)} + \sum_{i=1}^{s} \left\{ \mathbf{v}_i \cdot \frac{\partial}{\partial \mathbf{r}_i} + \frac{e}{m} \left[\mathbf{E}(\mathbf{r}_i, t) + \frac{\mathbf{v}_i}{c} \times \mathbf{B}(\mathbf{r}_i, t) \right] \cdot \frac{\partial}{\partial \mathbf{v}_i} \right\} F^{(s)}$$

$$- \frac{e^2}{m} \sum_{i,j}^{s'} \left(\frac{\partial}{\partial \mathbf{r}_i} \frac{1}{|\mathbf{r}_i - \mathbf{r}_j|} \right) \cdot \frac{\partial}{\partial \mathbf{v}_i} F^{(s)}$$

$$- \frac{Ne^2}{m} \sum_{i=1}^{s} \int d\mathbf{r}_{s+1} d\mathbf{v}_{s+1} \left(\frac{\partial}{\partial \mathbf{r}_i} \frac{1}{|\mathbf{r}_i - \mathbf{r}_{s+1}|} \right) \cdot \frac{\partial}{\partial \mathbf{v}_i} F^{(s+1)} = 0$$

which agrees with eq. (3.60) for the case $s = 1$.

4

The Boltzmann-Vlasov Equation

INTRODUCTION

In the previous chapter we saw that a completely reliable way for predicting the dynamical behaviour of a plasma is by means of Liouville's theorem supplemented by an initial distribution function selected to be maximally noncommittal with regard to all missing information. We also saw that this description is equivalent to solving Newton's laws of motion subject to initial conditions that were obtainable only in a statistical way. All macroscopic quantities of interest could be expressed in terms of certain phase-space integrals over the distribution function, and these macroscopic variables were presumed to be known once the solution of Liouville's equation was available. Unfortunately, except for very trivial systems, Newton's laws of motion cannot be explicitly solved, and thus, in order to proceed, it is necessary to make some mathematical approximations that will produce a more manageable equation out of Liouville's theorem.

Let us examine, for a moment, the related problem of obtaining a mathematically tractable equation from Liouville's theorem for the case of a dilute and neutral gas. This system is basically different from a plasma in that the interparticle forces for it are all of very short range in contrast to the long-range Coulomb forces. For the case of a dilute neutral gas, Bogoliubov has recently given a new derivation of the widely used, kinetic-theoretical Boltzmann equation by starting with the appropriate form of Liouville's theorem and expanding the solution of this equation in a power series of the particle density. Actually, of course, a dimensionless expansion parameter is required, and since the only other length in the problem is the force range r_0 this expansion parameter α must be given by

$$\alpha = nr_0^3 \tag{4.1}$$

where n is the particle density. For the case of a gas consisting exclusively of neutral particles, the force range r_0 is of order 10^{-8} cm and thus even for densities as large as 10^{20} particles per cc the parameter α is negligible compared to unity. We may expect, therefore, that the Boltzmann equation, which was originally obtained by assuming only that binary collisions dominate, will be valid for this system. On the other hand, for liquids with their much greater densities, the parameter α is of order unity and thus we cannot expect to make very accurate predictions in the same way. Physically, the explanation for this inability of the Boltzmann equation to predict the behavior of a very dense system is easy to see. The magnitude of the expansion parameter α may be thought of as being a measure of the probability that various numbers of particles will collide simultaneously. If α is very small compared to unity, then it is very unlikely that more than two particles will ever suffer a simultaneous collision; and, consequently, one expects that the familiar form of the Boltzmann equation, which allows only for binary collisions, will correctly describe the system. On the other hand, for liquids where α is of order unity, one anticipates that in order to obtain a correct description it will be necessary to modify the Boltzmann equation by including three or even possibly four particle-collision terms. Not unexpectedly this complicates the analysis enormously and is perhaps one of the main reasons why the kinetic theory of gases has been so extensively developed without corresponding developments in the theory of liquids.

Let us now examine the possibility of using the binary-collision form of the Boltzmann equation to describe a plasma. Assuming a relatively small density, say of the order of 10^{15} particles per cc, the problem confronting us becomes that of deciding the value for the force range r_o to use in eq. (4.1) in order to estimate the expansion parameter α. Since the range of the Coulomb force is essentially infinite, it would appear at first glance that α will always be very large regardless of the particle density, and that therefore Bogoliubov's approach would lead to the conclusion that nothing short of Liouville's equation itself would work. On the basis of our physical interpretation of the parameter α, it would seem therefore that each particle in the plasma experiences the forces due to many other particles; or stated in other words, most of the particles are constantly in simultaneous "collision" with each other. From another point of view, however, one could argue that this is not quite the case since—as we shall derive subsequently—there is a cutoff distance, the Debye shielding radius, beyond which the particles are oblivious to each other's Coulomb forces, and it is *this* distance that should be used in eq. (4.1). If T represents the absolute temperature of the plasma, then the Debye shielding distance, λ_D is given by the formula

$$\lambda_D = \left(\frac{\varepsilon_0 kT}{nq^2}\right)^{\frac{1}{2}} \tag{4.2}$$

where n is the number of particles per cubic centimeter and q is the electronic charge. On substituting this length for r_0 in eq. (4.1) one obtains

$$\alpha = \left(\frac{\varepsilon_0 k}{q^2}\right)^{\frac{3}{2}} T^{\frac{3}{2}} n^{-\frac{1}{2}} \tag{4.3}$$

and this shows that on this basis as well, α is still very large compared to unity for most physically interesting plasmas. For example, at a temperature of 10^5 °K, as the density varies between 10^{16} and 10^{12} particles per cc, α covers the range from 10 to 1000. Thus we conclude that for all reasonable densities and temperatures the particles in the plasma will suffer repeated, multiparticle, and simultaneous collisions and that consequently the binary-collision form of the Boltzmann equation is not applicable for such a plasma. Thus a correct and simple description cannot be obtained in this way.

The above physical interpretation that for large values of α a given particle experiences forces due to many other particles in the plasma can actually be used to some advantage. This feature will be seen in a quantitative way when we derive the Boltzmann-Vlasov equation by use of the method of Rostoker and Rosenbluth; and it can also be made plausible by noting that for large values of α, only if the particles move in some sort of a coherent or collective way will a typical particle in the plasma experience an appreciable force. Furthermore, such forces can be expected to be much more smoothly behaved functions of both space and time than the forces produced by the much rarer multiple-particle "collisions." When carried to its extreme, this argument leads us to suspect that in the lowest order we could replace all interparticle forces (the Coulombic as well as the magnetic) by certain macroscopically smoothed electromagnetic fields. According to this point of view every particle moves completely "independently" of all of the other particles but follows its predictable trajectory in these smoothed fields. There are still multiparticle correlations, of course, but presumably these can largely be taken into account by use of a suitable choice for the electromagnetic fields. Physically it is evident that this choice must consist of those fields that are produced by all of the particles in the plasma; and for obvious reasons these fields are often referred to as the *self-consistent fields*. In other words, the "independent" trajectories of the particles give rise to macroscopic charge and current densities which in turn produce those fields that will determine the motions of the particles in a self-consistent way. This method of solution turns out to be equivalent to the one obtained by solving for the single-particle distribution function from that form of the Boltzmann equation that is obtained by omitting the collision term but by supplementing the external force terms in this equation with the smoothed, self-consistent fields. These fields are obtained by solving Maxwell's equations with charge and current density expressed in terms of the distribution function by the last two of eqs. (3.35). This set of equations —namely, the collisionless Boltzmann equation plus the above described form of Maxwell's equation—will be referred to as the *Boltzmann-Vlasov (BV) equation.* The present chapter deals with a derivation and a study of this equation.

THE BV EQUATION BY USE
OF INDEPENDENT TRAJECTORIES

For reasons of simplicity let us first consider a gas of identical particles and generalize to multicomponent plasmas at a later stage. The assumption that forms the basis of the following discussion is that the particles follow "independent" trajectories, or equivalently that the N-particle distribution function, $F^{(N)}(t)$, may be expressed in the form

$$F^{(N)}(t) = \prod_{i=1}^{N} f(\mathbf{r}_i, \mathbf{p}_i, t) \tag{4.4}$$

where f is the single-particle distribution function. It will now be verified that the introduction of eq. (4.4) into Liouville's theorem produces the BV equation. Thus it will follow that the assumption in eq. (4.4) is equivalent to saying that each particle in the plasma follows a trajectory determined by forces due to any external fields plus the smoothed-out fields produced by all of the other particles in the plasma.

On substituting eq. (4.4) into eq. (3.26) and on integrating over the coordinates and momenta of all of the particles except those for say number 1, we find

$$\frac{\partial}{\partial t} f(\mathbf{r}_1, \mathbf{p}_1, t) = \int \left(\prod_{j=2}^{N} d\mathbf{r}_j \, d\mathbf{p}_j \right) \left\{ \mathbf{H}_{r_1} \cdot \frac{\partial}{\partial \mathbf{p}_1} - \mathbf{H}_{p_1} \cdot \frac{\partial}{\partial \mathbf{r}_1} \right\} \prod_{i=1}^{N} f(\mathbf{r}_i, \mathbf{p}_i, t) \tag{4.5}$$

where, as in the analogous derivation of eq. (3.59), various surface terms have been dropped. The vector functions $\mathbf{H}_{r_1}$ and $\mathbf{H}_{p_1}$ are given by eqs. (3.23) in which H now represents the full Hamiltonian as given in eq.

(3.21). It is convenient to split this Hamiltonian into two parts: one of these $H^{(1)}$ depends only on the coordinates and momenta of particle number 1, and the second of these $H^{(1j)}$ depends only on the coordinates and momenta of particles number 1 and j. Specifically, $H^{(1)}$ and $H^{(1j)}$ are given by

$$H^{(1)} = \frac{1}{2m}\left\{ \mathbf{p}_1 - \frac{e}{c}\mathbf{A}(\mathbf{r}_1,t) \right\}^2 + e\phi(\mathbf{r}_1,t)$$

$$H^{(1j)} = \frac{e^2}{r_{1j}} - \frac{e^2}{2m^2c^2}\left(\frac{\mathbf{p}_1 \cdot \mathbf{p}_j}{r_{1j}} + \frac{\mathbf{p}_1 \cdot \mathbf{r}_{1j}\,\mathbf{p}_j \cdot \mathbf{r}_{1j}}{r_{1j}^3} \right) \qquad (4.6)$$

Assuming that f has been normalized to unity, and making use of the symmetry under particle exchange of the integrand in eq. (4.5), this latter equation may be reduced to the form

$$\frac{\partial}{\partial t}f(\mathbf{r}_1,\mathbf{p}_1,t) = \mathbf{H}_{r_1}^{(1)} \cdot \frac{\partial}{\partial \mathbf{p}_1}f - \mathbf{H}_{p_1}^{(1)} \cdot \frac{\partial}{\partial \mathbf{r}_1}f$$

$$+ N\int dr_2\,dp_2\left\{ \mathbf{H}_{r_1}^{(12)} \cdot \frac{\partial}{\partial \mathbf{p}_1} - \mathbf{H}_{p_1}^{(12)} \cdot \frac{\partial}{\partial \mathbf{r}_1} \right\} f(\mathbf{r}_1,\mathbf{p}_1,t)f(\mathbf{r}_2,\mathbf{p}_2,t) \quad (4.7)$$

where the factor $(N-1)$ has been replaced by N. As in the derivation of eq. (3.59), we see that because of the existence of interparticle forces, complications of a nonlinear nature occur. This is a characteristic feature of all equations of this sort and only if there are no terms in the Hamiltonian involving the coordinates of two or more particles will appreciable simplifications occur.

In order to make some of the remaining intermediate steps more transparent, let us temporarily omit the interparticle magnetic interactions so that $H^{(12)}$ becomes simply

$$H^{(12)} = \frac{e^2}{r_{12}}$$

Substituting this form of $H^{(12)}$ as well as that for $H^{(1)}$ as given by eq. (4.6) into eq. (4.7) there results

$$\frac{\partial}{\partial t}f(\mathbf{r},\mathbf{p},t) + \mathbf{v} \cdot \frac{\partial}{\partial \mathbf{r}}f + \frac{e}{c}\left\{ \left(\mathbf{v} \cdot \frac{\partial}{\partial \mathbf{r}} \right)\mathbf{A} + \mathbf{v} \times \mathbf{B} - c\,\nabla\phi \right\} \cdot \frac{\partial}{\partial \mathbf{p}}f$$

$$= Ne^2\int dr_2\,dp_2\left(\frac{\partial}{\partial \mathbf{r}}\frac{1}{|\mathbf{r} - \mathbf{r}_2|} \right)f(\mathbf{r}_2,\mathbf{p}_2,t) \cdot \frac{\partial}{\partial \mathbf{p}}f(\mathbf{r},\mathbf{p},t) \qquad (4.8)$$

where $\mathbf{B}(\mathbf{r},\,t)$ is the external magnetic field and is expressed in terms of $\mathbf{A}$ by eq. (1.10) and where the subscripts on $\mathbf{r}$ and $\mathbf{p}$ have been consistently dropped. The symbol **v** is to be thought of as an abbreviation for the quantity

$$\frac{1}{m}\left\{\mathbf{p} - \frac{e}{c}\mathbf{A}(\mathbf{r},t)\right\} \tag{4.9}$$

As in the derivation of eq. (3.59), we now change variables from **r**, **p**, t to **r**, **v**, t. The derivatives in eq. (4.8) become replaced as in eq. (3.19) and thus eq. (4.8) becomes

$$\frac{\partial}{\partial t}f(\mathbf{r},\mathbf{v},t) + \mathbf{v}\cdot\frac{\partial}{\partial \mathbf{r}} + \frac{e}{m}\left[\mathbf{E} + \frac{\mathbf{v}}{c}\times\mathbf{B}\right]\cdot\frac{\partial}{\partial\mathbf{v}}f(\mathbf{r},\mathbf{v},t)$$

$$= \frac{Ne^2}{m}\int d\mathbf{r}_2\,d\mathbf{p}_2\left[\frac{\partial}{\partial\mathbf{r}}\frac{1}{|\mathbf{r}-\mathbf{r}_2|}\right]f(\mathbf{r}_2,\mathbf{p}_2,t)\cdot\frac{\partial}{\partial\mathbf{v}}f(\mathbf{r},\mathbf{v},t) \tag{4.10}$$

where **E** and **B** are the external fields and the factor $1/c$ in the force term is due to the present choice of units. It is evident that the term on the right-hand side of this equation has the same form as the external electric-field term on the left and that therefore the above integral may be thought of as representing an induced electric field in the interior of the plasma.

If in addition to the Coulomb repulsion between the particles we now also include the interparticle magnetic forces—that is, we now use that form of $H^{(12)}$ given in eq. (4.6)—then an additional term, which corresponds to an induced magnetic field, will be added to the right-hand side of eq. (4.10). Unfortunately, this added term cannot be simply expressed in terms of the independent variables used in eq. (4.10). In terms of the variables used in eq. (4.8), however, this added term has the form

$$-\frac{Ne^2}{m^2c^2}\int d\mathbf{r}_2\,d\mathbf{p}_2\left\{\mathbf{p}\times\left(\frac{\partial}{\partial\mathbf{r}}\times\frac{\mathbf{p}_2}{|\mathbf{r}-\mathbf{r}_2|}\right) + \left(\mathbf{p}\cdot\frac{\partial}{\partial\mathbf{r}}\right)\left[\frac{\mathbf{p}_2}{|\mathbf{r}-\mathbf{r}_2|}\right.\right.$$

$$\left.\left. -\frac{1}{2}\frac{\partial}{\partial\mathbf{r}}\left(\mathbf{p}_2\cdot\frac{\partial}{\partial\mathbf{r}}|\mathbf{r}-\mathbf{r}_2|\right)\right]\right\}f(\mathbf{r}_2,\mathbf{p}_2,t)\cdot\frac{\partial}{\partial\mathbf{p}}f(\mathbf{r},\mathbf{p},t)$$

$$+\frac{Ne^2}{m^2c^2}\int d\mathbf{r}_2\,d\mathbf{p}_2\left\{\frac{\mathbf{p}_2}{|\mathbf{r}-\mathbf{r}_2|}\right.$$

$$\left. -\frac{1}{2}\frac{\partial}{\partial\mathbf{r}}\left(\mathbf{p}_2\cdot\frac{\partial}{\partial\mathbf{r}}|\mathbf{r}-\mathbf{r}_2|\right)\right\}f(\mathbf{r}_2,\mathbf{p}_2,t)\cdot\frac{\partial}{\partial\mathbf{r}}f(\mathbf{r},\mathbf{p},t) \tag{4.11}$$

where each operator differentiates only the factor standing immediately to its right and where, to the same order in $1/c$, any of the factors **p**, $\mathbf{p}_2$ may be replaced by $\mathbf{p} - (e/c)\mathbf{A}$. This complicated-looking formula in eq. (4.11) may be simply interpreted in the following way. On adding eq. (4.11) to the right-hand side of eq. (4.10) the resulting terms may be described by saying that to order $(1/c)^2$ a particle located at the point $\mathbf{r}$ is acted upon by a particle—which is located at the point $\mathbf{r}_2$ and has momentum $\mathbf{p}_2$—by means of the scalar potential

$$\frac{e}{|\mathbf{r} - \mathbf{r}_2|} \tag{4.12}$$

and also by means of the vector potential

$$\frac{e}{mc}\left\{ \frac{\mathbf{p}_2}{|\mathbf{r} - \mathbf{r}_2|} - \frac{1}{2}\frac{\partial}{\partial \mathbf{r}}\left[\mathbf{p}_2 \cdot \frac{\partial}{\partial \mathbf{r}}|\mathbf{r} - \mathbf{r}_2| \right] \right\} \tag{4.13}$$

Of course, eq. (4.13) is not unique in that it is always possible to make a guage transformation by adding the gradient of a scalar quantity to this vector potential. The above vector potential has been arbitrarily selected to have zero divergence.

Proceeding with the derivation of the BV equation, we now add eq. (4.11) to the right-hand side of eq. (4.8) and the result thus obtained may be cast into the form

$$\frac{\partial}{\partial t}f(\mathbf{r},\mathbf{p},t) + \frac{1}{m}\left[\mathbf{p} - \frac{e}{c}(\mathbf{A} + \mathbf{A}_i) \right] \cdot \frac{\partial}{\partial \mathbf{r}}f$$

$$+ \frac{e}{mc}\left\{ \left(\left[\mathbf{p} - \frac{e}{c}(\mathbf{A} + \mathbf{A}_i) \right] \cdot \frac{\partial}{\partial \mathbf{r}} \right)(\mathbf{A} + \mathbf{A}_i) \right.$$

$$+ \left[\mathbf{p} - \frac{e}{c}(\mathbf{A} + \mathbf{A}_i) \right] \times (\mathbf{B} + \mathbf{B}_i)$$

$$\left. - mc[\nabla(\phi + \phi_i)] \right\} \cdot \frac{\partial}{\partial \mathbf{p}}f = 0 \tag{4.14}$$

where $\mathbf{A}_i$ and ϕ_i are the induced potentials which are *defined* by the formulas

$$\mathbf{A}_i(\mathbf{r},t) = \frac{Ne}{mc}\int d\mathbf{r}_2\, d\mathbf{p}_2 \left[\frac{\mathbf{p}_2}{|\mathbf{r} - \mathbf{r}_2|} \right.$$

$$\left. - \frac{1}{2}\frac{\partial}{\partial \mathbf{r}}\left(\mathbf{p}_2 \cdot \frac{\partial}{\partial \mathbf{r}}|\mathbf{r} - \mathbf{r}_2| \right) \right] f(\mathbf{r}_2,\mathbf{p}_2,t)$$

$$\phi_i(\mathbf{r},t) = Ne\int d\mathbf{r}_2\, d\mathbf{p}_2 \frac{1}{|\mathbf{r} - \mathbf{r}_2|}f(\mathbf{r}_2,\mathbf{p}_2,t) \tag{4.15}$$

and where $\mathbf{B}_i$ is the induced magnetic field and is the curl of $\mathbf{A}_i$. It is to be noted that $\mathbf{A}_i$ itself is of order $1/c$ and therefore some terms of order $(1/c)^3$ have been kept in eq. (4.14). These are not essential, however, and have been temporarily retained only in order to preserve some of the symmetry in eq. (4.14).

Following the now familiar pattern, we change the variables in eq. (4.14) from $\mathbf{r}$, $\mathbf{p}$, t to $\mathbf{r}$, $\mathbf{v}$, t where $\mathbf{v}$ is now defined by

$$\mathbf{v} = \frac{1}{m}\left[\mathbf{p} - \frac{e}{c}(\mathbf{A} + \mathbf{A}_i)\right]$$

The derivatives in eq. (4.14) are again transformed as in eq. (3.19) but with $\mathbf{A}$ now replaced by $\mathbf{A} + \mathbf{A}_i$. Thus we obtain the simple looking result

$$\frac{\partial}{\partial t}f(\mathbf{r},\mathbf{v},t) + \mathbf{v} \cdot \frac{\partial}{\partial \mathbf{r}}f + \frac{e}{m}\left[\mathbf{E} + \mathbf{E}_i + \frac{1}{c}\mathbf{v} \times (\mathbf{B} + \mathbf{B}_i)\right] \cdot \frac{\partial}{\partial \mathbf{v}}f = 0 \quad (4.16)$$

where again all terms of order $(1/c)^3$ have been dropped. In this equation, which is the BV equation for a single species, $\mathbf{E}$ and $\mathbf{B}$ are, of course, the external fields, while $\mathbf{E}_i$ and $\mathbf{B}_i$ are the induced electromagnetic fields and are *defined* in terms of $\mathbf{A}_i$ and ϕ_i by the familiar formulas

$$\mathbf{B}_i = \nabla \times \mathbf{A}_i$$

$$\mathbf{E}_i = -\nabla\phi_i - \frac{1}{c}\frac{\partial}{\partial t}\mathbf{A}_i \quad (4.17)$$

An immediate consequence of these last two relations is that $\mathbf{E}_i$ and $\mathbf{B}_i$ satisfy two of Maxwell's equations; that is, we have,

$$\nabla \cdot \mathbf{B}_i = 0$$

$$\nabla \times \mathbf{E}_i = -\frac{1}{c}\frac{\partial}{\partial t}\mathbf{B}_i \quad (4.18)$$

Furthermore, according to first of eqs. (4.15) we have $\nabla \cdot \mathbf{A}_i = 0$, and therefore according to the second of eqs. (4.17) it follows

$$\nabla \cdot \mathbf{E}_i = -\nabla^2\phi_i \quad (4.19)$$

By making use of the definition of ϕ_i as given in eq. (4.15), this relation in eq. (4.19) may be cast into the alternate form

$$\nabla \cdot \mathbf{E}_i = -Ne\int d\mathbf{r}'\, d\mathbf{p}'\left(\nabla^2\frac{1}{|\mathbf{r} - \mathbf{r}'|}\right)f(\mathbf{r}',p_,,t)$$

$$= 4\pi Ne\int d\mathbf{p}'\, f(\mathbf{r},\mathbf{p}',t) \quad (4.20)$$

where the second equality follows by use of the identity

$$\nabla^2\frac{1}{r} = -4\pi\,\delta(\mathbf{r}) \quad (4.21)$$

Moreover, according to eq. (3.53) the integral after the second equality in eq. (4.20) is proportional to the charge density $\rho_q(\mathbf{r}, t)$ and thus we have shown that $\mathbf{E}_i$ also satisfies the equation

$$\nabla \cdot \mathbf{E}_i = 4\pi\rho_q \tag{4.22}$$

which is one of Maxwell's equations as expressed in the present system of units.

The fact that the induced fields $\mathbf{E}_i$, $\mathbf{B}_i$ also satisfy the fourth of Maxwell's equations can be shown by taking the curl of the curl of the formula for $\mathbf{A}_i$ in eq. (4.15). On making use of the identity in eq. (4.21) and the fact that for any vector function $\mathbf{F}$ we have

$$\nabla \times (\nabla \times \mathbf{F}) = \nabla(\nabla \cdot \mathbf{F}) - \nabla^2 \mathbf{F}$$

we obtain

$$\nabla \times \mathbf{B}_i = \frac{4\pi Ne}{mc} \int d\mathbf{p}' \ \mathbf{p}' f(\mathbf{r},\mathbf{p}',t)$$
$$+ \frac{Ne}{mc} \nabla \left\{ \nabla \cdot \int d\mathbf{r}' \ d\mathbf{p}' \frac{\mathbf{p}}{|\mathbf{r} - \mathbf{r}'|} f(\mathbf{r}',\mathbf{p}',t) \right\} \tag{4.23}$$

If we make use of the continuity equation (see Problem 9, Chapter 3)

$$\nabla \cdot \int d\mathbf{p}' \frac{\mathbf{p}'}{m} f(\mathbf{r},\mathbf{p}',t) + \frac{\partial}{\partial t} \int d\mathbf{p}' f(\mathbf{r},\mathbf{p}',t) = 0 \tag{4.24}$$

the second term on the right-hand side of eq. (4.23) may be cast into the form

$$-\frac{1}{c} \frac{\partial}{\partial t} \nabla \phi_i \tag{4.25}$$

Finally, therefore, we make use of this result and the definition for the current density $\mathbf{j}$ in eqs. (3.35) and (3.54), and eq. (4.23) then takes on the familiar form

$$\nabla \times \mathbf{B}_i = \frac{4\pi}{c} \mathbf{j} + \frac{1}{c} \frac{\partial}{\partial t} \mathbf{E}_i \tag{4.26}$$

To summarize this lengthy discussion, we note that the assumption in eq. (4.4) produces the BV equation—that is, eq. (4.16)—provided $\mathbf{E}_i$ and $\mathbf{B}_i$ are the solution of Maxwell's equations—that is, eqs. (4.18), (4.22), and (4.26)—with charge and current density given by

$$\rho_q(\mathbf{r},t) = Ne \int d\mathbf{v} \ f(\mathbf{r},\mathbf{v},t)$$

$$\mathbf{j}(\mathbf{r},t) = Ne \int d\mathbf{v} \ \mathbf{v} f(\mathbf{r},\mathbf{v},t) \tag{4.27}$$

Furthermore eq. (4.16) has the form of Liouville's theorem for a single particle except that the external-field terms in this equation must be simultaneously determined with the distribution function itself. Therefore we can say that each particle in the plasma moves under the combined influence of any external fields plus the fields produced by all of the remaining particles in the plasma.

For the case where the plasma consists of two species of particles—say of charges e_-, e_+ and masses m_-, m_+, respectively—the generalization of the assumption in eq. (4.4) takes on the form

$$F^{(2N)}(t) = \left\{ \prod_{i=1}^{N} f_-(\mathbf{r}_i, \mathbf{p}_i, t) \right\} \left\{ \prod_{j=1}^{N} f_+(\mathbf{r}_j, \mathbf{p}_j, t) \right\} \tag{4.28}$$

where the first product goes over all of the electrons and the second over the positively charged ions. Here again we substitute this assumption into the applicable form of Liouville's theorem; and we then integrate (a) over the coordinates and momenta of all ions and of all electrons except for one, and (b) over the coordinates and momenta of all electrons, plus all of the ions except for one. In the first case, (a), we obtain an equation for the single-particle electronic distribution function f_-, and in (b) we obtain a corresponding equation for the single-particle ionic distribution function f_+. It should be evident that the detailed derivations of the equations satisfied by these two functions are essentially identical to the one carried out above for the case of a single species, and that the resulting equations are identical to eq. (4.16) except that for the present case the induced fields $\mathbf{E}_i$ and $\mathbf{B}_i$ are determined by the charge and current densities produced by both species. More specifically, the BV equations for a two-species plasma are given by

$$\frac{\partial}{\partial t} f_\pm(\mathbf{r}, \mathbf{v}, t) + \mathbf{v} \cdot \frac{\partial}{\partial \mathbf{r}} f_\pm + \frac{e_\pm}{m_\pm} \left\{ \mathbf{E} + \mathbf{E}_i + \frac{1}{c} \mathbf{v} \times (\mathbf{B} + \mathbf{B}_i) \right\} \cdot \frac{\partial}{\partial \mathbf{v}} f_\pm = 0 \tag{4.29}$$

where the induced fields $\mathbf{E}_i$ and $\mathbf{B}_i$ satisfy Maxwell's equations with charge and current densities given by

$$\rho_q(\mathbf{r}, t) = N \int d\mathbf{v} \, [e_+ f_+ + e_- f_-]$$

$$\mathbf{j}(\mathbf{r}, t) = N \int d\mathbf{v} \, \mathbf{v} [e_+ f_+ + e_- f_-] \tag{4.30}$$

The BV equations for plasmas that consist of more than two species can be obtained in a similar way. And the physical interpretations of all of these equations is, with obvious modifications, essentially the same as that of the single-component plasma.

Finally, the conversion of all of the above relations to rationalized mks units is obtained by dropping the $1/c$ factor in eqs. (4.29) and using that form of Maxwell's equations given in eqs. (1.5) through (1.8).

CORRECTIONS TO THE BV EQUATION

In the above discussion and derivation of the BV equation, two basic premises were made. First there was the assumption that Liouville's equation itself was applicable to the physical system under consideration and second we assumed it was legitimate to factor the N-particle distribution function as in eq. (4.4). The former of these two assumptions is hardly open to question in view of our present restricted interests to classical, nonrelativistic plasmas for which all inelastic processes such as radiative transitions, and so on, are negligible. However, the assumption that $F^{(N)}(t)$ may be factored into a product of single-particle distribution functions is not on a correspondingly firm basis, and in the present section this problem will be critically examined in order to find out more precisely under what circumstances the assumption in eq. (4.4) can be expected to be valid. Our method of attack will consist of producing explicit corrections to the BV equation.

On the basis of the above qualitative discussion it should be reasonably clear by now that in contrast to the neutral but dilute gas case, we can expect eq. (4.4) to be valid provided only that the parameter α, as given in eq. (4.3), is very large compared to unity. In order to obtain a more quantitative measure of the precise meaning of the phrase "large compared to unity," we shall at this point follow the method of Rostoker and Rosenbluth.* In essence, these authors expand the solution of Liouville's equations in a power series in $1/\alpha$, with α as given in eq. (4.3), and thereby obtain first-order corrections to the BV equation. So that the significant features of the following discussion will not be obscured in a morass of algebra, let us make the following simplifying assumptions:

    (1) The plasma consists of only one species of particles.

    (2) There are no external electromagnetic fields present.

    (3) The magnetic forces between the particles are negligible and thus only the Coulomb forces are operative.

Furthermore, for the purpose of this argument it is convenient to make a slight change in the normalization of the few particle distribution functions so that instead of eq. (3.52) we define $F^{(S)}(t)$ by the formula

$$F^{(s)}(t) = (V)^s \int \left(\prod_{j=s+1}^{N} d\mathbf{r}_j \, d\mathbf{p}_j \right) F^{(N)}(t) \tag{4.31}$$

---

* N. Rostoker and M. N. Rosenbluth, *Phys. of Fluids*, 3, 1 (1960).

where V is the plasma volume that is assumed to become infinitely large so that all surface effects are negligible. This change in normalization causes no essential alterations in the derivation for the equation that governs the temporal evolution of $F^{(s)}(t)$, and it is easily verified that the only change in eq. (3.60), for $s = 1$ (and Problem 15, Chapter 3 for a general $s(\ll N)$), is that the factor N becomes replaced by $n_o = N/V$, where n_o is the average number of particles per unit volume. Thus, in rationalized mks units, the equation for $F^{(S)}(t)$ is given by

$$\frac{\partial}{\partial t} F^{(s)}(t) + \sum_{j=1}^{s} \mathbf{v}_i \cdot \frac{\partial}{\partial \mathbf{r}_i} F^{(s)} + \frac{q^2}{4\pi m \varepsilon_o} \sum_{i,j}^{s}{}' \mathbf{E}_{ij} \cdot \frac{\partial}{\partial \mathbf{v}_i} F^{(s)}$$

$$+ \frac{n_o q^2}{4\pi \varepsilon_o m} \sum_{j=1}^{s} \int d\mathbf{r}_{s+1}\, d\mathbf{p}_{s+1}\, \mathbf{E}_{j,s+1} \cdot \frac{\partial}{\partial \mathbf{v}_j} F^{(s+1)} = 0 \quad (4.32)$$

where we have used the shorthand

$$\mathbf{E}_{ij} = -\frac{\partial}{\partial \mathbf{r}_i} \frac{1}{|\mathbf{r}_i - \mathbf{r}_j|} = \frac{(\mathbf{r}_i - \mathbf{r}_j)}{|\mathbf{r}_i - \mathbf{r}_j|^3} \quad (4.33)$$

and where the prime on the double summation indicates that the diagonal terms are to be omitted.

For our present purpose it is convenient to rewrite eq. (4.32) in dimensionless form by expressing all lengths in terms of the Debye shielding distance, λ_D,

$$\lambda_D = \left[\frac{n_o q^2}{\varepsilon_o k T} \right]^{-\frac{1}{2}}$$

where T is a representative temperature in the plasma and in addition by expressing all times in terms of the reciprocal of the *plasma frequency* ω_p which is given by

$$\omega_p = \left[\frac{n_o q^2}{m \varepsilon_o} \right]^{\frac{1}{2}} \quad (4.34)$$

We shall see the important part played by this parameter ω_p later; for the moment we may think of it as being the only quantity with dimensions of a reciprocal time that can be constructed out of the available constants—namely, n_0, q, m, and ε_0. Furthermore it is easy to verify that ω_p is the ratio of the thermal speed to the Debye shielding radius. If we temporarily use the same symbols for the dimensionless variables as for the normal ones, eq. (4.32) takes on the form

$$\frac{\partial}{\partial t}F^{(s)} + \sum_{i=1}^{s} \mathbf{v}_i \cdot \frac{\partial}{\partial \mathbf{r}_i}F^{(s)} + \frac{1}{4\pi\alpha}\sum_{i,j}' \mathbf{E}_{ij} \cdot \frac{\partial}{\partial \mathbf{v}_i}F^{(s)}$$

$$+ \frac{1}{4\pi}\sum_{i=1}^{s}\int d\mathbf{r}_{s+1}\,d\mathbf{p}_{s+1}\,\mathbf{E}_{i,s+1} \cdot \frac{\partial}{\partial \mathbf{v}_i}F^{(s+1)} = 0 \qquad (4.35)$$

where α is the very parameter that was defined in eq. (4.3) and here we see it appearing in a very natural way. As has been noted previously, for many cases of physical interest α is very large and consequently $1/\alpha$ is very small compared to unity. This suggests that we attempt to solve eq. (4.35) by expanding $F^{(S)}$ in a power series in $1/\alpha$ so that in lowest order, the third term in the equation for $F^{(S)}$ can be neglected.

Rather than proceed directly with this dimensionless equation, (4.35), however, it is more convenient to work directly with eq. (4.32). One procedure, which is equivalent to making a power-series expansion in terms of $1/\alpha$, involves taking the limits

$$q \to 0$$
$$m \to 0$$
$$n_0 \to \infty \qquad (4.36)$$

on eq. (4.32) but in such a way that the quantities $n_0 q$, $n_0 m$, and thus also q/m remain finite. On making use of these limits in eq. (4.36) we see that $1/\alpha$ is of order q, while ω_p and λ_D are both of order unity. The first two as well as the fourth term in eq. (4.32) are therefore of order unity while the third term alone is of order q. Thus we see that the application of the limits implied in eq. (4.36) to the equation for $F^{(S)}$—that is, eq. (4.32)—is equivalent to making a series expansion of eq. (4.35) in powers of $1/\alpha$.

This expansion of $F^{(S)}$ in a power series in $1/\alpha$ or equivalently in terms of the parameter q means that we may write

$$F^{(s)} = F_0^{(s)} + F_1^{(s)} + \cdots \qquad (4.37)$$

where $F_1^{(S)}$ is of order $1/\alpha$ relative to $F_0^{(S)}$. On substituting this assumed form for $F^{(S)}$ into eq. (4.32) and on equating the coefficients of the zeroth and first powers of $1/\alpha$ to zero, we obtain

$$\frac{\partial}{\partial t}F_0^{(s)} + \sum_{i=1}^{s} \mathbf{v}_i \cdot \frac{\partial}{\partial \mathbf{r}_i}F_0^{(s)}$$

$$+ \frac{n_0 q^2}{4\pi\varepsilon_0 m}\sum_{i=1}^{s}\int d\mathbf{r}_{s+1}\,d\mathbf{p}_{s+1}\,\mathbf{E}_{i,s+1} \cdot \frac{\partial}{\partial \mathbf{v}_i}F_0^{(s+1)} = 0 \qquad (4.38)$$

and

$$\frac{\partial}{\partial t}F_1^{(s)} + \sum_{i=1}^{s} \mathbf{v}_i \cdot \frac{\partial}{\partial \mathbf{r}_i}F_1^{(s)} + \frac{n_0 q^2}{4\pi\varepsilon_0 m} \sum_{i=1}^{s} \int d\mathbf{r}_{s+1}\, d\mathbf{p}_{s+1}\, \mathbf{E}_{i,s+1} \cdot \frac{\partial}{\partial \mathbf{v}_i}F_1^{(s+1)}$$

$$+ \frac{q^2}{4\pi\varepsilon_0 m} \sum_{i,j}' \mathbf{E}_{ij} \cdot \frac{\partial}{\partial \mathbf{v}_i}F_0^{(s)} = 0 \tag{4.39}$$

It is to be noted that each of eqs. (4.38) and (4.39) actually represents a set of equations—that is, one for each value of s where s can be any positive integer which is much smaller than N but greater than or equal to unity.

Let us first study the lowest-order equation—that is, eq. (4.38). By definition, $F_0^{(S)}$ is the s-particle distribution function in the limit $\alpha \to \infty$. As we have seen, in this limit all of the particles in the plasma are within a Debye radius of each other and consequently no particle is shielded from the Coulomb field of any other one. Thus, since N is very large, the few-particle collisions are completely negligible compared to the forces produced by the overwhelmingly large number of particles whose associated Coulombic force fields cannot be shielded from any region of the plasma. Therefore, since any macroscopically fluctuating field can only be associated with "few-particle collisions," and since these do not exist in the limit $\alpha \to \infty$, we conclude that the actual fields existing in the plasma vary only over macroscopic space and time intervals, and consequently that the BV equation is an exact description. This argument suggests that we attempt to find a solution for eq. (4.38) by making use of the *ansatz*

$$F_0^{(s)} = \prod_{i=1}^{s} f_0(\mathbf{r}_i, \mathbf{v}_i, t) \tag{4.40}$$

where f_0 may be thought of as the single-particle distribution function in the limit $\alpha \to \infty$. Although this equation looks very similar to the assumption in eq. (4.4), it is on a completely different footing. For in the present context, eq. (4.40) is only the first term in a power series in $1/\alpha$, for which higher-order corrections can be obtained in a systematic way; while on the other hand, the assumption in eq. (4.4) implies no further corrections.

In order to find the equation satisfied by f_0, we substitute eq. (4.40) into eq. (4.38) and obtain

$$\sum_{i=1}^{s} \left\{ \left[\prod_{j=1}^{s}{}' f_0(\mathbf{r}_j, \mathbf{v}_j, t) \right] \left[\frac{\partial}{\partial t} + \mathbf{v}_i \cdot \frac{\partial}{\partial \mathbf{r}_i} \right. \right.$$

$$\left. \left. + \frac{n_0 q^2}{4\pi\varepsilon_0 m} \int d\mathbf{r}_{s+1}\, d\mathbf{p}_{s+1}\, f_0(\mathbf{r}_{s+1}, \mathbf{p}_{s+1}, t)\mathbf{E}_{i,s+1} \cdot \frac{\partial}{\partial \mathbf{v}_i} \right] f_0(\mathbf{r}_i, \mathbf{v}_i, t) \right\} = 0$$

$$\tag{4.41}$$

where the prime on the product means omit the term $j = i$. An examination of eq. (4.41) now shows that this equation will always be satisfied provided that f_0 is a solution of

$$\frac{\partial}{\partial t}f_0 + \mathbf{v} \cdot \frac{\partial}{\partial \mathbf{r}}f_0 + \frac{q}{m}\mathbf{E}_0 \cdot \frac{\partial}{\partial \mathbf{v}}f_0 = 0 \qquad (4.42)$$

where $\mathbf{E}_0(\mathbf{r}, t)$ is given by

$$\mathbf{E}_0(\mathbf{r},t) = -\frac{n_0 q}{4\pi\varepsilon_0}\int d\mathbf{r}'\, d\mathbf{v}'\, f_0(\mathbf{r}',\mathbf{v}',t)\frac{\partial}{\partial \mathbf{r}}\frac{1}{|\mathbf{r}-\mathbf{r}'|} \qquad (4.43)$$

and thus satisfies Maxwell's equations with the charge density determined in the familiar self-consistent way in terms of f_0. Evidently, in the present case for which there are no external fields and for which the interparticle magnetic forces are negligible, eqs. (4.42) and (4.43) represent the applicable form of the BV equation. Thus it has been established that in the limit $\alpha \to \infty$ the single-particle distribution function f_0 satisfies the BV equation. It is to be emphasized, however, that f_0 is not the true single-particle distribution function since the correct $F^{(1)}$ will, in general, contain $1/\alpha$ corrections. And this is the essential distinction between eqs. (4.4) and (4.40).

The main advantage of the present approach is that it is now possible to go beyond the BV equation by calculating corrections to it and these are obtained by use of eq. (4.39). In order to solve this latter equation, we write

$$F^{(2)}(x_1,x_2,t) = [f_0(x_1,t)+f_1(x_1,t)][f_0(x_2,t)+f_1(x_2,t) \qquad (4.44)$$
$$+ P(x_1,x_2,t)$$

where we have used the notation $x_i = (\mathbf{r}_i, \mathbf{v}_i)$. For our purposes, it is only necessary to take f_1 and P to be of order $1/\alpha$. Thus on comparison with eq. (4.37) we may write

$$F_0^{(2)} = f_0(x_1,t)f_0(x_2,t) \qquad (4.45)$$

and

$$F_1^{(2)} = f_0(x_1,t)f_1(x_2,t)+f_1(x_1,t)f_0(x_2,t)+P(x_1,x_2,t) \qquad (4.46)$$

For self-evident reasons, the quantity $P(x_1,x_2,t)$ is often called the two-particle correlation function and may be thought of as being defined by eq. (4.44) provided only that the quantity $f_0(x_1,t)+f_1(x_1,t)$ is the actual single-particle distribution function. We saw above that the part of $F^{(S)}$ which is independent of $1/\alpha$ can be taken to be expressible in terms of a product of single-particle functions. This suggests that we seek a solution for $F^{(S)}$ in a form that involves only functions containing the coordinates and momenta of at most two particles. Thus, on comparison with eq. (4.46) we now try the *ansatz*

$$F_1^{(s)} = \sum_{i=1}^{s} \left\{ \prod_{j=1}^{s}{}' f_0(x_j,t) \right\} f_1(x_i,t)$$

$$+ \frac{1}{2} \sum_{i,j}^{s}{}' P(x_i,x_j,t) \left\{ \prod_{k=1}^{s}{}'' f_0(x_k,t) \right\} \tag{4.47}$$

where as usual the primes and double primes mean omit the terms $i = j$ and $i = k, j = k$. To complete the story it is now necessary to find equations that will determine the functions f_1 and P and these may be obtained by substituting eq. (4.47) into those forms of eq. (4.39) that result for the two special cases $s = 1$ and $s = 2$. For the case $s = 1$, we obtain

$$\frac{\partial}{\partial t} f_1(x_1,t) + \mathbf{v}_1 \cdot \frac{\partial}{\partial \mathbf{r}_1} f_1 + \frac{q}{m} \left\{ \mathbf{E}_0 \cdot \frac{\partial}{\partial \mathbf{v}_1} f_1 + \mathbf{E}_1 \cdot \frac{\partial}{\partial \mathbf{v}_1} f_0 \right\}$$

$$+ \frac{n_0 q^2}{4\pi\varepsilon_0 m} \int d\mathbf{r}_2 \, d\mathbf{v}_2 \, \mathbf{E}_{12} \cdot \frac{\partial}{\partial \mathbf{v}_1} P(x_1,x_2,t) = 0 \tag{4.48}$$

where $\mathbf{E}_0$ is defined in eq. (4.43) and $\mathbf{E}_1$ is given in a similar way by the formula

$$\mathbf{E}_1(\mathbf{r},t) = -\frac{n_0' q}{4\pi\varepsilon_0} \int d\mathbf{r}' \, d\mathbf{v}' \, f_1(\mathbf{r}',\mathbf{v}',t) \frac{\partial}{\partial \mathbf{r}} \frac{1}{|\mathbf{r}-\mathbf{r}'|} \tag{4.49}$$

The manipulations for the case $s = 2$ are slightly more involved, but on making use of eq. (4.48) as well as the BV equation as given in eq. (4.42), the result may be cast into the form

$$\left\{ \frac{\partial}{\partial t} + \mathbf{v}_1 \cdot \frac{\partial}{\partial \mathbf{r}_1} + \mathbf{v}_2 \cdot \frac{\partial}{\partial \mathbf{r}_2} \right.$$

$$+ \frac{q}{m} \left[\mathbf{E}_0(\mathbf{r}_1,t) \cdot \frac{\partial}{\partial \mathbf{v}_1} + \mathbf{E}_0(\mathbf{r}_2,t) \cdot \frac{\partial}{\partial \mathbf{v}_2} \right] \right\} P(x_1,x_2,t)$$

$$+ \frac{n_0 q^2}{4\pi\varepsilon_0 m} \left\{ \int d\mathbf{r}_3 \, d\mathbf{v}_3 \, \mathbf{E}_{13} P(x_2,x_3,t) \cdot \frac{\partial}{\partial \mathbf{v}_1} f_0(x_1,t) + (1 \longleftrightarrow 2) \right\}$$

$$+ \frac{q^2}{4\pi\varepsilon_0 m} \left\{ f_0(x_1,t) \mathbf{E}_{21} \cdot \frac{\partial}{\partial \mathbf{v}_2} f_0(x_2,t) + (1 \longleftrightarrow 2) \right\} = 0 \tag{4.50}$$

where the symbol $(1 \leftrightarrow 2)$ means repeat the preceding term but with the subscripts 1 and 2 interchanged and where $\mathbf{E}_{12}$ is defined in eq. (4.33). As in the discussion following eq. (3.29), these equations—namely eqs.

(4.48) and (4.50)—can be utilized to determine uniquely f_1 and P at any time t in terms of their initial values. Finally, we note that the *ansatz* in eq. (4.47) is self-consistent; for on substituting this form into eq. (4.39) we see this equation is satisfied for values of s greater than 2, provided only that the functions f_1 and P satisfy the eqs. (4.48) through (4.50).

In summary, the preceding arguments have shown that in the limit $\alpha \to \infty$, $F^{(S)}$ is completely determined by the BV equation, and, furthermore, equations that yield the $1/\alpha$ corrections to $F^{(S)}$ have also been derived. Of course, the discussion has been somewhat restrictive in that we have neglected external fields as well as interparticle magnetic forces, but these omissions are clearly not serious and could have been included at the price of a vast deluge of algebra. Furthermore, the equations that determine the corrections to the BV equation—namely, eqs. (4.48)–(4.50)—are already very formidable, and an analysis of these equations is still the subject of a number of current research efforts. Therefore, except for recognizing the fact that this systematic way exists for solving for the distribution function in a power series in $1/\alpha$, we shall pursue the matter no further here. The obtaining of the zeroth order solution of this set—that is, the self-consistent solution of the BV equation—is itself sufficiently complicated to warrant further studies for many cases of physical interest. Consequently, most of our remaining effort will be directed towards the application of the BV equation to various physical systems. In so doing we must keep in mind the limitations that are inherent in such results in the light of the above $1/\alpha$ expansion.

Before we go into this detailed study of the BV equation, however, it should be noted that there are approaches, other than the one considered here, that have been used for obtaining corrections to the BV equation. Reference to some of these can be found at the end of this chapter. Perhaps most noteworthy among these is a "diagrammatic method" which is associated with the names of Prigogine and Balescu. Most of these derivations, some of which are perhaps more heuristic than the one considered above, have as their final goal the replacement of the zero on the right-hand side of the BV equation with a collision term that is a functional of the single-particle distribution function only. Physically, such a term describes changes in the distribution function brought about by few-particle or close-encounter collisions and may therefore be interpreted as having the same effect as our $1/\alpha$ corrections. One of the most important of these modified forms of the BV equation is known as the *Fokker-Planck equation* and has been the subject of many investigations. For this case, those terms that are added to the right-hand side of the BV equation are known as the *Fokker-Planck terms* and are not associated with the smoothed-out macroscopic fields already included on the left-hand side of the BV equation, nor are they associated with the violent, close-encounter collisions usually described by the Boltzmann collision integrals and negligible for the case $\alpha \gg 1$. But rather, these Fokker-Planck terms are based on a physical mechanism that lies between these two. This mechanism may be thought of as producing changes in the distribution function as a result of gradual alterations in the particle trajectories due to many small momentum transfer or large impact parameter scatterings. Since such scatterings can occur only for particles within a Debye radius of each other, it is clear that the Fokker-Planck equation is related to our own approach which involves a series expansion in powers of $1/\alpha$. Indeed, we would hope to be able to eliminate the correlation function P between eqs. (4.48) and (4.50), combine the resulting equation for f_1 with the BV equation for f_0 and thus obtain a form of the Fokker-Planck equation. Unfortunately, the detailed carrying out of such a derivation, although straightforward in principle, is much too involved to be further examined here. Instead, let us refer the interested reader to the article by Bernstein and Trehan where he will find a very physical derivation of the Landau form of the Fokker-Planck terms as well as additional references.

THE MOMENT EQUATIONS

It has been noted previously that the distribution function* is not in itself of direct physical interest except insofar as it determines all macroscopic variables. Let us therefore turn now to the possibility of making use of the BV equation in order to obtain equations for macroscopic quantities and thereby possibly circumvent the BV equation altogether. The resultant, so-called moment equations, on being combined with certain phenomenological relations such as Ohm's law, are known as the *equations of magnetohydrodynamics* (MHD) and will be examined in greater detail in the next chapter. For the present, our interests lie more in the direction of obtaining a better understanding of the BV equation and this will be done by showing that the moment equations, which are derived from it, are physically reasonable and have the form one expects intuitively. In order to simplify this discussion, let us assume that the plasma consists of a single species only.

For this purpose of deriving the moment equations it is convenient to rewrite the BV equation in terms of slightly different variables. In place of the velocity $\mathbf{v}$, we introduce the vector $\mathbf{w}$, which represents the velocity of a

---

* From now on, by "distribution function" we shall mean the single-particle distribution function; the N- and s-particle functions will no longer enter the discussion.

typical particle relative to the mean fluid velocity **u**, and which is defined by the formula

$$\mathbf{w} = \mathbf{v} - \mathbf{u}(\mathbf{r},t) \tag{4.51}$$

where the fluid velocity **u** is given by

$$\mathbf{u} = \frac{N}{n(\mathbf{r},t)} \int d\mathbf{v} \ \mathbf{v} f(\mathbf{r},\mathbf{v},t) \tag{4.52}$$

and where, in turn, the particle density $n(\mathbf{r},t)$ is given by

$$n(\mathbf{r},t) = N \int d\mathbf{v} \ f(\mathbf{r},v,t) \tag{4.53}$$

We now change the variables in the BV equation from **r**, **v**, t to **r**, **w**, t with **w** as defined in eq. (4.51). A short calculation shows that the derivatives transform according to the formulas

$$\frac{\partial}{\partial t} \rightarrow \frac{\partial}{\partial t} - \left(\frac{\partial \mathbf{u}}{\partial t}\right) \cdot \frac{\partial}{\partial \mathbf{w}}$$

$$\frac{\partial}{\partial \mathbf{r}} \rightarrow \frac{\partial}{\partial \mathbf{r}} - \sum_{j=1}^{3} \left(\frac{\partial}{\partial \mathbf{r}} u_j\right) \frac{\partial}{\partial w_j}$$

$$\frac{\partial}{\partial \mathbf{v}} \rightarrow \frac{\partial}{\partial \mathbf{w}} \tag{4.54}$$

and on making use of these substitutions in the BV equation the latter may be cast into the form

$$\frac{\partial}{\partial t} f(\mathbf{r},\mathbf{w},t) + \frac{\partial}{\partial \mathbf{r}} \cdot [(\mathbf{w}+\mathbf{u})f] + \frac{\partial}{\partial \mathbf{w}} \cdot [\mathbf{a}f] = 0 \tag{4.55}$$

where the vector **a** is given by

$$\mathbf{a} = \frac{q}{m}(\mathbf{E}+\mathbf{u}\times\mathbf{B}) - \frac{d}{dt}\mathbf{u} + \frac{q}{m}\mathbf{w}\times\mathbf{B} - \left(\mathbf{w}\cdot\frac{\partial}{\partial \mathbf{r}}\right)\mathbf{u} \tag{4.56}$$

and where the symbol d/dt is defined by

$$\frac{d}{dt} = \frac{\partial}{\partial t} + \mathbf{u}\cdot\frac{\partial}{\partial \mathbf{r}} \tag{4.57}$$

and represents the time derivatives as we follow a given element of the plasma. Throughout all the above formulas, **u** is to be thought of as an unknown function of time and **E** and **B** represent the total fields—that is, the external plus the internally generated self-consistent fields.

In terms of the relative velocity **w**, eq. (3.42) for the particle density and eq. (3.55) for the pressure tensor become, respectively,

$$n(\mathbf{r},t) = N \int d\mathbf{w}\, f(\mathbf{r},\mathbf{w},t) \tag{4.58}$$

and

$$p_{ij}(\mathbf{r},t) = Nm \int d\mathbf{w}\, w_i w_j f(\mathbf{r},\mathbf{w},t) \tag{4.59}$$

while the second moment of the distribution function—that is,

$$\int d\mathbf{w}\, \mathbf{w} f(\mathbf{r},\mathbf{w},t)$$

may be shown to vanish by virtue of the relations

$$0 = \frac{N}{n} \int d\mathbf{v}\, \mathbf{v} f(\mathbf{r},\mathbf{v},t) - \mathbf{u}(\mathbf{r},t) = \frac{N}{n} \int d\mathbf{v}\, (\mathbf{v} - \mathbf{u}) f(\mathbf{r},\mathbf{v},t)$$

$$= \frac{N}{n} \int d\mathbf{w}\, \mathbf{w} f(\mathbf{r},\mathbf{w},t) \tag{4.60}$$

The equation for the first moment of the BV equation is obtained by multiplying eq. (4.55) by N and integrating over the variable **w**. Since the third term in eq. (4.55) is a perfect derivative with respect to **w**, it will vanish in this process, while the first term, on comparison with eq. (4.58) becomes the time derivative of the particle density. Making use of the fact that according to eq. (4.60) the second moment vanishes, the integral over the second term in the BV equation becomes

$$N \frac{\partial}{\partial \mathbf{r}} \cdot \int d\mathbf{w}\, (\mathbf{w} + \mathbf{u}) f(\mathbf{r},\mathbf{w},t) = \frac{\partial}{\partial \mathbf{r}} \cdot \left\{ N\mathbf{u} \int d\mathbf{w} f \right\} = \frac{\partial}{\partial \mathbf{r}} \cdot (\mathbf{u}n) \tag{4.61}$$

Combining these results, then, the first moment of eq. (4.55) yields the equation

$$\frac{\partial}{\partial t} n + \nabla \cdot (\mathbf{u}n) = 0 \tag{4.62}$$

and this formula, as has been seen in Problem 9, Chapter 3, may be interpreted as the statement of the conservation of the number of particles. Or equivalently, by multiplying eq. (4.62) by q or by m this equation becomes the relation that expresses the conservation of charge or mass, respectively. Thus we see that the first moment of the BV equation produces a very meaningful physical result and one that can be expected to play a very important and necessary role in any macroscopic theory.

From a mathematical point of view, eq. (4.62) is, of course, incomplete. That is, as in the discussion after eq. (3.29), eq. (4.62) cannot be used to obtain the density at any time t given only its initial value; for, in addition, we must know $\mathbf{u}(\mathbf{r}, t)$ for all times t. This suggests that in order to obtain a closed set of equations, we need to find an equation that contains $\partial \mathbf{u}/\partial t$, and this can be obtained by taking the second moment of the BV equation.

Therefore we shall multiply the BV equation by mw_i and integrate over all values of $\mathbf{w}$. This time the first term in eq. (4.55) will vanish since it becomes simply the time derivative of the second moment, which according to eq. (4.60) is zero. On the other hand, the second term splits up into a vanishing second moment plus a term that is quadratic in $\mathbf{w}$. Comparing this result with eq. (4.59), we see that the second term in the BV equation becomes

$$\sum_{j=1}^{3} \frac{\partial}{\partial x_j} p_{ij} \qquad (4.63)$$

and this will be referred to as the divergence of the pressure tensor. Finally, the last term in eq. (4.55) may be transformed by use of an integration by parts into the forms

$$Nm \int d\mathbf{w} \; w_i \frac{\partial}{\partial \mathbf{w}} \cdot (\mathbf{a}f) = -Nm \int d\mathbf{w} \; a_i f$$

$$= -Nq(\mathbf{E} + \mathbf{u} \times \mathbf{B})_i \int f \, d\mathbf{w} + Nm \left(\frac{d}{dt} u_i \right) \int f \, d\mathbf{w}$$

$$= -qn(\mathbf{r},t)(\mathbf{E} + \mathbf{u} \times \mathbf{B})_i + mn(\mathbf{r},t) \frac{d}{dt} u_i \qquad (4.64)$$

where after the second equality we have dropped two terms of the form $\int w_j f \, d\mathbf{w}$ since they vanish, and where in writing the third equality we have used eq. (4.58). We now add up the results in eqs. (4.63), (4.64) and find thus that the second moment of the BV equation becomes

$$\rho \left[\frac{\partial}{\partial t} u_i + \left(\mathbf{u} \cdot \frac{\partial}{\partial \mathbf{r}} \right) u_i \right] = \rho_q E_i + (\mathbf{j} \times \mathbf{B})_i - \sum_{j=1}^{3} \frac{\partial}{\partial x_j} p_{ij} \qquad (4.65)$$

where ρ is the mass density mn, ρ_q is the charge density qn, and $\mathbf{j} = qn\mathbf{u}$ is the current density. Again, even assuming that $\mathbf{E}$ and $\mathbf{B}$ were given functions of space and time, this equation when combined with eq. (4.62) is not complete. For in order to find ρ and $\mathbf{u}$ at any time t in terms of their initial values, it is now necessary to specify in addition $p_{ij}(\mathbf{r}, t)$ for all time t and this means that one must derive an equation containing $\partial p_{ij}/\partial t$. Such an equation will be derived below but we may already anticipate that new quantities will arise and that we can never obtain a finite closed set of equations for the macroscopic quantities in this way. Thus, our effort to circumvent the BV equation is not successful, unless, of course, we can truncate this hierarchy of moment equations at some stage. Indeed, this is precisely what will be done in the next chapter.

The physical interpretation of eq. (4.65) may be obtained by integrating this equation over a small volume element ΔV. The left-hand side of the resultant equation may then be interpreted as the mass times the acceleration of the plasma inside ΔV. We anticipate, therefore, that the right-hand side of eq. (4.65) will then represent the force on this volume element, and indeed this is the case. For the integral over ΔV of $\rho_q \mathbf{E} + \mathbf{j} \times \mathbf{B}$ is just the electromagnetic force on this element. Finally, the integral over the divergence of the pressure tensor, may, by use of Gauss' law, be recast into the form

$$\sum_{j=1}^{3} \int_{\Delta s} p_{ij} \, ds_j \tag{4.66}$$

where Δs is the closed surface bounding ΔV and ds_j is an open element of area whose normal is oriented along the direction j. Making note of the definition of p_{ij} in eq. (4.59), we see that the result in eq. (4.66) represents a force on ΔV since it may be directly interpreted as a flow of momentum per unit time out of the volume ΔV. Thus, the second moment of the BV equation is also physically reasonable and corresponds to Newton's law of motion for those particles contained in an arbitrary volume element.

In order to make certain that the physical significance and the essential incompleteness of the moment equations are clearly understood, let us finally take the third moment of the BV equation and thus obtain the equation involving $(\partial/\partial t)p_{ij}$. This time we multiply eq. (4.55) by the factor $Nm w_i w_j$ and again integrate over all values of $\mathbf{w}$. On making use of eq. (4.59) the $\partial f/\partial t$ term in the BV equation becomes simply

$$\frac{\partial}{\partial t} p_{ij} \tag{4.67}$$

Similarly, the second term in eq. (4.55) yields the two terms

$$\nabla \cdot (\mathbf{u} p_{ij}) + \sum_{k=1}^{3} \frac{\partial}{\partial x_k} Q_{ijk} \tag{4.68}$$

where Q_{ijk} is a completely symmetric tensor of rank three, is called the *heat-flow tensor*, and is explicitly given by

$$Q_{ijk}(\mathbf{r},t) = Nm \int d\mathbf{w} \, w_i w_j w_k f(\mathbf{r},\mathbf{w},t) \tag{4.69}$$

According to eq. (4.59), the pressure tensor is symmetric; that is,

$$p_{ij} = p_{ji} \tag{4.70}$$

and therefore there are only six independent elements in this tensor. Similarly, the heat-flow tensor Q_{ijk} is symmetric under exchange of any two of its three indices, and a brief calculation shows that Q_{ijk} therefore, has only seven independent elements. Again, in order to obtain a closed set of macroscopic equations we must obtain at least seven new equations that will yield the evolution in time of these independent elements of the heat-flow tensor.

Before we turn to an examination of the physical significance of this tensor, however, let us complete the derivation for the third moment of the BV equation. On multiplying the third term in eq. (4.55) by Nmw_iw_j and integrating over all $\mathbf{w}$, we find on integrating by parts that the result may be written as

$$- Nm \int d\mathbf{w} \, [w_i a_j + w_j a_i] f(\mathbf{r},\mathbf{w},t) \tag{4.71}$$

which on making use of eq. (4.60) and the definition for $\mathbf{a}$ in eq. (4.56) may be cast into the form

$$- Nm \int d\mathbf{w} \, f(\mathbf{r},\mathbf{w},t) \left\{ w_i(\mathbf{w} \times \mathbf{B})_j + w_j(\mathbf{w} \times \mathbf{B})_i \right.$$

$$\left. + \sum_{k=1}^{3} \left(w_i w_k \frac{\partial}{\partial x_k} u_j + w_j w_k \frac{\partial}{\partial x_k} u_i \right) \right\} \tag{4.72}$$

Let us now introduce the totally antisymmetric tensor of rank three, ε_{ijk} by the definition

$$(\mathbf{F} \times \mathbf{G})_k = \sum_{i=1}^{3} \sum_{j=1}^{3} \varepsilon_{ijk} F_i G_j \tag{4.73}$$

where $\mathbf{F}$ and $\mathbf{G}$ are two arbitrary vectors. On making use of this tensor as well as the definition for p_{ij} in eq. (4.59), the various terms in eq. (4.72) may be cast into the form

$$- \sum_{e,m=1}^{3} B_m \left[\varepsilon_{emj} p_{il} + \varepsilon_{emi} p_{je} \right]$$

$$+ \sum_{k=1}^{3} \left[p_{ik} \frac{\partial}{\partial x_k} u_j + p_{jk} \frac{\partial}{\partial x_k} u_i \right] \tag{4.74}$$

Finally, on collecting the results contained in eqs. (4.67), (4.68), and (4.74), we find that the third moment of the BV equation has the form

$$\frac{\partial}{\partial t}P_{ij} + \nabla \cdot [\mathbf{u}P_{ij}] + \sum_{k=1}^{3}\left\{\frac{\partial}{\partial x_k}Q_{ijk} + P_{ik}\frac{\partial}{\partial x_k}u_j + P_{jk}\frac{\partial}{\partial x_k}u_i\right\}$$

$$= \sum_{e,m=1}^{3} B_m\left\{\varepsilon_{emj}P_{ie} + \varepsilon_{emi}P_{je}\right\} \tag{4.75}$$

The physical interpretation of the various terms in this formula is not as transparent as the corresponding interpretations in the equations for the first two moments and this is perhaps the reason why moments higher than the third are not extensively used.

In order to obtain at least a partial understanding of eq. (4.75), however, let us take its trace; that is, we set $j = i$ and sum on i from 1 to 3. If in addition we divide the result by a factor of two, we obtain

$$\frac{\partial}{\partial t}\left[\frac{3}{2}nkT(\mathbf{r},t)\right] + \nabla \cdot \left[\mathbf{u}\,\frac{3}{2}\,nkT\right] + \frac{1}{2}\sum_{i,j=1}^{3}\frac{\partial}{\partial x_j}Q_{iij} + \sum_{i,j=1}^{3}P_{ij}\frac{\partial}{\partial x_j}u_i = 0 \tag{4.76}$$

where the vanishing of the right-hand side follows from the fact that the quantity

$$\sum_{i,e=1}^{3}\varepsilon_{emi}P_{ie}$$

is zero since p_{ie} is symmetric in its indices while ε_{emi} is antisymmetric in the corresponding two indices. The quantity $(3/2)n(\mathbf{r}, t)kT(\mathbf{r}, t)$ represents the internal or thermal energy of the plasma and has been previously defined in eq. (3.55) by the suggestive formula

$$\frac{3}{2}nkT = \frac{1}{2}\sum_{i=1}^{3}P_{ij} = N\int d\mathbf{w}\,\frac{mw^2}{2}f(\mathbf{r},\mathbf{w},t) \tag{4.77}$$

In order to simplify eq. (4.76) further, let us cast the last term in this equation into the form

$$\sum_{i,j=1}^{3}\left\{\frac{\partial}{\partial x_j}(p_{ij}u_i) - u_i\frac{\partial}{\partial x_j}p_{ij}\right\} \tag{4.78}$$

and substitute for the factor $(\partial p_{ij}/\partial x_j)$ from the equation of motion that is eq. (4.65). In this way one finds the relation

$$\sum_{i,j=1}^{3} u_i \frac{\partial}{\partial x_j} p_{ij} = \mathbf{j} \cdot \mathbf{E} - \frac{1}{2} \rho \frac{d}{dt} \mathbf{u}^2 \tag{4.79}$$

which on being substituted back into eq. (4.78) enables us to write the final version of eq. (4.76) as

$$\frac{\partial}{\partial t}\left[\frac{3}{2} nkT\right] + \frac{1}{2}\rho \frac{d}{dt}\mathbf{u}^2 + \nabla \cdot \left[\frac{3}{2}nkT\mathbf{u}\right]$$

$$+ \sum_{i,j=1}^{3} \frac{\partial}{\partial x_j}\left[\frac{1}{2}Q_{iij} + u_i p_{ij}\right] = \mathbf{j} \cdot \mathbf{E} \tag{4.80}$$

and in this form the various terms have simple physical interpretations.

To this end, let us integrate both sides of eq. (4.80) over a small volume element ΔV. The right-hand side may then be simply interpreted as a transfer of power from the fluid to the electromagnetic field. The first two terms on the left-hand side, moreover, have the obvious significance of representing the rate of increase of the internal energy and the kinetic energy, respectively. By an application of Gauss' law the remaining three terms may be cast into integrals over the surface bounding ΔV, and these three terms may be thought of as representing, respectively, the outward flow of internal energy with the stream velocity, the outward flow of the internal energy with the thermal velocity, and, finally, the term

$$\int_{\Delta s} \sum_{i,j=1}^{3} u_i p_{ij}\ ds_j$$

may be thought of as the power expended by the force $(\sum_i ds_j\, p_{ij})$ in pushing on the surface Δs with the fluid velocity. Thus, we see that eq. (4.80) may be interpreted as representing the statement of the conservation of energy.

Let us summarize this discussion by noting that by taking the first, second, and third moments of Liouville's equation we have obtained three equations that may be interpreted respectively as the *continuity equation* (eq. (4.62)), the hydrodynamical *equation of motion* (eq. (4.65)) and eq. (4.75) which may be called the *heat-flow equation*. These equations are not closed and every time an attempt is made to form a closed set by taking a higher moment of the BV equation, new terms enter and the resultant equations are again not closed. In the next chapter, we shall, somewhat arbitrarily, truncate this hierarchy by assuming that the heat-flow term is negligible, and in this way obtain a closed set of equations.

RELATIVISTIC FORM OF THE BV EQUATION

Under some conditions of physical interest, it may happen that some component of a plasma becomes characterized by a velocity close to that of light and under this circumstances the distribution function will no longer satisfy that form of the BV equation that we have just studied. This situation can arise, for example, if the temperature of the plasma becomes very high or possibly because nuclear processes, such as beta decay, inject relativistic electrons into the plasma. As we have previously noted, Maxwell's equations are applicable for arbitrary velocities and thus we need concern ourselves only with obtaining a more general form of an equation for the distribution function than that given in eq. (4.16).

In general, the problem of obtaining the trajectories of two relativistic charged particles is impossibly difficult from a mathematical point of view. The source of this difficulty is easy to see. For the force on one of these charged particles at a given instant is *not* produced by the electromagnetic fields generated by the other particle at the same instant, but rather by the fields produced by the second particle at an appropriate retarded time. This feature is due to the fact that all electromagnetic signals propagate with the speed of light and only if the particles move very slowly can we assume that the forces act instantaneously. As a matter of principle, we may solve for the trajectories by use of an iterative scheme. That is, we assume some trajectory for one of the particles and calculate the motion of the second in the known fields produced by the first. The trajectory for the first particle may then be corrected by use of the known motion of the second, and so on. The problems involved when more than two particles interact are evidently very complicated.

Fortunately, in our own case we describe the plasma by use of the BV equation, and thus we approximate the plasma dynamics by saying that the motion of each particle is governed by the external forces plus the macroscopically averaged forces due to the electromagnetic fields of all of the other particles. Thus, provided we use relativistic dynamics for the motion of a typical particle, the effects of retardation are automatically included in the solutions of Maxwell's equations. Therefore, we need only find the relativistic form of the equation for the distribution function and this is simply the appropriate form of Liouville's equation for a single particle.

It has been previously verified (Problem 1, Chapter 3) that the single-particle Hamiltonian

$$H = c\left[(\mathbf{p} - q\mathbf{A})^2 + m^2 c^2\right]^{1/2} + q\phi(\mathbf{r}, t) \tag{4.81}$$

produces the correct relativistic equations of motion in eq. (2.1) and therefore the relativistic form of Liouville's theorem is, according to eq. (3.8), given by

$$\frac{\partial}{\partial t}f + \mathbf{v} \cdot \frac{\partial}{\partial \mathbf{r}}f + q\left\{\mathbf{v} \times \mathbf{B} - \nabla\phi + \left(\mathbf{v} \cdot \frac{\partial}{\partial \mathbf{r}}\right)\mathbf{A}\right\} \cdot \frac{\partial}{\partial \mathbf{p}}f = 0 \quad (4.82)$$

where $\mathbf{v}$ is expressed in terms of the momentum $\mathbf{p}$ and the vector potential by means of the formula

$$\mathbf{v} = c(\mathbf{p} - q\mathbf{A})[(\mathbf{p} - q\mathbf{A})^2 + m^2c^2]^{-\frac{1}{2}} \quad (4.83)$$

In order to write eq. (4.82) in more convenient form—that is, in terms of $\mathbf{E}$ and $\mathbf{B}$ rather than in terms of the potentials—we define a new momentum $\mathbf{P}$ by the formula

$$\mathbf{P} = \mathbf{p} - q\mathbf{A}(\mathbf{r},t) \quad (4.84)$$

and as a function of the new variable, $\mathbf{r}$, $\mathbf{P}$, t, Liouville's theorem in eq. (4.82) takes on the form

$$\frac{\partial}{\partial t}f(\mathbf{r},\mathbf{P},t) + \frac{c\mathbf{P}}{(\mathbf{P}^2 + m^2c^2)^{\frac{1}{2}}} \cdot \frac{\partial}{\partial \mathbf{r}}f$$

$$+ q\left\{\mathbf{E} + \frac{c\mathbf{P} \times \mathbf{B}}{(\mathbf{P}^2 + m^2c^2)^{\frac{1}{2}}}\right\} \cdot \frac{\partial}{\partial \mathbf{P}}f = 0 \quad (4.85)$$

We now interpret this equation as the BV equation; that is, f becomes the distribution function and the fields $\mathbf{E}$ and $\mathbf{B}$ represent the sum of the external fields and the solution of Maxwell's equations with charge and current densities expressed in terms of the distribution function f by the formulas

$$\rho_q = Nq \int d\mathbf{P}\, f(\mathbf{r},\mathbf{P},t)$$

$$\mathbf{j} = Nqc \int d\mathbf{P}\, \frac{\mathbf{P}}{(\mathbf{P}^2 + m^2c^2)^{\frac{1}{2}}}f(\mathbf{r},\mathbf{P},t) \quad (4.86)$$

It is eq. (4.85) with the interpretation of $\mathbf{E}$ and $\mathbf{B}$ implied by eq. (4.86) that will be called the relativistic form of the BV equation. Of course, we are in no position to calculate corrections to eq. (4.85) as we were able to do in the nonrelativistic case. In the nonrelativistic limit, $\mathbf{P}^2 \ll m^2c^2$, the BV equation in eq. (4.85) reduces to eq. (4.16) provided we remember from eq. (4.84) that $\mathbf{v}$ and $\mathbf{P}$ are related by the formula $\mathbf{v} = \mathbf{P}/m$.

Finally, let us rewrite eq. (4.85) in terms of the velocity **v**, which is defined by

$$\mathbf{v} = \frac{c\mathbf{P}}{(\mathbf{P}^2 + m^2 c^2)^{1/2}} \tag{4.87}$$

On making use of the relations

$$\frac{\partial}{\partial P_i} = \sum_{j=1}^{3} \frac{\partial v_j}{\partial P_i} \frac{\partial}{\partial v_j}$$

$$= \frac{1}{m\gamma} \left[\frac{\partial}{\partial v_i} - \frac{1}{c^2} \mathbf{v} \cdot \frac{\partial}{\partial \mathbf{v}} \right] \tag{4.88}$$

where γ is as usual given by

$$\gamma = [1 - v^2/c^2]^{-1/2}$$

and is expressible in terms of **P** as

$$\gamma = \frac{1}{mc}[\mathbf{P}^2 + m^2 c^2]^{1/2}$$

the relativistic BV equation may be written

$$\frac{\partial}{\partial t} f(\mathbf{r}, \mathbf{v}, t) + \mathbf{v} \cdot \frac{\partial}{\partial \mathbf{r}} f + \frac{q}{m\gamma} \left\{ \mathbf{E} + \mathbf{v} \times \mathbf{B} - \frac{1}{c^2} \mathbf{v} \cdot \mathbf{E}\mathbf{v} \right\} \cdot \frac{\partial}{\partial \mathbf{v}} f = 0 \tag{4.89}$$

and this is precisely the form one would expect on the basis of our non-relativistic discussion and an application of eq. (2.1).

The basic distinction between eqs. (4.85) and (4.89) may be seen most easily in the following way. Suppose, first, we integrate eq. (4.85) over the variable **P**. It is evident that the third term integrates to zero since it involves essentially a perfect derivative with respect to **P**. That is, the operator $\partial/\partial \mathbf{P}$ may be moved through the electromagnetic force terms since the derivatives of such terms vanish exactly, and the integrals over the first two terms in eq. (4.89) reproduce the continuity equation which expresses the conservation of mass and charge. On the other hand, if we integrate eq. (4.89) over the variable **v**, the third term does *not* vanish and consequently we do not obtain the conservation of mass in this way. However, let us first multiply eq. (4.89) by γ^5 and then integrate over all **v**. Since it is easily verified that

$$\frac{\partial}{\partial \mathbf{v}} \cdot \left[\gamma^4 \left(\mathbf{E} + \mathbf{v} \times \mathbf{B} - \frac{1}{c^2} \mathbf{v} \cdot \mathbf{E}\mathbf{v} \right) \right] = 0$$

it follows that the third term in eq. (4.89) will vanish after integration over **v**, and the remaining terms may then again be interpreted in terms of the continuity equation. In particular, the charge and current densities are now given by

$$\rho_q(\mathbf{r},t) = Nq \int d\mathbf{v} \; \gamma^5 f(\mathbf{r},\mathbf{v},t) \tag{4.90}$$

and

$$\mathbf{j}(\mathbf{r},t) = Nq \int d\mathbf{v} \; \mathbf{v}\gamma^5 f(\mathbf{r},\mathbf{v},t) \tag{4.91}$$

The factor γ^5 in these formulas may be interpreted in terms of the Jacobian of the transformation between the variables $\mathbf{P}$ and $\mathbf{v}$, and it is easily verified that this Jacobian is indeed γ^5. It is largely because of this factor of γ^5 in eqs. (4.90) and (4.91) that the BV equation in the form of eq. (4.85) in terms of $\mathbf{P}$ is easier to deal with.

THE DEBYE SHIELDING RADIUS

In the previous parts of this chapter we developed, in a rather formal way, the BV equation and studied some of its more important physical properties and limitations. Let us now examine some elementary applications of this equation.

As a first example, we shall consider a "test" particle of charge Q, which is fixed in position at the origin of a coordinate system, and we shall assume that all of physical space is occupied by a plasma that consists of electrons of charge $-q$ and mass m_- and an equal number of ions of charge $+q$ and mass m_+. Now assuming that the system is in equilibrium at the temperature T and that the average number of particles per unit volume n_0 is the same for each species, the problem becomes that of determining the distribution of particles in the plasma and, further, the electric field in the immediate neighborhood of the test particle. Intuitively we expect that the test particle of charge Q will attract plasma particles of the opposite sign towards the origin and repel particles of like sign away from itself and in this way, the electrostatic field produced by the test particle will be shielded from the remote portions of the plasma.

More quantitatively, let us solve this problem by explicitly calculating the distribution functions $f_\pm$ for each species. Since the plasma is in equilibrium, all derivatives with respect to time must vanish and thus f_+ and f_- satisfy the equations

$$\mathbf{v} \cdot \frac{\partial}{\partial \mathbf{r}} f_- - \frac{q}{m_-} \mathbf{E} \cdot \frac{\partial}{\partial \mathbf{v}} f_- = 0$$

$$\mathbf{v} \cdot \frac{\partial}{\partial \mathbf{r}} f_+ + \frac{q}{m_+} \mathbf{E} \cdot \frac{\partial}{\partial \mathbf{v}} f_+ = 0 \tag{4.92}$$

where **E** is the sum of the external field that is produced by the test particle and the self-consisted field that is produced by the plasma particles themselves. Obviously, this electric field **E** must be an electrostatic one and thus according to the discussion following eq. (1.16) **E** may be described in terms of a scalar potential ϕ by the formula

$$\mathbf{E} = -\nabla\phi \tag{4.93}$$

Consequently the applicable form of Maxwell's equations may be written as

$$\nabla^2\phi = -\frac{1}{\varepsilon_0}\rho_q - \frac{1}{\varepsilon_0}Q\delta(\mathbf{r}) \tag{4.94}$$

where ρ_q is the charge density in the plasma and is expressed in terms of the distribution functions by

$$\rho_q(\mathbf{r}) = Nq\int d\mathbf{v}[f_+(\mathbf{r},\mathbf{v}) - f_-(\mathbf{r},\mathbf{v})] \tag{4.95}$$

Thus the problem of the density distribution of the plasma in the neighborhood of the test particle has been reduced to a mathematical one of finding a simultaneous solution of eqs. (4.92) to (4.95).

In order to solve this system of equations, we first note that if $\mathbf{E} = -\nabla\phi$ were a given external electrostatic field, then each of the eqs. (4.92) would represent the time independent form of Liouville's theorem for a single particle whose motion is governed by the Hamiltonian

$$H_{\pm} = \frac{\mathbf{p}^2}{2m_{\pm}} \pm q\phi \tag{4.96}$$

and it is easily verified that an arbitrary function of this Hamiltonian satisfies eq. (4.92). Furthermore, since both species of particles are in equilibrium at temperature T—that is, the mean energy per particle is $(3/2)kT$—it follows (see Problem 11, Chapter 3) that the two distribution functions $f_{\pm}$ are exponential functions of their respective Hamiltonians. After multiplying by appropriate normalization factors, we may therefore write

$$f_{\pm} = \frac{\exp\{-\beta[\frac{1}{2}m_{\pm}v^2 \pm q\phi]\}}{\int\int d\mathbf{r}\, d\mathbf{v}\, \exp\{-\beta[\frac{1}{2}m_{\pm}v^2 \pm q\phi]\}} \tag{4.97}$$

where $\beta = 1/kT$. It is a simple matter to verify the facts that eqs. (4.97) satisfy eq. (4.92) for all functions ϕ, that $f_{\pm}$ are both normalized to unity, and that the mean energy per particle is equal to $(3/2)kT$. Thus, all that remains now is to calculate the potential function ϕ and an equation to determine this function can be obtained by substituting eqs. (4.97) into eq. (4.94) with the result

$$\nabla^2\phi = -\frac{Q}{\varepsilon_0}\delta(\mathbf{r}) - \frac{Nq}{\varepsilon_0}\left\{\frac{\exp\{-\beta q\phi\}}{\int d\mathbf{r}\,\exp\{-\beta q\phi\}} - \frac{\exp\{\beta q\phi\}}{\int d\mathbf{r}\,\exp\{\beta q\phi\}}\right\}$$

(4.98)

The solution of this nonlinear equation when combined with the distribution functions in eq. (4.97) enables us then to calculate any desired physical property of the plasma.

Because of the rather complicated nature of eq. (4.98), it is necessary to resort to approximation schemes in order to calculate ϕ. We expect that on going away from the origin, the exponential factor $\beta q\phi$ will become small compared to unity, and this suggests the attempt to solve eq. (4.98) by expanding all of the exponentials on the right-hand side of eq. (4.98) and by keeping only the leading terms. On carrying out this expansion—whose validity will be verified subsequently—we obtain the simple linear equation

$$\nabla^2\phi = -\frac{Q}{\varepsilon_0}\delta(\mathbf{r}) - \frac{N}{\int d\mathbf{r}}\frac{q}{\varepsilon_0}[-2\beta q\phi(\mathbf{r})]$$

$$= -\frac{Q}{\varepsilon_0}\delta(\mathbf{r}) + \frac{2n_0 q^2}{kT\varepsilon_0}\phi(\mathbf{r})$$

(4.99)

Taking note of the fact that the mean plasma density is $2n_0$, and that therefore the coefficient of $\phi(\mathbf{r})$ on the right-hand side of eq. (4.99) is the square of the reciprocal of the Debye shielding radius λ_D, this equation may be cast into the form

$$\nabla^2\phi - \frac{1}{\lambda_D^2}\phi = -\frac{Q}{\varepsilon_0}\delta(\mathbf{r})$$

(4.100)

The only physically meaningful solution of this equation—that is, one that goes to zero for large r—is easily seen to be given by

$$\phi(r) = \frac{Q}{4\pi\varepsilon_0}\frac{1}{r}\exp\left\{-\frac{r}{\lambda_D}\right\}$$

(4.101)

Thus we see that for distances small compared to λ_D, the potential in the vicinity of the test particle is due to its Coulomb field but that this potential is exponentially damped as the distance becomes larger than a Debye shielding radius. Needless to say, we can now take this solution in eq. (4.101), substitute it back into eq. (4.97) and thus calculate many other physically interesting quantities. However, such calculations can be left for the problems; the essential and physically significant result is already displayed in eq. (4.101).

As a final point let us examine the above approximation, which was based on the assumption that the arguments of the exponentials in eq. (4.98) were small. Making use of the explicit formula for the potential in eq. (4.101), this assumption is equivalent to assuming the validity of the inequality

$$1 \gg \beta q\phi = \frac{qQ}{4\pi\varepsilon_0 kT} \frac{1}{r} \exp\left\{-\frac{r}{\lambda_D}\right\} \cong \frac{1}{n_0\lambda_D^3}\left(\frac{\lambda_D}{r}\right)$$

By hypothesis, the BV equation is only valid for the case $n_0\lambda_D^3 \gg 1$, and thus we conclude that the above approximation of expanding the exponentials in eq. (4.97) is valid—except for very small values of $|\mathbf{r}|$—provided only that the BV equation itself is applicable to the situation.

THE ELECTRON GAS
IN A RIGID CONDUCTOR

As a second application of the BV equation to a physical situation, let us consider the distribution of electrons in an idealized metal for which the electrons can be described classically and for which the positive ions are held rigidly in place and serve only to define the boundaries of the conductor and to supply a uniform background of positive charge. Let us assume that the metal has a width $2a$, that it is infinite in its other two dimensions, and that the electrons are in equilibrium at the temperature T. Since, in the present approximation, there must be many electrons inside a sphere of radius λ_D, and since we wish to make use of a continuous distribution of electrons, it follows that the width of the metal $2a$ must be much larger than λ_D. Assuming now that we have selected a coordinate system so that the two infinite sides of the conductor coincide with the planes $z = \pm a$, it is clear that our problem is one-dimensional in nature and may be described in terms of the single variable z. The boundaries of the metal will be taken into account by assuming that there is a very large repulsive potential at $z = \pm a$, so that any electrons striking these surfaces are elastically reflected.

As in the previous illustration, the equation for the distribution function of the electrons inside the metal is given by

$$\mathbf{v} \cdot \frac{\partial}{\partial \mathbf{r}} f(z,\mathbf{v}) + \frac{q}{m}\frac{\partial}{\partial z}\phi(z)\frac{\partial}{\partial v_z}f = 0 \tag{4.102}$$

where we have made use of the fact that the self-consistent potential is a function only of z. Assuming that f has been normalized to unity, the applicable form of Maxwell's equations becomes

$$\frac{d^2}{dz^2}\phi = -\frac{1}{\varepsilon_0}[n_0 q - Nq\int d\mathbf{v}\, f(z,\mathbf{v})] \tag{4.103}$$

where the term $n_0 q$ represents the contribution to the charge density by the ions that are distributed with uniform density n_0. Again, the solution of eq. (4.102) that is appropriate for the electronic equilibrium at temperature T is given by

$$f(z,\mathbf{v}) = \frac{\exp\{-\beta[\frac{1}{2}mv^2 - q\phi(z)\}}{\int\int d\mathbf{r}\, d\mathbf{v}\, \exp\{-\beta[\frac{1}{2}mv^2 - q\phi(z)\}} \tag{4.104}$$

and on substituting this form into eq. (4.103), there results the equation for $\phi(z)$

$$\frac{d^2}{dz^2}\phi = -\frac{qn_0}{\varepsilon_0}[1 - \exp\{\beta q(\phi(z) - A)\}] \tag{4.105}$$

where the constant A is to be determined by the condition

$$\exp\{\beta q A\} = \frac{1}{2a}\int_{-a}^{a} dz\, \exp\{-\beta q\phi(z)\} \tag{4.106}$$

As in the previous case, it is now necessary to solve this nonlinear equation (4.105) for $\phi(z)$ in order to obtain f and this represents, as a rule, a very complicated mathematical problem.

In the present case, however, it turns out that it is possible to obtain an explicit solution for ϕ in terms of a definite integral. In order to display this solution, let us multiply both sides of eq. (4.105) by $d\phi/dz$, integrate the result, and thereby obtain the equation

$$\frac{1}{2}\left[\frac{d\phi}{dz}\right]^2 = -\frac{qn_0}{\varepsilon_0}\left[\phi(z) + \frac{\exp\{+\beta q A\}}{\beta q} - \frac{\exp\{-\beta q(\phi - A)\}}{\beta q}\right] \tag{4.107}$$

where we have used the fact that along the plane of symmetry, $z = 0$, we have

$$\frac{d\phi}{dz} = 0$$

and have selected the zero of potential to lie along this same plane. A second integration of eq. (4.107) can also be carried out and after an obvious change of dummy variables we obtain

$$|z| = \lambda_D \int_0^{\beta q\phi(z)} dy[\exp\{y - y_0\} - \exp\{-y_0\} - y]^{-\frac{1}{2}} \tag{4.108}$$

where y_0 is given in terms of A by the formula

$$y_0 = -\beta q A \tag{4.109}$$

Equation (4.108) completely solves our problem. In principle, this equation may be integrated to yield the potential as an explicit function of z and A, and the latter is determined by the transcendental equation that results when eq. (4.106) is used. Physically, we expect that the potential will start out parabolically near $z = 0$, and rapidly become very negative for values of z near $\pm a$ so that the electrons do not escape through the surface.

It is possible to proceed a little further by assuming that both $\beta q A = -y_0$ as well as $\beta q \phi(z)$ are small compared to unity, so that the exponentials in the denominator of eq. (4.108) may be expanded, and that it suffices to keep only the first nonvanishing term. This procedure leads to the result

$$|z| = \sqrt{2}\,\lambda_D \int_{y_0}^{y_0 + \beta q \phi(z)} dy \, [y^2 - y_0^2]^{-\frac{1}{2}}$$

$$= \sqrt{2}\,\lambda_D \cosh^{-1}\left[\frac{\phi(z)}{A} + 1\right] \tag{4.110}$$

and therefore we find

$$\phi(z) = A\left[\cosh\left(\frac{z}{\sqrt{2}\,\lambda_D}\right) - 1\right] \tag{4.111}$$

a result that could have been obtained directly by expanding the exponential in eq. (4.105). The self-consistency of this form requires that on substituting eq. (4.111) into eq. (4.106), the resulting transcendental equation for A have a solution for which $\beta q A$ is very small compared to unity. Making use of the fact that on physical grounds we must have the inequality,

$$a \gg \lambda_D$$

this calculation may be carried out in a straightforward but approximate way and with the eventual result

$$\beta q A \cong -2 \exp\left\{-\frac{a}{\sqrt{2}\,\lambda_D}\right\} \tag{4.112}$$

which is indeed small compared to unity. Substituting this result back into eq. (4.111) we find

$$\beta q \phi(z) = -2 \exp\left\{-\frac{a}{\sqrt{2}\,\lambda_D}\right\}\left[\cosh\left(\frac{z}{\sqrt{2}\,\lambda_D}\right) - 1\right] \tag{4.113}$$

This potential, which as expected is attractive, is parabolic for small values of z; and for values of $|z|$ near a it has the form

$$\beta q \phi(z) \cong -\exp\left\{\frac{|z| - a}{\sqrt{2}\,\lambda_D}\right\}$$

and grows exponentially in this region. Thus, as was anticipated, the electrons with their negative charge are very strongly repelled inward whenever they get within a Debye shielding distance of the surface of the conductor. Our formula for $\phi(z)$ is, of course, not applicable for points within a Debye shielding distance of the surface since in this region $\beta q \phi(z)$ becomes of order unity and it is no longer legitimate to expand the exponentials.

PLASMA OSCILLATIONS

As a third application of the BV equation, let us make a brief study of the collective or plasma oscillations of an electron plasma. Only the simplest situation will be considered here, and a more detailed analysis will be found in a subsequent chapter.

For this present purpose, let us consider again a plasma that is of infinite extent and consists of a gas of free electrons imbedded in a neutralizing background of relatively immobile, positive ions. Initially, the system is in equilibrium with both the ions and the electrons distributed throughout all of physical space with a uniform density n_0; and the ions are at rest while the electrons have a Maxwellian velocity distribution. In other words, our assumption is that initially the electrons are described by the equilibrium distribution function,

$$f(\mathbf{r},\mathbf{v}) = n_0 f_0(\mathbf{v}) = n_0 \left[\frac{m\beta}{2\pi}\right]^{3/2} \exp\left\{-\beta \frac{mv^2}{2}\right\} \qquad (4.114)$$

where $1/\beta k$ is the electron temperature and f has been normalized to the total number of particles. Suppose now that at, say, $t = 0$, a small disturbance is created in the plasma so that the distribution function for times subsequent to $t = 0$ takes on the form

$$f(\mathbf{r},\mathbf{v},t) = n_0 f_0(\mathbf{v}) + g(\mathbf{r},\mathbf{v},t) \qquad (4.115)$$

where $g(\mathbf{r}, \mathbf{v}, t)$ is a perturbation that vanishes for negative times and is always small compared to $n_0 f_0$. It is clear, on physical grounds, that the disturbance g will eventually be damped out and that the system will return to equilibrium. Thus our problem becomes one of predicting the details of this approach to equilibrium and in particular of calculating the frequencies and damping constants that are associated with this relaxation phenomenon.

The following analysis will be confined to the longitudinal modes of oscillation. This means that the induced magnetic field is neglected while the induced electric field may be described in terms of the gradient of a scalar ϕ. Thus the applicable form of the BV equation may be written

$$\frac{\partial}{\partial t}f + \mathbf{v} \cdot \frac{\partial}{\partial \mathbf{r}}f + \frac{q}{m}(\nabla\phi) \cdot \frac{\partial}{\partial \mathbf{v}}f = 0 \qquad (4.116)$$

with the self-consistent potential ϕ determined by the equation

$$\nabla^2 \phi = -\frac{n_0 q}{\varepsilon_0} + \frac{q}{\varepsilon_0} \int d\mathbf{v}\, f(\mathbf{r}, \mathbf{v}, t)$$

$$= -\frac{n_0 q}{\varepsilon_0} + \frac{n_0 q}{\varepsilon_0} \int d\mathbf{v}\, f_0(\mathbf{v}) + \frac{q}{\varepsilon_0} \int d\mathbf{v}\, g(\mathbf{r}, \mathbf{v}, t)$$

$$= \frac{q}{\varepsilon_0} \int d\mathbf{v}\, g(\mathbf{r}, \mathbf{v}, t) \tag{4.117}$$

where the second equality follows by an application of eq. (4.115) and the third then follows by virtue of the fact that $f_0(\mathbf{v})$ is normalized to unity. The term $(-n_0 q)$ in eq. (4.117) represents the uniform charge density of the positive ions. We now substitute that form of f given in eq. (4.115) into eq. (4.116) and noting that according to eq. (4.117), ϕ is of order g, we obtain in zeroth order the result

$$\frac{\partial}{\partial t}(n_0 f_0) + \mathbf{v} \cdot \frac{\partial}{\partial \mathbf{r}}(n_0 f_0) = 0 \tag{4.118}$$

while to first order in g, we obtain

$$\frac{\partial}{\partial t} g + \mathbf{v} \cdot \frac{\partial}{\partial \mathbf{r}} g + \frac{n_0 q}{m}(\nabla \phi) \cdot \frac{\partial}{\partial \mathbf{v}} f_0 = 0 \tag{4.119}$$

Now the zeroth order, eq. (4.118), is satisfied by an arbitrary function of the velocity alone and in particular by the Maxwellian form given in eq. (4.114); and thus, eq. (4.118) yields essentially no information. The first order eq. (4.119) is not so easily satisfied, however, and our task thus becomes one of finding a simultaneous solution of eq. (4.117) and the linearized form of the BV equation—that is, eq. (4.119).

A simple way for solving these equations is to Fourier analyze them both in space and time by making direct use of eqs. (1.29) and (1.46). This may be accomplished by multiplying eqs. (4.117) and (4.119) by the factor

$$\frac{1}{(2\pi)^4} \exp\{-i(\mathbf{k} \cdot \mathbf{r} - \omega t)\}$$

and integrating over all of physical space and over all positive times. We find after carrying out some straightforward manipulations the results

$$-k^2 \phi_\omega(\mathbf{k}) = \frac{q}{\varepsilon_0} \int d\mathbf{v}\, g_\omega(\mathbf{k}, \mathbf{v}) \tag{4.120}$$

and

$$-g_0 + i(\mathbf{k} \cdot \mathbf{v} - \omega) g_\omega(\mathbf{k}, \mathbf{v}) + \frac{i q n_0}{m} \phi_\omega(\mathbf{k}) \mathbf{k} \cdot \frac{\partial}{\partial \mathbf{v}} f_0(\mathbf{v}) = 0 \tag{4.121}$$

where, for example, $g_\omega(\mathbf{k}, \mathbf{v})$ is given by

$$g_\omega(\mathbf{k},\mathbf{v}) = \frac{1}{(2\pi)^4} \int d\mathbf{r} \int_0^\infty dt\, g(\mathbf{r},\mathbf{v},t) \exp\{-i(\mathbf{k}\cdot\mathbf{r} - {}_\omega t)\} \qquad (4.122)$$

and where

$$g_0 \equiv g_0(\mathbf{k},\mathbf{v})$$

is the Fourier transform—in space only—of the initial value for g and is thus a function only of $\mathbf{k}$ and $\mathbf{v}$. To proceed now, we solve eq. (4.121) for $g_\omega(\mathbf{k}, \mathbf{v})$ and thus obtain the expression

$$g_\omega(\mathbf{k},\mathbf{v}) = \frac{1}{i(\mathbf{k}\cdot\mathbf{v} - \omega)}\left[g_0 - \frac{iqn_0}{m}\phi_\omega(\mathbf{k})\mathbf{k}\cdot\frac{\partial}{\partial\mathbf{v}}f_0\right] \qquad (4.123)$$

which may be integrated over all velocities. The result, on being substituted into eq. (4.120) yields the relation

$$-k^2\phi_\omega(\mathbf{k}) = \frac{q}{\varepsilon_0}\int d\mathbf{v}\,\frac{g_0(\mathbf{k},\mathbf{v})}{i(\mathbf{k}\cdot\mathbf{v} - \omega)} - \frac{q^2 n_0}{m\varepsilon_0}\phi_\omega\int d\mathbf{v}\,\frac{\mathbf{k}\cdot\dfrac{\partial}{\partial\mathbf{v}}f_0}{\mathbf{k}\cdot\mathbf{v} - \omega} \qquad (4.124)$$

which now involves the potential $\phi_\omega(\mathbf{k})$ only in an algebraic way. Thus we have essentially obtained an explicit formula for $\phi_\omega(\mathbf{k})$ and this is given by

$$\phi_\omega(\mathbf{k}) = \frac{\dfrac{iq}{\varepsilon_0}\displaystyle\int d\mathbf{v}\,\frac{g_0(\mathbf{k},\mathbf{v})}{\mathbf{k}\cdot\mathbf{v} - \omega}}{k^2 - \omega_P^2\displaystyle\int d\mathbf{v}\,\frac{1}{\mathbf{k}\cdot\mathbf{v} - \omega}\mathbf{k}\cdot\frac{\partial}{\partial\mathbf{v}}f_0} \qquad (4.125)$$

where ω_p is the plasma frequency and has been previously defined in eq. (4.34). The result given in eq. (4.125) when combined with eq. (4.123) thus represents the complete solution to our problem.

As stated above, our present interests are restricted to obtaining the frequencies and decay constants of this system and these may be directly obtained by taking the inverse Fourier transform in time of, say, the potential $\phi_\omega(\mathbf{k})$. On making use of eq. (1.30) we may write

$$\phi(\mathbf{k},t) = \frac{iq}{\varepsilon_0}\int_{-\infty}^\infty d\omega\, e^{-i\omega t}\,\frac{\displaystyle\int d\mathbf{v}\,\frac{g_0(\mathbf{k},\mathbf{v})}{\mathbf{k}\cdot\mathbf{v} - \omega}}{k^2 - \omega_P^2\displaystyle\int d\mathbf{v}\,\frac{1}{\mathbf{k}\cdot\mathbf{v} - \omega}\mathbf{k}\cdot\frac{\partial}{\partial\mathbf{v}}f_0} \qquad (4.126)$$

and this integral over ω may be explicitly evaluated by closing the contour with a large semicircle in the lower half of the complex ω plane and by making use of Cauchy's theorem. Thus $\phi(\mathbf{k}, t)$ takes on the form of a sum of terms the jth of which has a time dependence $e^{-i\omega_j t}$ where ω_j is the jth pole of the integrand in eq. (4.126). The integrand in eq. (4.126) may have poles either because the numerator is singular or else because the denominator has a zero. Furthermore since all singularities of the numerator are associated with details of the initial perturbation and not with intrinsic properties of the plasma, they are of no interest in our present considerations. Thus, the physically interesting singularities are associated only with the zeros in the denominator of the integrand in eq. (4.126). These zeros occur at those values of ω that satisfy the relation

$$0 = k^2 - \omega_P^2 \int d\mathbf{v} \frac{\mathbf{k} \cdot (\partial/\partial \mathbf{v}) f_0(\mathbf{v})}{\mathbf{k} \cdot \mathbf{v} - \omega}$$

$$= k^2 - \omega_P^2 \int_{-\infty}^{\infty} dv \frac{(d/dv) f_0(v)}{v - \omega/k} \tag{4.127}$$

where the second equality follows from carrying out the integrations at right angles to $\mathbf{k}$ so that $f_0(v)$ is the integral of $f_0(\mathbf{v})$ over two components of the velocity. This formula is called a *dispersion relation* since with it we can calculate ω as a function of $\mathbf{k}$. A fairly detailed analysis of eq. (4.127) will be given in a subsequent chapter; for the present purpose, we note that the solution of the problem is obtained by finding those values of ω for which eq. (4.127) is satisfied, and associated with a typical root, ω_0, there is a time dependence of the form $e^{-i\omega_0 t}$ in both $\phi(\mathbf{k}, t)$ as well as in $g(\mathbf{k}, \mathbf{v}, t)$. And thus, the real parts of the roots of eq. (4.127) represent the natural frequencies of the plasma and the imaginary parts represent the associated damping* constants.

Let us close this brief introduction to these plasma oscillations by calculating a root of eq. (4.127) in the long wavelength limit—that is, as $|\mathbf{k}| \to 0$. On making use of the explicit formula for $f_0(v)$ given in eq. (4.114), there results

$$k^2 = \omega_p^2 \left(\frac{\beta m}{2\pi}\right)^{1/2} \int_{-\infty}^{\infty} \frac{dv}{(v - \omega/k)^2} \exp\left\{-\beta \frac{mv^2}{2}\right\} \tag{4.128}$$

where we have made use of an integration by parts. Now assuming that k is small, and therefore that ω/k is very large, the integrand may be expanded in a power series in k/ω of the form

$$\left(\frac{\beta m}{2\pi}\right)^{1/2} \int_{-\infty}^{\infty} \frac{dv \exp\{-(\beta m v^2)/2\}}{(\omega/k)^2 (1 - kv/\omega)^2} \cong \left(\frac{k}{\omega}\right)^2 \left[1 + 3\left(\frac{k}{\omega}\right)^2 \frac{1}{\beta m} + \cdots\right]$$

---

* It will be subsequently shown that the choice for f_0 in eq. (4.114) allows only roots with negative imaginary parts.

On substituting this back into eq. (4.128) we obtain, after consistently neglecting terms of order k^4, the formula

$$\omega^2 \cong \omega_p^2 + 3k^2 u^2 \tag{4.129}$$

where u^2 is the rms velocity and is expressible in terms of β by the formula

$$u^2 = \frac{1}{\beta m} \tag{4.130}$$

The approximate root given in eq. (4.129), which is valid only for small values of k, was first obtained by Vlasov. A more refined derivation of this result was subsequently given by Landau, who showed that in addition to the real part given in eq. (4.129) this root also has an imaginary part ω_i; this is given approximately by

$$\omega_i = -\left(\frac{\pi}{8}\right)^{1/2} \omega_p \left(\frac{\omega_p}{ku}\right)^2 \exp\left\{-\frac{\omega_p^2}{2k^2 u^2}\right\} \tag{4.131}$$

The exponential decay of plasma waves associated with this value of ω_i is often called *Landau damping*, and will be studied in greater detail subsequently.

PLASMA CONDUCTIVITY

As a final illustration of the usage of the BV equation we shall now derive in a rather elementary way a formula for the conductivity of a plasma. For the purpose of this simplified discussion it is again convenient to assume that the ions are essentially stationary and serve only to supply a neutralizing background of positive charge. And as in the above discussion of plasma oscillations, the electrons in their unperturbed state are assumed to be in equilibrium at the temperature T, but as a result of the existence of a weak, external, electric field $E(r, t)$, this electronic distribution function $f(r, v, t)$ takes on the form

$$f(\mathbf{r}, \mathbf{v}, t) = n_0 f_0 + g(\mathbf{r}, \mathbf{v}, t) \tag{4.132}$$

where the perturbation g is of order E and is therefore assumed to be small compared to the equilibrium distribution function $n_0 f_0$. This form for $f(\mathbf{r}, \mathbf{v}, t)$ is similar to that assumed in eq. (4.115); however, in that case g represented a perturbation due to an initial disturbance whereas in the present context g represents a modification in the distribution function due to the presence of the external field $E(\mathbf{r}, t)$.

In our previous derivation of the conductivity in Chapter 1, we found it very important to include a term that took into account the collisions between the mobile electrons and the relatively stationary ions. Similarly, we can expect the collision frequency ω_c also to play an important role in the present calculation. These collisional effects can be easily taken into account in a phenomenological way by modifying the BV equation so that it becomes

$$\frac{\partial}{\partial t}f + \mathbf{v} \cdot \frac{\partial}{\partial \mathbf{r}}f - \frac{q}{m}\mathbf{E}(\mathbf{r},t) \cdot \frac{\partial}{\partial \mathbf{v}}f = -\omega_c g \tag{4.133}$$

where g is as defined in eq. (4.132) and $\mathbf{E}(\mathbf{r}, t)$ is the external electric field. The addition of the term $-\omega_c g$ to the right-hand side of the BV equation can be made plausible by first linearizing eq. (4.133) in order to obtain

$$\frac{\partial}{\partial t}g + \mathbf{v} \cdot \frac{\partial}{\partial \mathbf{r}}g - \frac{n_0 q}{m}\mathbf{E} \cdot \frac{\partial}{\partial \mathbf{v}}f_0 = -\omega_c g \tag{4.134}$$

and then noting that in the absence of the electric field, this equation implies that g would decay exponentially from some initial value to zero in a time of order $1/\omega_c$. This is in accord with our intuition which tells us that in the absence of Landau damping the plasma would approach equilibrium only by virtue of collisions. Order of magnitude estimates for ω_c can be found in the references at the end of this chapter; for our immediate needs it is sufficient to note that for most physically interesting systems we have the inequality

$$\omega_c \ll \omega_p$$

and therefore plasma oscillations will be damped out long before collisional effects come into play.

The technique, which will be used to calculate the conductivity σ, will consist of solving eq. (4.134) for g, and then using this formula to calculate the current density $\mathbf{j}$. The result will turn out to be proportional to $\mathbf{E}$, and by definition the coefficient of proportionality is called the *conductivity*.

In order to solve eq. (4.134), it is again convenient to reduce this differential equation to an algebraic one by taking Fourier transforms in both space and time. The result may be easily solved for $g_\omega(\mathbf{k}, \mathbf{v})$ and we obtain

$$g_\omega(\mathbf{k},\mathbf{v}) = \frac{(n_0 q)/m\mathbf{E}_\omega(\mathbf{k}) \cdot \partial/\partial\mathbf{v}f_0}{i(\mathbf{k} \cdot \mathbf{v} - \omega - i\omega_c)} \tag{4.135}$$

where, for example, $\mathbf{E}_\omega(\mathbf{k})$ is given by

$$\mathbf{E}_\omega(\mathbf{k}) = \frac{1}{(2\pi)^4}\int d\mathbf{r}\, dt\, \mathbf{E}(\mathbf{r},t)\exp\{-i(\mathbf{k}\cdot\mathbf{r} - \omega t)\} \tag{4.136}$$

On making use of that form of $g_\omega(\mathbf{k}, \mathbf{v})$ as given in eq. (4.135), the Fourier transform of the current density is easily calculated and we obtain

$$\mathbf{j}_\omega(\mathbf{k}) = -\frac{n_0 q^2}{m} \int d\mathbf{v}\, \mathbf{v} \frac{\mathbf{E}_\omega(\mathbf{k}) \cdot \partial/\partial \mathbf{v} f_0(\mathbf{v})}{i(\mathbf{k} \cdot \mathbf{v} - \omega - i\omega_c)} \tag{4.137}$$

where we have made use of the fact that the current density associated with the equilibrium distribution function f_0 vanishes. Evidently, $\mathbf{j}_\omega(\mathbf{k})$ is not simply proportional to $\mathbf{E}_\omega(\mathbf{k})$; nevertheless we may write Ohm's law in the form

$$(\mathbf{j}_\omega)_i = \sum_{j=1}^{3} \sigma_{ij}(\mathbf{E}_\omega)_j \tag{4.138}$$

where the conductivity tensor σ_{ij} is given by

$$\sigma_{ij} = -\frac{n_0 q^2}{m} \int d\mathbf{v}\, \frac{v_i\, \partial/\partial v_j\, f_0}{i(\mathbf{k} \cdot \mathbf{v} - \omega - i\omega_c)} \tag{4.139}$$

It is often stated that the simpler form for the conductivity as given in eq. (1.4) is the zero temperature limit of eq. (4.139). The verification of this statement is straightforward and depends on the fact that the neglect of thermal motion means that $f_0(\mathbf{v})$ has the form of a delta function; that is,

$$f_0(\mathbf{v}) = \delta(\mathbf{v})$$

and on substituting this into eq. (4.139) we obtain after an integration by parts the result

$$\begin{aligned}
\sigma_{ij} &= \frac{n_0 q^2}{m} \int d\mathbf{v}\, \delta(\mathbf{v}) \frac{\partial}{\partial v_j} \left[\frac{v_i}{i(\mathbf{k} \cdot \mathbf{v} - \omega - i\omega_c)} \right] \\
&= \frac{n_0 q^2}{m} \frac{\partial}{\partial v_j} \left[\frac{v_i}{i(\mathbf{k} \cdot \mathbf{v} - \omega - i\omega_c)} \right]_{\mathbf{v}=0} \\
&= \frac{n_0 q^2}{m} \frac{1}{\omega_c - i\omega} \delta_{ij}
\end{aligned} \tag{4.140}$$

As expected this is identical to eq. (1.4). An alternate way for obtaining this result is by assuming that the external field is uniform and that therefore the wave vector $\mathbf{k}$ vanishes. In this case eq. (4.139) may be written

$$\begin{aligned}
\sigma_{ij} &= -\frac{n_0 q^2}{m} \frac{1}{\omega_c - i\omega} \int d\mathbf{v}\, v_i \frac{\partial}{\partial v_j} f_0(\mathbf{v}) \\
&= \frac{n_0 q^2}{m} \frac{1}{\omega_c - i\omega} \delta_{ij}
\end{aligned} \tag{4.141}$$

where the second equality follows by use of an integration by parts. Thus we see that eq. (4.139) for the conductivity tensor reduces to the form given in eq. (1.4) in the limit of zero temperature as well as in the long wavelength limit.

The physical interpretation of the imaginary part of the conductivity tensor can be obtained most simply perhaps by relating it to a complex dielectric constant. This relationship can be easily derived by noting that in the presence of an external field, the plasma becomes polarized and acquires a dipole moment per unit volume $P_\omega(k)$, which may be expressed by the relation

$$P_\omega(\mathbf{k})_i = \varepsilon_0 \sum_{j=1}^{3} \left[\kappa_\omega(\mathbf{k})_{ij} - \delta_{ij} \right] E_\omega(k)_j \tag{4.142}$$

where $\kappa_{\omega ij}$ is the dielectric tensor. On making use of this fact and Maxwell's equations it is easy to show that σ_{ij} and κ_{ij} are related by

$$\kappa_\omega(\mathbf{k})_{ij} = \delta_{ij} + \frac{i}{\omega \varepsilon_0} \sigma_{ij} \tag{4.143}$$

Finally, since the dielectric constant can be related to the index of refraction, and since the imaginary part of the index of refraction is known to be associated with the absorption of energy by the plasma, it follows that the existence of a real part to the conductivity tensor implies that energy will be absorbed from any impinging electromagnetic wave.

Suggested Reading and References

1. Corrections to the BV equation

R. Balescu, "General Theory of Nonequilibrium Phenomena," contained in *Lectures in Theoretical Physics III, at Boulder, Colorado, 1960* (edited by W. E. Brittin, B. W. Downs, and J. W. Downs). New York: Interscience Publishers, 1961.

H. Grad, "Principles of the Kinetic Theory Gases," *Handbuch der Physik, B.* XII. Berlin: Springer-Verlag, 1958.

A. N. Kaufman, "Plasma Transport Theory," contained in *"La theorie des gaz neutres et ionises"* (edited by C. DeWitt and J. F. Detoeuf). New York: John Wiley & Sons, Inc., 1960.

N. Rostoker and M. N. Rosenbluth, "Test Particles in a Completely Ionized Plasma," *Phys, of Fluids.* 3, 1 (1960).

W. B. Thompson, "Fluctuations: The Fokker Plank Equation for a Plasma," contained in *International Summer Course in Plasma Physics 1960, Risö Report No.* 18 (Danish Atomic Energy Commission at Risö) November, 1960, pp. 101–17.

2. Plasma Conductivity

V. L. Ginzburg, *Propagation of Electromagnetic Waves in Plasma* (English translation), Gordon and Breach, Chap. II. New York: Science Publishers, Inc., 1961.

3. Plasma Oscillations

J. D. Jackson, "Plasma Oscillations," *J. Nuclear Energy* Part C. 1, 141 (1960).

A. Simon, "Collisionless Boltzmann Equation," contained in *International Summer Course in Plasma Physics, 1960, Risö Report No.* 18 (Danish Atomic Energy Commission at Risö) November 1960, pp. 101–17.

Problems

1. Calculate the distribution of electrons in a rigid conducting sphere of radius b in the linear approximation. Assume that the center of the sphere is at zero potential, that the mean number of electrons per cubic centimeter is n_0, that the electron gas is in equilibrium at the temperature T, and that the radius of the sphere is much greater than the applicable value for λ_D.

2. Consider a plasma consisting of two species, the particles of which have charges $\pm q$ and masses m, M, respectively.

(a) Write down the linearized BV equation for each species in terms of their respective equilibrium distribution functions f_{0+}, f_{0-}.

(b) Show that the dispersion relation for longitudinal oscilations is the same as that given in eq. (4.127) but with the replacement

$$f_0(\mathbf{v}) \rightarrow f_{0-}(\mathbf{v}) + \frac{m}{M} f_{0+}(\mathbf{v})$$

(c) Calculate the frequency and the damping constant in the long wavelength limit.

3. Derive the dispersion relation for the longitudinal oscillations of an electron gas for the case where the temperature is sufficiently high so that a relativistic treatment is required.

4. (a) Find explicit formulas for the roots of the dispersion relation for the case where the one-dimensional equilibrium distribution function $f_0(v)$ has the form

$$f_0(v) = \frac{\Delta}{\pi} \left\{ \frac{1}{(v-u)^2 + \Delta^2} + \frac{1}{(v+u)^2 + \Delta^2} \right\}$$

where Δ is the velocity spread about the two maxima at $\pm u$.

(b) Verify the fact that for $u < \Delta$ there are no exponentially growing waves—that is, that for this range of the parameters u, Δ, regardless of the wave number, there are no roots with positive imaginary parts.

(c) Show that for $u > \Delta$, there are instabilities—that is, roots with positive imaginary parts—only for values of k between zero and $\frac{1}{2}\omega_p$. Note that the above electron distribution may be thought of as the overlap of two streams of electrons that have the respective mean velocities $\pm u$. The instability just calculated is an example of what is known as the *two-stream instability*.

5. Set up the problem for calculating the dispersion relation for the longitudinal modes of oscillation of an electron gas in the presence of a uniform external magnetic field B_0. Carry out the analysis as far as possible. Assuming that the magnetic field is weak, calculate the first nonvanishing corrections to the dispersion relation in eq. (4.127).

6. Show that for the case where the equilibrium distribution function is Maxwellian, the dispersion relation may be expressed in the form

$$1 + \frac{k^2 u^2}{\omega_p^2} = - i\omega \int_0^\infty dt \, \exp\{i\omega t - \tfrac{1}{2}k^2 u^2 t^2\}$$

where u is the rms velocity.

7. (a) Show that the dispersion relations for the *transverse* oscillations of an electronic plasma is given by

$$\omega^2 - k^2 c^2 + \omega \omega_p^2 \int dv \, \frac{f_0(\mathbf{v})}{\mathbf{k}\cdot\mathbf{v} - \omega} = 0$$

(By definition, the transverse electric field has the property $\nabla\cdot\mathbf{E} = 0$ or in Fourier-transformed language $\mathbf{k}\cdot\mathbf{E}_\omega(k) = 0$.)

(b) Show that in the limit of small wave numbers an approximate root of this dispersion relation is given by

$$\omega^2 \cong \omega_p^2 + k^2 c^2$$

8. Extend the result of Problem 1, Chapter 1, by assuming that in addition to the external electric field there is also a uniform, static magnetic field $\mathbf{B}_0$ at right angles to the electric field.

9. Derive a formula for the conductivity tensor assuming that the electron gas is relativistic. Find an explicit formula that is valid in the long wavelength limit.

10. Calculate the conductivity tensor for the case that the plasma is a mixture of two species of charges $\pm q$, and masses m, M, respectively, and that both species are in equilibrium at the temperature T. Evaluate the result in the zero temperature limit and compare it to the formula in the text.

11. Consider a noninteracting gas of particles confined to one dimensional motion in a box of length a.

(a) Show that if $f_0(x, v)$ is the initial distribution of the particles inside the box, then the function $F(x, v)$ which is defined by

$$F(x,v) = (2a)^{-\frac{1}{2}} \sum_{n=-\infty}^{\infty} a_n(v) \exp\left\{\frac{in\pi x}{a}\right\}$$

where $a_n(v)$ is given by

$$a_n(v) = (2a)^{-\frac{1}{2}}\left[\int_0^a dx\, f_0(x,v) \exp\left\{-\frac{in\pi x}{a}\right\}\right.$$
$$\left. + \int_{-a}^0 dx\, f_0(-x-v) \exp\left\{-\frac{in\pi x}{a}\right\}\right]$$

is identical to $f_0(x, v)$ inside the box that has been taken to be located on the interval $o < x < a$.

(b) Show further that because of the periodicity of the function F, the reflections of the particles by the containing walls at $x = 0$, a are automatically taken into account provided we describe the particles inside the box in terms of F.

(c) Making use of the fact that the particles are noninteracting, show that at any subsequent time t, the distribution of particles is given by the function $F(x - vt, v)$.

(d) Apply this result in order to calculate the distribution function at time t for a gas that is initially located with uniform density on the interval $o < x < a/2$—that is, the left half of the box—and has a Maxwellian velocity distribution.

(e) Calculate the approximate time required until the particles are distributed uniformly throughout the box.

12. Make use of the technique in Problem 11 in order to set up a dispersion relation for an electron gas in a one-dimensional box of length a.

13. Generalize the results in Problem 11 to the three-dimensional case.

14. (a) Consider the motion of a particle of charge q and mass m in a very strong external magnetic field that is oriented along the z axis and is described by the vector potential

$$\mathbf{A} = \frac{1}{2}\mathbf{B} \times \mathbf{r}$$

Show that the transformation from the customary variables to new ones that are defined by

$$P_x = 2^{-\frac{1}{2}}\left(p_x - \frac{m\omega}{2}y\right); \quad P_y = 2^{-\frac{1}{2}}\left(p_x + \frac{m\omega}{2}y\right)$$

$$X = 2^{-\frac{1}{2}}\left(x + \frac{2}{m\omega}p_y\right); \quad Y = 2^{-\frac{1}{2}}\left(x - \frac{2}{m\omega}p_y\right)$$

is a canonical transformation and that the Hamiltonian in terms of the new variables is given by

$$H = \frac{1}{m}P_y^2 + \frac{1}{4}m\omega^2 Y^2 + \frac{p_z^2}{2m}$$

where ω is the Larmor frequency. What is the physical significance of P_y and Y?

(b) Write down Liouville's theorem in terms of the new variables. In addition to the variables appearing in this equation, on what other ones may the distribution function depend?

(c) Consider now a gas of particles in a magnetic field and suppose that the interactions between the particles may be neglected. Show that if θ and v are defined by

$$\theta = \tan^{-1}\left(\frac{Y}{P_y}\frac{m\omega}{2}\right) \qquad v^2 = \left(\frac{2}{m^2}P_y^2 + \frac{\omega^2}{2}Y^2\right)$$

and if $f(X, P_x, \theta, v, z, p_z)$ is the initial distribution function, then

$$f\left(X, P_x, \theta - \omega t, v, z - \frac{p_z t}{m}, p_z\right)$$

is the distribution function at any subsequent time.

15. An approximate description of a plasma that is confined to a magnetic bottle may be obtained by assuming that the field is completely uniform and that the ends of the bottle consist of perfectly reflecting walls.

(a) Combine the results of Problems 11 and 14 in order to obtain the distribution function at any time t (in terms of its initial value) for a plasma that is confined to the interval along the z direction $0 < z < a$ and that is in the presence of a uniform magnetic field along this same direction.

(b) Suppose that in such a bottle there is a plasma that is at the temperature T, has a mean velocity u_0 along the z axis, and is originally of uniform density in the region $0 < z < a/2$, $r < b$. Find the distribution function at any subsequent time assuming, of course, that the interparticle forces can be consistently neglected.

5

Magnetohydrodynamics

INTRODUCTION

It has been previously suggested that a description of the dynamics of a plasma in terms of the BV equation might be expected to be unnecessarily complicated since a knowledge of the single-particle distribution function is equivalent to having available an infinity of macroscopic variables in addition to those few that are actually of direct physical interest. Unfortunately, equations that give directly the unique time development for these physically interesting macroscopic variables cannot be obtained from the BV equation. For as we saw in the previous chapter each time we take a moment of the BV equation in order to obtain an equation involving the time derivative of some given physical quantity, this same equation invariably contains the next higher moment; and, consequently, the resulting set of equations is not closed. Despite the lack of completeness of these moment equations, however, they do deal directly with physically interesting and therefore intuitive quantities; this makes it tempting to close these equations by use of various physical assumptions. Generally speaking, the equations of magnetohydrodynamics (MHD) are those equations that are obtained by truncating the moment equations in some way. The precise way in which these equations are closed depends, of course, on the properties of the physical system under consideration; and consequently various types of truncations have been studied in the past and are found in the literature.

For a plasma consisting of a single species, we previously derived the associated moment equations, and the first two of these were shown to be

$$\frac{\partial}{\partial t} n + \nabla \cdot (\mathbf{u}n) = 0 \tag{5.1}$$

and

$$\rho \left\{ \frac{\partial}{\partial t} u_i + (\mathbf{u} \cdot \nabla) u_i \right\} = \rho_q E_i + (\mathbf{j} \times \mathbf{B})_i - \sum_{j=1}^{3} \frac{\partial}{\partial x_j} p_{ij} \tag{5.2}$$

where n, ρ, and ρ_q are the particle density, the mass density, and the charge density, respectively; $\mathbf{u}$ is the mean fluid velocity; $\mathbf{j}$ is the current density; $\mathbf{E}$ and $\mathbf{B}$ are the total electromagnetic fields—that is, the external fields plus those produced by the sources ρ_q and $\mathbf{j}$; and p_{ij} is the pressure tensor. For the case where the plasma consists of more than one species, it is a simple matter to verify the fact that there will be equations of the types (5.1) and (5.2) for each species but the associated electromagnetic fields $\mathbf{E}$ and $\mathbf{B}$ will now represent the sum of the external fields and the fields produced by all of the particles in the plasma rather than only those associated with the given species. Furthermore, even though for each species the quantities ρ, ρ_q, and $\mathbf{j}$ can be expressed in terms of the particle density n, it is clear that the first two of the moment equations for a multicomponent plasma are incomplete since the time development of the various pressure tensors is not known. The simplest method for constructing a closed set from these moment equations involves the assumption that this problem essentially does not exist and postulating a relation between the pressure tensor and the other macroscopic quantities.

In particular a commonly used assumption is that the pressure tensor is a scalar; that is, we have the relation

$$p_{ij} = p\delta_{ij} \tag{5.3}$$

where p is the ordinary pressure. If, in addition, we assume the existence of an equation of state—that is, a unique relationship between the scalar pressure p and the mass density ρ—eqs. (5.1) and (5.2) comprise a closed set of equations. Physically speaking, the assumption in eq. (5.3) may be expected to be valid provided the transport of momentum in the local rest frame of the plasma is isotropic—that is, provided that the momentum transported across any element of surface in the plasma lies along the normal to this surface and furthermore that the magnitude of this momentum transport is independent of the orientation of the surface. For example, this assumption is *not* expected to be valid if the plasma is permeated by anisotropies such as those produced by a large magnetic field. The second assumption—namely, the existence of an equation of state—relates to the local equilibrium of the plasma and may be employed if the density and temperature are such that the plasma relaxes to equilibrium in a time that is very short compared to any other relevant times. Thus we see that for certain physical situations it is possible to obtain a complete description for the plasma by simply appending to the moment equations some physically reasonable assumptions.

A second possible way for obtaining a closed set of equations is one that unfortunately leads to much more complicated mathematics. It involves the assumption that the heat-flow tensor Q_{ijk}, which was defined in eq. (4.69), is negligible compared to the other terms in eq. (4.75). In this case, the temporal evolution of the pressure tensor is uniquely given by eq. (4.75) and when taken in combination with eqs. (5.1) and (5.2) a closed system of equations results. Indeed, we can proceed in this same way in order to obtain a larger but closed system of equations by including the equation that involves the time derivative of the heat-flow tensor. This is not desirable, however, not only because the mathematics quickly gets out of hand, but also because the physical significance of the higher moments is more obscure, thus defeating our underlying motivation for dealing only with the physically interesting and intuitive macroscopic variables.

For purposes of obtaining a physical feeling for various quantities and phenomena, we shall begin our discussion of magnetohydrodynamics by first studying certain phenomenological relations that will be seen to be very similar to the moment equations. Subsequently we shall examine the problem of deriving these relations and thereby develop methods for dealing with complicating features such as those produced by anisotropies.

THE ONE-FLUID MODEL

In the simplest version of the equations of magnetohydrodynamics, we think of the plasma as consisting of a *single* conducting fluid which is electrically neutral macroscopically—that is, the macroscopic charge density vanishes everywhere in the interior of the plasma—and which is sufficiently homogeneous and isotropic so that it can be completely described in terms of the four macroscopic variables: the fluid velocity $\mathbf{u}(\mathbf{r}, t)$ and the mass density $\rho(\mathbf{r}, t)$. Physically, of course, the plasma consists of two or more species and thus, for example, $\mathbf{j}$ is not simply proportional to $\mathbf{u}$. Moreover, in the present description it is assumed that any deviation from electrical neutrality is immediately eliminated by means of the very powerful electrostatic restoring forces which, as we have seen, result in damped, high-frequency, plasma oscillations. In other words, in describing a plasma via the one-fluid model we must restrict ourselves to those low-frequency phenomena that are usually associated with the motions of the more massive constituents of the plasma. The electrons serve primarily to maintain the over-all electrical neutrality of the plasma.

An immediate consequence of this restriction to low-frequency phenomena is that for reasons of consistency, we must drop the displacement current—that is, the term $\partial E/\partial t$—from Maxwell's eq. (1.8). Furthermore, since the charge density is also assumed to vanish, we have $\nabla \cdot E = 0$, and therefore all electric fields are purely transverse. Thus, in the one-fluid model, the equations for the induced electromagnetic fields are written:

$$\mathbf{V} \cdot \mathbf{B} = 0 \tag{5.4}$$

$$\mathbf{V} \cdot \mathbf{E} = 0 \tag{5.5}$$

$$\mathbf{V} \times \mathbf{E} = -\frac{\partial}{\partial t}\mathbf{B} \tag{5.6}$$

$$\mathbf{V} \times \mathbf{B} = \mu_0 \mathbf{j} \tag{5.7}$$

This last equation is, of course, consistent with charge conservation, since eq. (5.7) implies $\nabla \cdot \mathbf{j} = 0$, and therefore since ρ_q is assumed to vanish, there is no difficulty with eq. (1.9).

The equations that describe the motion of the fluid are obviously identical to eqs. (5.1) and (5.2) for which now, however, all macroscopic variables are to be associated with the entire fluid and not only with a given species.* Before we can make use of eq. (5.2), however, it is necessary to simplify the form of the pressure tensor. It is, of course, possible to make direct usage of the assumption in eq. (5.3); however, a slight generalization of this formula enables us to include viscous effects also, and therefore we shall employ this latter form. In treatises on gas dynamics and fluid mechanics† it is shown in a fairly general way that for the case of an isotropic and homogeneous fluid, the gradient of the pressure tensor may be expressed by the formula

$$-\sum_{j=1}^{3} \frac{\partial}{\partial x_j} p_{ij} = -\frac{\partial}{\partial x_i} p + \frac{\eta}{3} \frac{\partial}{\partial x_i} \mathbf{V} \cdot \mathbf{u} + \eta \nabla^2 u_i$$

where p is the scalar pressure, $\mathbf{u}$ is the velocity field, and η is an empirical parameter that is known as the *coefficient of viscosity*. In the limit of vanishingly small η, this result is, of course, identical to that in eq. (5.3). Furthermore, in the one-fluid model, it is conventionally assumed that the

---

* This feature will become clearer upon our subsequent examination of the two-fluid model.

† See, for example, Horace Lamb, *Hydrodynamics*, Chap. XI. New York: Dover Publications, Inc., 1945.

fluid is incompressible. Mathematically, this feature is expressed by the relation

$$\frac{\partial}{\partial t}\rho + (\mathbf{u}\cdot\nabla)\rho = 0$$

which on being combined with the statement of mass conservation, namely,

$$\frac{\partial}{\partial t}\rho + \nabla\cdot(\mathbf{u}\rho) = 0 \tag{5.8}$$

shows that the incompressibility of the fluid may be alternatively expressed by the relation

$$\nabla\cdot\mathbf{u} = 0$$

Finally, on making use of this fact, as well as the above form for the gradient of the pressure tensor, the equation of motion for the fluid becomes

$$\rho\left\{\frac{\partial}{\partial t}\mathbf{u} + (\mathbf{u}\cdot\nabla)\mathbf{u}\right\} = \mathbf{j}\times\mathbf{B} - \nabla p + \eta\nabla^2\mathbf{u} \tag{5.9}$$

Eqs. (5.4) through (5.9), when combined with an equation of state of the form

$$p = p(\rho) \tag{5.10}$$

are essentially the working equations for the one-fluid model of magneto-hydrodynamics.

Let us first examine the problem of the completeness of this set of equations. As we have already seen, completeness in the present context means that given *all* macroscopic variables at some instant of time then a sufficient number of equations are needed for a calculation of these same quantities at an infinitesimally small later instant of time. This calculation may be accomplished either because we have an equation such as eq. (5.10) that relates two of the variables, or else because we have an equation that involves the time derivative of one of the variables. For example, if we have the equation

$$\frac{\partial}{\partial t}h(\mathbf{r},t) = K(\mathbf{r},t) \tag{5.11}$$

where $K(\mathbf{r},t)$ is a "known" function which can even be explicitly dependent on the unknown function $h(\mathbf{r},t)$ and possibly its spatial derivatives (but *not* its time derivatives), then given $h(\mathbf{r},0)$, at a later instant of time Δt, we have

$$h(\mathbf{r},\Delta t) = h(\mathbf{r},0) + \Delta t K(\mathbf{r},0)$$

for sufficiently small Δt.

For the case of the one-fluid model of magnetohydrodynamics, the complete set of macroscopic variables consists of the six quantities ρ, **u**, **j**, p, **E**, and **B**. Let us suppose that all of these are completely known throughout all of physical space at time $t = 0$. Our problem thus becomes: are the equations (5.4) through (5.10) sufficient to enable us to calculate these six quantities at time Δt? First, by the respective usage of eqs. (5.6), (5.8), and (5.9), **B**, ρ, and **u** are immediately calculable at time Δt. Making use of these formulas for **B** and ρ at this later time, **j** and p may also be obtained via eqs. (5.7) and (5.10), respectively. Thus we see that five out of the entire set of six macroscopic variables are available in terms of their initial values, but unfortunately we cannot calculate the electric field **E** at time Δt with any of the eqs. (5.4) through (5.10). Thus we conclude that this set of equations is *not* complete unless we can add to it an additional equation that either involves the time derivative of the electric field or relates **E** to some of the remaining variables.

The simplest assumption we can make in order to obtain a closed set from eqs. (5.4) through (5.10) is to assume the validity of Ohm's law. In the light of the discussion that was given in deriving eq. (1.27), Ohm's law has the simple form

$$\mathbf{j} = \sigma(\mathbf{E} + \mathbf{u} \times \mathbf{B}) \tag{5.12}$$

where the parameter σ is the conductivity and is conventionally assumed to be a known parameter. For some physical situations, we can take the conductivity to be effectively infinite, and in this case Ohm's law takes on the form

$$\mathbf{E} + \mathbf{u} \times \mathbf{B} = 0 \tag{5.13}$$

which, for reasons of simplicity, is often used in place of eq. (5.12).

To sum up the situation then, we see that the equations of the one-fluid model of magnetohydrodynamics consist of Maxwell's equations—that is, eqs. (5.4) through (5.7)—the conservation of mass relation in eq. (5.8), the equation of motion in eq. (5.9), an equation of state of the form in eq. (5.10), and Ohm's law in either of the forms (5.12) or (5.13). As has just been shown, this system of equations is complete in that, given all macroscopic variables at one instant, we can calculate them all at a slightly later time. The key assumptions that have been made in writing down these equations are:

(1) The charge density vanishes and thus only low-frequency phenomena are describable.
(2) The pressure tensor is expressible as the sum of a scalar pressure plus a viscous term.
(3) The fluid is incompressible.

(4) An equation of state is applicable.

(5) The validity of Ohm's law can be established.

Some of these restrictions and assumptions will be eliminated in a subsequent discussion that deals with the two-fluid model. For this latter model it is also possible to study high-frequency effects such as plasma oscillations which, however, are beyond the scope of the one-fluid analysis. Before we turn to these matters, however, let us first explore some consequences of the one-fluid equations.

MAGNETIC AND MECHANICAL EFFECTS

Let us now examine some direct conclusions that can be drawn from the equations for the one-fluid model.

As a first application we shall suppose that the conductivity σ is constant throughout all of space and solve Ohm's law for the electric field and thus obtain

$$\mathbf{E} = \frac{1}{\sigma}\mathbf{j} - \mathbf{u} \times \mathbf{B} \tag{5.14}$$

On substituting the curl of this expression into eq. (5.6) and making use of eq. (5.7) in order to eliminate $\mathbf{j}$, we find

$$\frac{\partial}{\partial t}\mathbf{B} = \nabla \times (\mathbf{u} \times \mathbf{B}) + \frac{1}{\sigma\mu_0}\nabla^2\mathbf{B} \tag{5.15}$$

where we have made use of the identity

$$\nabla \times (\nabla \times \mathbf{B}) = \nabla(\nabla \cdot \mathbf{B}) - \nabla^2\mathbf{B}$$

as well as eq. (5.4). Eq. (5.15) is in a form convenient for study since it involves only the magnetic field.

If the fluid is essentially at rest so that $\mathbf{u} = 0$, then eq. (5.15) reduces to the familiar diffusion equation

$$\frac{\partial}{\partial t}\mathbf{B} = \frac{1}{\sigma\mu_0}\nabla^2\mathbf{B} \tag{5.16}$$

and the quantity $1/\sigma\mu_0$ is often called the *magnetic diffusity*. This equation may be interpreted as implying that starting with some initial magnetic field distribution, this field will diffuse away in a time τ which is given by

$$\tau = \mu_0\sigma b^2 \tag{5.17}$$

where b is a typical distance over which the magnetic field varies appreciably. For example, in a good conductor, say copper, $\tau \sim 1$ sec for $b \sim 1$ cm, while for the earth for which $b \sim 10^3$ miles, we find $\tau \sim 10^4$ years. And for large astrophysical plasmas this diffusion time can even become comparable to the lifetime of the universe.

At the other extreme for which the conductivity is essentially infinite, or in other words, for times very short compared to a diffusion time τ, the second term on the right-hand side of eq. (5.15) may be neglected compared to the first term, and we now find

$$\frac{\partial}{\partial t} \mathbf{B} = \nabla \times (\mathbf{u} \times \mathbf{B}) \tag{5.18}$$

This result may be interpreted by integrating both sides of this equation over some open surface S. On making use of the results obtained in connection with our discussion of Faraday's law for moving surfaces in Chapter 1, we obtain

$$\frac{d}{dt} \int_S \mathbf{B} \cdot d\mathbf{S} = 0 \tag{5.19}$$

where we have taken the surface S to be instantaneously at rest with respect to an element of the fluid. Eq. (5.19) may be interpreted to mean that the magnetic lines of force are frozen into the fluid and therefore follow its motion completely. This result is consistent with the notions of drift velocity developed in connection with our discussion of orbit theory, since for the present case $\sigma = \infty$, and thus the fluid as well as the field lines travel with the velocity

$$\mathbf{u} = (\mathbf{E} \times \mathbf{B})\mathbf{B}^{-2}$$

according to eq. (5.13). For the purpose of this discussion, it has been assumed that $\mathbf{E}$, $\mathbf{u}$, and $\mathbf{B}$ form a mutually orthogonal set.

These two extremes—namely, of the diffusion of the magnetic field lines and of their being frozen into the plasma—may be conveniently distinguished by means of a dimensionless parameter R_m which is called the *magnetic Reynold's number*. This quantity is defined by the equation

$$R_m = \tau \frac{v}{b} \tag{5.20}$$

where τ is the diffusion time and v and b are the characteristic velocity and length of the given physical system. If we rewrite eq. (5.15) in terms of dimensionless quantities by use of v, τ, and b, we conclude that if $R_m \gg 1$, then the magnetic field lines are essentially frozen into the fluid while at the other extreme for which $R_m \ll 1$, the magnetic field diffuses away. Of course, if $R_m \sim 1$, then no clear-cut physical picture is available.

As a second application of the equations of the one-fluid model, let us explore some consequences of the equation of motion—that is, eq. (5.9).

On neglecting the nonlinear term $(\mathbf{u}\cdot\nabla)\mathbf{u}$, this equation may be cast into the form

$$\rho\frac{\partial}{\partial t}\mathbf{u} = \mathbf{F} + \sigma\{(\mathbf{E}\times\mathbf{B}) - \mathbf{u}_\perp B^2\} \tag{5.21}$$

where $\mathbf{F}$ stands for all forces of nonelectromagnetic origin, and where we have substituted the expression for the current density given by Ohm's law. The symbol $\mathbf{u}_\perp$ represents the component of the fluid velocity at right angles to the magnetic field. First, we note that the motion of the fluid along the magnetic field is governed exclusively by the nonelectromagnetic forces $\mathbf{F}$; of course, this is what we would expect on the basis of our orbit theory considerations. With regard to the motions at right angles to $\mathbf{B}$, we find on solving eq. (5.21) in an order of magnitude way, the result

$$\mathbf{u}_\perp(t) = \mathbf{u}_\perp(0)\exp\left\{-t\frac{\sigma B^2}{\rho}\right\}$$
$$+ \frac{1}{\sigma B^2}[\mathbf{F}_\perp + \sigma(\mathbf{E}\times\mathbf{B})]\left[1 - \exp\left\{-t\frac{\sigma B^2}{\rho}\right\}\right] \tag{5.22}$$

where $\mathbf{u}_\perp(0)$ is the initial value for $\mathbf{u}_\perp$. This formula tells us that starting from some initial value, the velocity $\mathbf{u}_\perp$ approaches its final form

$$\mathbf{u}_\perp(\infty) = \frac{1}{\sigma B^2}\mathbf{F}_\perp + \frac{1}{B^2}(\mathbf{E}\times\mathbf{B}) \tag{5.23}$$

in a time τ', which is given by

$$\tau' = \frac{\rho}{\sigma B^2} \tag{5.24}$$

It is interesting to note that the term proportional to B^2 in eq. (5.21) may be interpreted as an effective viscous or frictional drag and according to eqs. (5.22) and (5.23) it tends to prevent the flow of the fluid at right angles to the magnetic field. This term is often called the *magnetic viscosity*.

STEADY-STATE SOLUTIONS

A considerable amount of insight into the equations of the one-fluid model of magnetohydrodynamics can often be obtained by making a study of solutions that are independent of time. These solutions are called *steady state* and often are approximately valid for phenomena that are weakly time-dependent. From the microscopic point of view, these stationary solutions are applicable if the initial distribution function is a true constant of the motion, and thus we can expect these steady-state solutions to be valid if the system is sufficiently near equilibrium.

Formally the equations for the steady state may be obtained by setting the partial derivatives with respect to time of all macroscopic quantities to zero. Therefore, in the steady state both the divergence and the curl of the electric field vanish, and any electric field that is present must come from an external source. Furthermore, the equations for the magnetic field are just those of magnetostatics, that is eqs. (5.4) and (5.7). The equation of mass conservation becomes now

$$\nabla \cdot (\rho \mathbf{u}) = 0 \tag{5.25}$$

which is essentially equivalent to the statement for the incompressibility of the fluid; that is, $\nabla \cdot \mathbf{u} = 0$. Finally, for a stationary state, eq. (5.9) becomes

$$\rho(\mathbf{u} \cdot \nabla)\mathbf{u} = -\nabla p + \mathbf{j} \times \mathbf{B} + \eta \nabla^2 \mathbf{u}$$

which by use of the identity

$$(\mathbf{A} \cdot \nabla)\mathbf{A} = \frac{1}{2}\nabla(\mathbf{A}^2) - \mathbf{A} \times (\nabla \times \mathbf{A})$$

as well as eq. (5.7) may be cast into the form

$$\frac{1}{2}\rho\nabla\mathbf{u}^2 - \rho\mathbf{u} \times (\nabla \times \mathbf{u}) = -\nabla p + \frac{1}{\mu_0}(\mathbf{B} \cdot \nabla)\mathbf{B}$$

$$-\nabla\left(\frac{B^2}{2\mu_0}\right) + \eta\nabla^2\mathbf{u} \tag{5.26}$$

Assuming now that the velocity field is irrotational, that is, $\nabla \times \mathbf{u} = 0$, that the term $(\mathbf{B} \cdot \nabla)\mathbf{B}$ vanishes (this happens, for example, if the magnetic field varies only at right angles to the direction in which it points), that the density does not vary in the direction of the fluid velocity, and making use of the fact that for an incompressible and irrotational fluid the viscous term vanishes, we find that eq. (5.26) may be integrated once to yield

$$\frac{1}{2}\rho\mathbf{u}^2 + p + \frac{B^2}{2\mu_0} = \text{constant} \tag{5.27}$$

The physical interpretation of the various terms in this relation is clear. The first term is the kinetic pressure (the velocity $\mathbf{u}$, of course, is not to be confused with the thermal velocity); the second is the ordinary pressure; and, finally, the last term is the pressure produced by the magnetic field. The content of eq. (5.27) is that in the steady state the sum of these various pressures is constant from point to point in the fluid. Thus, for example, in our discussion (Chapter 2) of the pinch effect by use of the independent particle model (neglecting for the moment the fact that in this case the current surface actually collapsed), equilibrium could have been maintained if the interior kinetic pressure had just balanced the external magnetic pressure $\mathbf{B}^2/2\mu_0$. Actually, we assumed in that discussion that the kinetic pressure was negligible compared to $\mathbf{B}^2/2\mu_0$ and thus the cylinder collapsed. Eventually, of course, the kinetic pressure inside builds up to such an extent that it balances the magnetic pressure and at this stage the radius of the cylinder approaches the minimum value. Any increase of the particles' velocities after this point is reached would result in an unbalance in the other direction—that is, an outward expansion of the plasma.

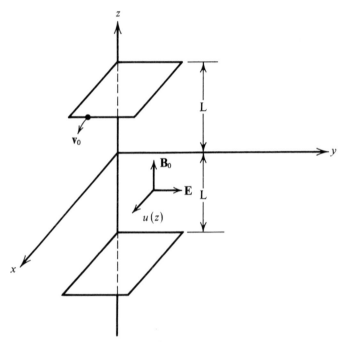

Fig. 5.1

As a particular and more detailed illustration of a steady-state solution, let us study the physical system that was first analyzed by Hartmann.* To this end, we shall consider an incompressible but viscous conducting fluid that flows in the x direction between two infinite bounding surfaces at $z = \pm L$, the upper one of which has a velocity v_0 along the x direction (Fig. 5.1). A uniform magnetic field $\mathbf{B}_0$ points along the z axis and since we expect the fluid to move faster along the wall at $z = +L$ than at the lower boundary, the fluid tends to pull the lines of force in its direction of motion;

* J. Hartmann, "Theory of the Laminar Flow of an Electrically Conducting Liquid in a Homogeneous Magnetic Field," *Kgl. Videnshap Selskab, Math-Fys.*, 15, No. 6 (1937).

therefore, there will be an induced magnetic field **B** in the x direction. In addition, let us assume that there is an external electric field present and that this field is oriented along the y axis. Finally, the system is taken to be infinite in the x and y directions and thus we shall look for a steady-state solution, for which all macroscopic quantities depend only on the single variable z.

Since the fluid velocity **u** has only a component in the x direction, and the external electric field has only a component in the y direction, it follows from Ohm's law that the current density is oriented along the y axis and this component $j(z)$ is given by

$$j(z) = \sigma\{E - B_0 u(z)\} \tag{5.28}$$

where $u(z)$ is the nonvanishing component of the velocity field. Furthermore, since $u(z)$ is a function only of z, the nonlinear velocity terms in eq. (5.9) vanish, and thus the equation of motion appropriate to the present situation may be written

$$\nabla p = \mathbf{j} \times \mathbf{B} + \eta \nabla^2 \mathbf{u} \tag{5.29}$$

On making use of eq. (5.28), the components of this equation become

$$\frac{\partial}{\partial x} p = \sigma B_0 \{E - B_0 u(z)\} + \eta \frac{\partial^2}{\partial z^2} u$$

$$\frac{\partial}{\partial y} p = 0$$

$$\frac{\partial}{\partial z} p = -\sigma B\{E - B_0 u(z)\} \tag{5.30}$$

where B is the nonvanishing x component of the induced field. Making use of the fact that all quantities are independent of x and y—a fact that is clearly consistent with the second of eqs. (5.30)—the first of these equations becomes

$$\frac{d^2 u}{dz^2} - \left(\frac{M}{L}\right)^2 u = -\left(\frac{M}{L}\right)^2 \frac{E}{B_0} \tag{5.31}$$

where M is the Hartmann number and is given by the formula

$$M = \left(\frac{\sigma B_0 L^2}{\eta}\right)^{1/2}$$

and is essentially the square root of the ratio of the magnetic to the ordinary viscosity. The solution of eq. (5.31) is well known, and on making use of the facts that $u(-L) = 0$ and $u(+L) = v_0$, it may be written

$$u(z) = \frac{v_0}{2}\left\{\frac{\sinh{(M/L)z}}{\sinh{M}} + \frac{\cosh{(M/L)z}}{\cosh{M}}\right\}$$

$$+ \frac{E}{B_0}\left\{1 - \frac{\cosh{(M/L)z}}{\cosh{M}}\right\} \tag{5.32}$$

In the limit of small Hartmann number—that is, $B_0 \approx 0$ or $\eta \to \infty$—eq. (5.32) becomes

$$u(z) \cong \frac{v_0}{2} + \frac{v_0}{2L}z \tag{5.33}$$

while at the opposite extreme of small η or large B_0, we find for $z > 0$

$$u(z) \cong \frac{E}{B_0} + \left(v_0 - \frac{E}{B_0}\right)\exp\left\{\frac{M}{L}(z - L)\right\} \tag{5.34}$$

and for $z < 0$

$$u(z) \cong \frac{E}{B_0}\left[1 - \exp\left\{-\frac{M}{L}(z + L)\right\}\right] \tag{5.35}$$

We note that for the case $M \gg 1$, at $z = -L$, the velocity vanishes but that very rapidly in a distance of order L/M it assumes the expected value of its drift velocity E/B_0 which it maintains until its approach within a distance L/M of $z = +L$, beyond which it drops very rapidly to v_0.

Making use of the explicit formula for $u(z)$ in eq. (5.32), the current density, which as we have already seen points in the y direction, may be obtained by substitution into eq. (5.28). In terms of this current, the induced magnetic field in the x direction is obtained from Maxwell's eq. (5.7) to be

$$\frac{\partial}{\partial z}B(z) = \mu_0 j(z) = \mu_0\sigma\{E - B_0 u(z)\} \tag{5.36}$$

In order to integrate this equation, it is clear that some boundary conditions on B need to be specified and in general these will depend on the details of how this steady state was reached as well as on the actual physical situation to which the present infinitely large configuration is an approximation. To be specific, let us assume somewhat arbitrarily that B vanishes at both surfaces. It follows from eq. (5.36) that the total current flow also vanishes under this assumption. Making use of eq. (5.32), it follows that this latter condition will be satisfied, provided the parameters v_0, B_0, and E are related by

$$v_0 = \frac{2E}{B_0}$$

and in this case $u(z)$ takes on the form

$$u(z) = \frac{E}{B_0}\left\{1 + \frac{\sinh (M/L)z}{\sinh M}\right\} \tag{5.37}$$

Substituting this result into eq. (5.36), we find after a simple integration

$$B(z) = B_0 R_m \frac{\cosh M - \cosh (M/L)z}{M \sinh M} \tag{5.38}$$

where R_m is the magnetic Reynolds number defined in eq. (5.20) and in terms of the present parameters is given by

$$R_m = \mu_0 \sigma L v_0$$

It follows by inspection of eq. (5.38) that the induced field is maximum at the center of the channel and that this maximum is largest for the small values of the Hartmann number. Plots of $u(z)$ and $B(z)$ for the two extremes

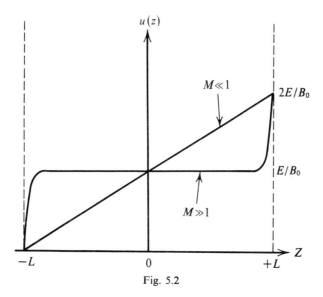

Fig. 5.2

of very large and very small values of M will be found in Figures 5.2 and 5.3. The substitution of reasonable numerical values for L, σ, and η into the solutions given by eqs. (5.37) and (5.38) show that our previous qualitative conclusions on the transport of the lines of force and of their being frozen into the fluid are substantiated. Finally, by substituting the above expressions for $B(z)$ and $u(z)$ into the third of eqs. (5.30), a formula for the pressure may be obtained.

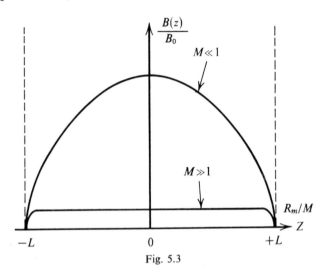

Fig. 5.3

Various other steady-state solutions of the one-fluid equations will be found in the references. Of particular interest, perhaps, is the steady-state analysis of the pinch that can be found, for example, in the book by Spitzer.

MAGNETOHYDRODYNAMIC WAVES

As a second application of the equations of the one-fluid model of magnetohydrodynamics we shall now study the problem of the propagation of a small disturbance that has been created in a plasma initially in a steady state.

For reasons of simplicity let us consider the case of a nonviscous plasma of infinite physical dimensions—that is, our interests are in phenomena that take place in regions far away from the bounding surfaces—and of infinite conductivity. Following the methods found to be so useful in ordinary hydrodynamics, we shall assume that the plasma is originally in an unperturbed state characterized by the variables of: density ρ_0, pressure p_0, velocity field $\mathbf{u}_0 = 0$, and an external uniform magnetic field $\mathbf{B}_0$, all of which have their equilibrium values and are thus time independent and spatially uniform. Let us suppose now that a small inhomogeneity is created in, say, the density; the problem will be how this small disturbance is propagated and what happens to the other dynamical variables.

Making use of the facts that $\sigma = \infty$, $\eta = 0$, and that there is no external electric field present, we may make direct use of eq. (5.18) for the magnetic field and thus the equations that describe the plasma are

$$\frac{\partial}{\partial t} \rho + \nabla \cdot (\mathbf{u}\rho) = 0$$

$$\rho \left\{ \frac{\partial}{\partial t} \mathbf{u} + (\mathbf{u} \cdot \nabla)\mathbf{u} \right\} = -\nabla p - \frac{1}{\mu_0} \mathbf{B} \times (\nabla \times \mathbf{B})$$

$$\frac{\partial}{\partial t} \mathbf{B} = \nabla \times (\mathbf{u} \times \mathbf{B}) \tag{5.39}$$

plus, of course, some equation of state. We now assume that the departure of all variables from their equilibrium or initial values are small and thus write

$$\mathbf{B(r},t) = \mathbf{B_0} + \mathbf{B'(r},t)$$
$$\rho(\mathbf{r},t) = \rho_0 + \rho'(\mathbf{r},t)$$
$$\mathbf{u(r},t) = \mathbf{u'(r},t)$$
$$p(\mathbf{r},t) = p_0 + p'(\mathbf{r},t) \tag{5.40}$$

where the primed quantities represent the small perturbations. Substituting the forms assumed in eq. (5.40) into eq. (5.39), we find correct to first order in the primed quantities (as in the analogous discussion of plasma oscillations in the previous chapter, this process is called *linearizing* the equations)

$$\frac{\partial}{\partial t} \rho + \rho_0 \nabla \cdot \mathbf{u} = 0$$

$$\rho_0 \frac{\partial}{\partial t} \mathbf{u} = -s^2 \nabla \rho - \frac{1}{\mu_0} \mathbf{B_0} \times (\nabla \times \mathbf{B})$$

$$\frac{\partial}{\partial t} \mathbf{B} = \nabla \times (\mathbf{u} \times \mathbf{B_0}) \tag{5.41}$$

where in the interests of simplicity the primes on all of the variables have been dropped. The quantity s^2 is called the *square of the speed of sound* and is explicitly given by the relation

$$s^2 = \frac{\partial p_0}{\partial \rho_0} \tag{5.42}$$

and arises from the term ∇p in the second of eqs. (5.39) by virtue of the equation of state that implies that p is function only of ρ. Thus we have to first order in the small quantities

$$\nabla p = \nabla p(\rho_0 + \rho') = \nabla p(\rho_0) + \nabla \left[\rho' \frac{\partial}{\partial \rho_0} p_0 \right] = s^2 \nabla \rho' \tag{5.43}$$

The simplest way of studying the implications of the linearized eqs. (5.41) is to Fourier analyze the variables ρ, $\mathbf{u}$, and $\mathbf{B}$ in both space and time. If we recall from the discussion in Chapter 1 that this analysis may be carried out by simply making the replacements

$$\frac{\partial}{\partial t} \to -i\omega \qquad \nabla \to i\mathbf{k}$$

we obtain the results

$$\omega\rho = \rho_0 \mathbf{k} \cdot \mathbf{u}$$

$$\omega\rho_0 \mathbf{u} = s^2 \mathbf{k}\rho + \frac{1}{\mu_0}\mathbf{B}_0 \times (\mathbf{k} \times \mathbf{B})$$

$$-\omega\mathbf{B} = \mathbf{k} \times (\mathbf{u} \times \mathbf{B}_0) \qquad\qquad (5.44)$$

The quantities ρ, $\mathbf{u}$, and $\mathbf{B}$ are now, of course, functions of $\mathbf{k}$ and ω instead of $\mathbf{r}$ and t as above, but for convenience we have used the same symbols in the both cases since there is little danger of confusion. It is apparent that eqs. (5.44) are a set of seven homogeneous equations in the seven unknowns ρ, $\mathbf{u}$, and $\mathbf{B}$, and hence will have a solution only if the determinant of the coefficients vanishes. We may interpret this fact by saying that for a fixed value of $\mathbf{k}$, there will be at most seven distinct frequencies ω for which there are nontrivial solutions. The resulting possibilities are associated with magnetohydrodynamic waves.

Rather than set up this determinant, however, a simpler way for obtaining these frequencies consists of solving the first of eqs. (5.44) for ρ and the last equation for $\mathbf{B}$ and substituting these into the second of eqs. (5.44). The result may be expressed in the form

$$\omega^2 \mathbf{u} = s^2 \mathbf{k}\mathbf{k}\cdot\mathbf{u} - \mathbf{v}_0 \times \{\mathbf{k} \times [\mathbf{k} \times (\mathbf{u} \times \mathbf{v}_0)]\} \qquad (5.45)$$

where $\mathbf{v}_0$ is a very important quantity that is called the *Alfven velocity* and is explicitly given by the formula

$$\mathbf{v}_0 = \frac{\mathbf{B}_0}{(\mu_0\rho_0)^{\frac{1}{2}}} \qquad\qquad (5.46)$$

The obtaining of the characteristic frequencies is still somewhat complex in general and therefore we shall examine only some special cases.

The *longitudinal magnetosonic wave* is defined as the wave for which the velocity $\mathbf{u}$ is parallel to the propagation vector $\mathbf{k}$ and its properties may be obtained by dotting eq. (5.45) with $\mathbf{k}$. The result is expressed by the formula

$$\mathbf{k}\cdot\mathbf{u}\{\omega^2 - s^2 k^2 - v_0^2 k^2\} = -k^2 \mathbf{k}\cdot\mathbf{v}_0\,\mathbf{u}\cdot\mathbf{v}_0 \qquad (5.47)$$

The factor $\mathbf{u} \cdot \mathbf{v}_0$ may be calculated by dotting the second of eqs. (5.44) with the vector $\mathbf{v}_0$; making use of the first of eqs. (5.44) there results

$$\mathbf{u} \cdot \mathbf{v}_0 = \frac{s^2}{\omega^2} \mathbf{k} \cdot \mathbf{v}_0 \, \mathbf{k} \cdot \mathbf{u} \tag{5.48}$$

which on being combined with eq. (5.47) yields directly the formula

$$\mathbf{k} \cdot \mathbf{u} \left\{ \omega^2 - k^2(s^2 + v_0^2) + \frac{k^2 s^2}{\omega^2} (\mathbf{k} \cdot \mathbf{v}_0)^2 \right\} = 0 \tag{5.49}$$

Finally, therefore, in order to have a nontrivial solution the only allowed values of ω are those that satisfy the equation

$$\omega^4 - \omega^2 k^2(s^2 + v_0^2) + k^2 s^2 (\mathbf{k} \cdot \mathbf{v}_0)^2 = 0 \tag{5.50}$$

This has the real roots

$$\frac{\omega^2}{k^2} = \frac{1}{2}(s^2 + v_0^2) \pm \left[\frac{1}{4}(s^2 + v_0^2)^2 - s^2 v_0^2 \cos^2\alpha \right]^{\frac{1}{2}} \tag{5.51}$$

where α is the angle between $\mathbf{k}$ and $\mathbf{B}_0$. In particular, for disturbances for which $\mathbf{k}$ is parallel to $\mathbf{B}_0$, the two roots are $\omega^2 = k^2 s^2$ and $\omega^2 = k^2 v_0^2$; the first of these has an associated phase velocity $\partial\omega/\partial k$ equal to the speed of sound, while the second has an associated phase velocity equal to the Alfven velocity. The wave that has the phase velocity s is evidently an ordinary sound wave and has associated with it a vanishing magnetic field. On the other hand, the disturbance that propagates with the phase velocity v_0 is to be associated with a purely magnetohydrodynamic phenomenon since it is essentially independent of the detailed properties of the plasma and depends only on the external field and the density. For the case that the vector $\mathbf{k}$ is at right angles to $\mathbf{B}_0$—that is, for $\alpha = \pi/2$—we conclude that one of the roots is zero while the physically interesting one is given by

$$\omega^2 = k^2(s^2 + v_0^2) \tag{5.52}$$

and has an associated phase velocity

$$\frac{\partial\omega}{\partial k} = (s^2 + v_0^2)^{\frac{1}{2}} \tag{5.53}$$

and is thus proportional to the square root of the sum of the ordinary pressure and magnetic pressure. As a rule, for laboratory magnetic fields and densities the Alfven velocity is always very small compared to the speed of sound. For the case of astrophysical plasmas for which the densities are so much lower, however, these two velocities can easily become comparable and thus the velocity of the longitudinal magnetosonic wave can be appreciably different from that of an ordinary sound wave. Finally, we note from the third of eqs. (5.44) that the magnetic field associated with this wave is given by

$$\mathbf{B} = |\mathbf{u}|\mathbf{B}_0(s^2 + v_0^2)^{-\frac{1}{2}}$$

and thus is at right angles to $\mathbf{k}$.

In addition to the longitudinal modes just examined there is also a transverse mode—that is, one for which $\mathbf{k \cdot u} = 0$, and it is left as a simple exercise to show that this wave propagates with the Alfven speed and has an associated magnetic field that is antiparallel to $\mathbf{u}$.

The modifications required in the above discussion for the case where the conductivity is finite or where viscous effects are important are straightforward. The analysis may be carried out as given above and the analogue of eq. (5.45) will involve complex numbers, which in turn will depend upon η and σ. As anticipated the frequencies of the associated waves are complex and it is not hard to become convinced that the waves will be damped. In the above analysis for which we assumed $\sigma = \infty$, $\eta = 0$, there is no physical mechanism available for damping and thus the associated frequencies were purely real.

Finally, let us examine briefly the problem of transforming the above solutions back into the time domain. At first glance there would seem to be a difficulty, since according to eq. (1.30) this transformation involves an integral over ω and as things stand there do not appear to be any delta functions of frequency that would enable us to obtain the expected results. Actually, of course, while taking the Fourier transforms over time in order to obtain eq. (5.44) no mention was made of the fact that the perturbations all vanish for negative times and consequently the Fourier transforms of all time derivatives yield surface terms in addition to those given in eq. (5.44). This situation has previously been encountered in our study of plasma oscillations. More explicitly, the origin of these surface terms can be seen by reference to the relations

$$\int_0^\infty dt\, e^{i\omega t} \frac{\partial}{\partial t}\rho = e^{i\omega t}\rho(t)\Big|_0^\infty - i\omega \int_0^\infty e^{i\omega t}\rho(t)\, dt$$

$$= -\rho(0) - i\omega\rho_\omega$$

where $\rho(0)$ is the initial perturbation in the density and represents an ω-independent constant not explicitly included in the first eqs. (5.44). Thus the corrected version of eqs. (5.44) is not at all a set of homogeneous equations in the seven unknowns, but rather a set of ordinary linear equations. Furthermore, if we solve these equations by the use of determinants, then in the denominator of each of the unknowns there would appear the previously alluded-to determinant of the coefficients. Now let us Fourier transform these corrected results back into the time domain by carrying out the integration along the real ω axis and closing the contour in the lower half plane. The integral may be evaluated by use of Cauchy's theorem to be $2\pi i$ times the sum of the residues inside the contour. The poles in the integrand are evidently at the zeroes of the denominator and at each of these poles we get a contribution that has the form $\exp\{-i\omega_i t\}$ where ω_i is one of the roots of the determinant of the coefficients. Thus, all conclusions based on the homogeneous eqs. (5.44) are reproduced in this more careful analysis. Furthermore, the original method is preferable since it enables us to focus on the actual physical properties of the plasma—that is, its "normal modes"—and these do not depend on the particular means used to excite these modes.

THE TWO-FLUID MODEL

It has been previously noted that when the plasma density has decreased sufficiently so that, for example, the charge density no longer vanishes, then the one-fluid model of magnetohydrodynamics is no longer applicable, and it becomes necessary to go to the next approximation in which we think of the plasma as consisting of a mixture of two, or possibly three, distinct fluids. In particular for the two-fluid model, each of the fluids is again assumed to be completely described in terms of the three macroscopic variables of pressure, density, and velocity field. The associated charge and current densities, which in turn determine the induced electromagnetic fields, will now depend upon the variables of both fluids and the resulting equations may therefore be expected to be correspondingly more complex.

Specifically, let us assume that the two fluids consist of electrons of charge $-q$ and mass m and of a single type of ion of charge $+q$ and of mass M. Let n_e, n_I, $\mathbf{u}_e$, $\mathbf{u}_I$, p_e, p_I be the particle densities, the velocity fields, and the assumed scalar pressures of the electrons and ions, respectively. According to eq. (4.62), the equations expressing the conservation of the number of particles are given by

$$\frac{\partial}{\partial t} n_e + \nabla \cdot (n_e \mathbf{u}_e) = 0$$

$$\frac{\partial}{\partial t} n_I + \nabla \cdot (n_I \mathbf{u}_I) = 0 \tag{5.54}$$

which upon multiplication by m and M, respectively, and addition yield the equation of mass conservation. Similarly, by multiplication by $-q$ and q and addition we obtain the equation of charge conservation. Assuming that the pressure tensors are both scalar and that the viscous terms are negligible, the analogues of eq. (4.65) for the present case become

$$mn_e\left\{\frac{\partial}{\partial t}\mathbf{u}_e + (\mathbf{u}_e\cdot\nabla)\mathbf{u}_e\right\} = -qn_e\mathbf{E} - qn_e\mathbf{u}_e\times\mathbf{B} - \nabla p_e \qquad (5.55)$$

and

$$Mn_I\left\{\frac{\partial}{\partial t}\mathbf{u}_I + (\mathbf{u}_I\cdot\nabla)\mathbf{u}_I\right\} = qn_I\mathbf{E} + qn_I\mathbf{u}_I\times\mathbf{B} - \nabla p_I \qquad (5.56)$$

The electromagnetic fields $\mathbf{E}$ and $\mathbf{B}$ in these equations are determined by Maxwell's equations (1.5) through (1.8) with charge density ρ_q and current density $\mathbf{j}$ expressed in terms of the variables of the two species by the relations

$$\rho_q = q(n_I - n_e) \qquad (5.57)$$

and

$$\mathbf{j} = q(n_I\mathbf{u}_I - n_e\mathbf{u}_e) \qquad (5.58)$$

and these, therefore, represent the only couplings between the two fluids. It is, of course, necessary to assume an equation of state for each species in addition to the above. That is, p_e and p_I are again presumed to be given functions of mn_e and Mn_I, respectively. Brief reflection shows that eqs. (5.54) through (5.58) plus the two equations of state and Maxwell's equations are sufficient to determine the behavior in time of all macroscopic quantities in terms of their initial values. Unlike the case of the one-fluid model, it is no longer necessary to assume the validity of Ohm's law. The reason for this is that since the motion of the electrons is now explicitly included, we are no longer confined to low-frequency phenomena and thus the time derivative of the electric field must be retained in Maxwell's equations. The charge density $\mathbf{j}$ is, of course, fixed by eq. (5.58).

The derivation of the corresponding forms of the one-fluid equations by use of eqs. (5.54) through (5.56) is relatively straightforward. The velocity field $\mathbf{u}$, the pressure p, and the mass density ρ are given in terms of the two-fluid variables by the relations

$$\rho = mn_e + Mn_I$$

$$p = p_e + p_I$$

$$\mathbf{u} = \frac{1}{\rho}[Mn_I\mathbf{u}_I + mn_e\mathbf{u}_e] \qquad (5.59)$$

As has already been noted, eq. (5.8) is obtained by taking the appropriate linear combinations of eqs. (5.54). The derivation of eq. (5.9), however, requires a little more detailed discussion. First, we note that in the one-fluid model, the charge density vanishes and thus according to eq. (5.57) this means that $n_e = n_I$. Second, since in the one-fluid model the entire plasma behaves as a single fluid, it follows that $\mathbf{u}_e$ and $\mathbf{u}_I$ are both of the same order of magnitude. And, finally, therefore, since $m \ll M$, we may neglect the ratio m/M compared to unity and thus the first and third of eqs. (5.59) may be written in the one-fluid approximation as

$$\rho = (M + m)n_I \cong Mn_I$$

$$\mathbf{u} = \frac{1}{Mn_I}[n_I M\mathbf{u}_I + n_e m\mathbf{u}_e] \cong \mathbf{u}_I \tag{5.60}$$

while the current density becomes

$$\mathbf{j} = qn_I(\mathbf{u}_I - \mathbf{u}_e) \tag{5.61}$$

Therefore, making use of eqs. (5.60) and (5.61) and consistently neglecting terms of order m/M, we find on adding eqs. (5.55) and (5.56) the result

$$\rho\left\{\frac{\partial}{\partial t}\mathbf{u} + (\mathbf{u} \cdot \nabla)\mathbf{u}\right\} = \mathbf{j} \times \mathbf{B} - \nabla p \tag{5.62}$$

where use has also been made of the second of eqs. (5.59). Eq. (5.62) is, of course, essentially the same as eq. (5.9) and thus we see that with the above approximations the one-fluid equations follow from eqs. (5.54) through (5.58). Needless to say, this argument is not appreciably altered by the inclusion of the viscous term.

To summarize this discussion then, we see that the two-fluid model of magnetohydrodynamics is described by eqs. (5.54) through (5.56), plus an equation of state for each species and Maxwell's equations with charge and current density given by eqs. (5.57) and (5.58). In this model it is also possible to describe high-frequency phenomena such as plasma oscillations. Finally, we note that the generalization of the above arguments to the case of fluids consisting of more than two species may be expected to be straightforward and will be examined from a slightly different point of view below.

PLASMA OSCILLATIONS

In our study of MHD waves by use of the one-fluid model, we have seen that these waves involve only low frequencies since the underlying motion is that of the heavy ions; the electrons serving only to re-establish electrical neutrality whenever it is violated. Now, by use of the two-fluid model, it also becomes possible to study the time scale of the electronic vibrations. On the basis of our previous analysis of plasma oscillations by use of the BV equation we may anticipate that the electronic frequencies are generally very large compared to those associated with MHD waves and, consequently, for purposes of the present considerations we can completely ignore the motions of the ions. The only role played by these ions is to create a static uniform background of positive charge that preserves the over-all electrical neutrality.

Let us assume therefore that we have an infinitely large electron plasma that is originally in equilibrium and is characterized in this state by the macroscopic variables n_0, p_0, and $\mathbf{u}_0 = 0$. For the time scales involved the corresponding variables for the ions do not change. We shall suppose now that a small disturbance is introduced into this plasma and let n, p, and $\mathbf{u}$ be the perturbations associated with n_0, p_0, and $\mathbf{u}_0$ $(= 0)$, respectively, so that the charge and current densities instead of vanishing are now given by

$$\rho = -qn$$

$$\mathbf{j} = -qn_0\mathbf{u} \tag{5.63}$$

where q is positive. As in the analogous discussion of MHD waves, correct to first order in the small quantities, eqs. (5.54) and (5.55) become

$$\frac{\partial}{\partial t}n + n_0\nabla\cdot\mathbf{u} = 0 \tag{5.64}$$

and

$$\frac{\partial}{\partial t}\mathbf{u} + \frac{1}{n_0}s^2\nabla n = -\frac{q}{m}\mathbf{E} - \frac{q}{m}\mathbf{u}\times\mathbf{B}_0 \tag{5.65}$$

where s^2 is given by

$$s^2 = \frac{\partial p_0}{\partial \rho_0}$$

We have also assumed the existence of, an external, uniform magnetic field $\mathbf{B}_0$. The electromagnetic fields are determined by the familiar equations

$$\nabla\cdot\mathbf{B} = 0$$

$$\nabla\times\mathbf{E} = -\frac{\partial}{\partial t}\mathbf{B}$$

$$\nabla\cdot\mathbf{E} = -\frac{1}{\varepsilon_0}qn$$

$$\nabla\times\mathbf{B} = -\mu_0qn_0\mathbf{u} + \frac{1}{c^2}\frac{\partial}{\partial t}\mathbf{E} \tag{5.66}$$

and since $\mathbf{E}$ and $\mathbf{B}$ are thus both of first order in the perturbation, the term $\mathbf{u}\times\mathbf{B}$ was not included in eq. (5.65) since such a term is of second order in the small quantities.

Following the familiar pattern, we now Fourier analyze eqs. (5.64)—(5.66) in both space and time. Again let us neglect the surface terms since as we have seen they are not essential for purposes of obtaining the dispersion relation. The result of this Fourier-analysis is given by

$$n = \frac{n_0}{\omega} \mathbf{k} \cdot \mathbf{u}$$

$$\mathbf{u} = \mathbf{k} \frac{n}{n_0} \frac{s^2}{\omega} - \frac{iq}{m\omega}(\mathbf{E} + \mathbf{u} \times \mathbf{B_0})$$

$$\mathbf{k} \cdot \mathbf{B} = 0$$

$$\mathbf{k} \cdot \mathbf{E} = \frac{i}{\varepsilon_0} qn$$

$$\mathbf{k} \times \mathbf{E} = \omega \mathbf{B}$$

$$\mathbf{k} \times \mathbf{B} = i\mu_0 q n_0 \mathbf{u} - \frac{\omega}{c^2} \mathbf{E} \tag{5.67}$$

which may again be interpreted as a set of ten homogeneous equations in the ten unknowns n, $\mathbf{u}$, $\mathbf{E}$, and $\mathbf{B}$. The fact that eqs. (5.67) are actually twelve equations is easily understandable since some of these equations are redundant. For example, the third of eqs. (5.67) may be derived from the fifth by dotting the latter through with $\mathbf{k}$. In order to study the implications of these relations, let us examine some special cases.

Suppose first that the external magnetic field $\mathbf{B_0}$ vanishes. For this case, eqs. (5.67) may be put into a more manageable form by first solving Maxwell's equations for $\mathbf{u}$ in terms of $\mathbf{E}$ and thus we obtain

$$\mathbf{u} = -\frac{iq}{m\omega} \frac{1}{\omega_p^2} [\mathbf{E}(\omega^2 - k^2 c^2) + c^2 \mathbf{kk} \cdot \mathbf{E}] \tag{5.68}$$

where ω_p is the plasma frequency as previously defined in eq. (4.34). Substituting eq. (5.68) into the second of eqs. (5.67) and on making use of the first and fourth of these equations, we may obtain an equation involving only the electric field and this is given by

$$\mathbf{E}(\omega^2 - \omega_p^2 - k^2 c^2) + \mathbf{kk} \cdot \mathbf{E}(c^2 - s^2) = 0 \tag{5.69}$$

In turn, this equation may be written as two equations; one for the longitudinal and the other for the transverse components. These are

$$\mathbf{E}_t(\omega^2 - \omega_p^2 - k^2 c^2) = 0 \tag{5.70}$$

and

$$\mathbf{E}_l(\omega^2 - \omega_p^2 - k^2 s^2) = 0 \tag{5.71}$$

Thus we conclude that there is one longitudinal wave with an associated frequency $(\omega_p^2 + k^2 s^2)^{1/2}$ and this is to be compared with the corresponding but very approximate result obtained by use of the BV equation and explicitly given in eq. (4.129). It follows from the fifth of eqs. (5.67) that there is no magnetic field associated with this wave and the remaining variables may also be obtained by use of these equations. With regard to the transverse modes, eq. (5.70) implies that there are two such waves, and each of these has a frequency

$$\omega = [\omega_p^2 + k^2 c^2]^{\frac{1}{2}} \tag{5.72}$$

and this is the same as the result obtained by use of the BV equation in Problem 7 of the previous chapter. It is to be noted that eq. (5.72) is an exact result of the present theory, while it is only a long wavelength approximation as far as the BV equation is concerned.

As a second application of eqs. (5.67) let us examine these equations for the case where the external magnetic is finite—that is, $\mathbf{B}_o \neq 0$—but where the term obtained by use of an electronic equation of state (that is, $kns^2/n_0\omega$) is negligible. The resulting set of equations may be simplified in the following way. We solve Maxwell's equations and the first of eqs. (5.67) in order to obtain $\mathbf{E}$ in terms of $\mathbf{u}$ and n with the result

$$\mathbf{E} = -\frac{iqc^2/\varepsilon_0}{\omega^2 - k^2 c^2}\left[kn - \frac{\omega n_0}{c^2}\mathbf{u}\right] \tag{5.73}$$

On substituting this formula into the second of eqs. (5.67) we obtain after some simplifications

$$\mathbf{u} = -\frac{c^2\omega_p^2}{\omega(\omega^2 - \omega_p^2 - k^2 c^2)}\frac{n}{n_0}\mathbf{k} - i\frac{\omega_L}{\omega}\frac{\omega^2 - k^2 c^2}{\omega^2 - \omega_p^2 - k^2 c^2}\mathbf{u} \times \mathbf{b} \tag{5.74}$$

where ω_L is the Larmor frequency qB_0/m, and $\mathbf{b}$ is a unit vector in the direction $\mathbf{B}_0$. The explicit solution of eq. (5.74) in order to obtain $\mathbf{u}$ as a function of n is somewhat involved but can be obtained by making use of the fact that the expression for $\mathbf{u}$ can only be a linear combination of the three vectors $\mathbf{k}$, $\mathbf{b}$, and $\mathbf{k} \times \mathbf{b}$. Making use of this observation, the result is found to be

$$\mathbf{u} = \frac{-\omega_p^2 c^2 (n/n_0)}{\omega(\omega^2 - \omega_p^2 - k^2 c^2)}\frac{1}{(1 - a^2)}[\mathbf{k} - ba^2\mathbf{k}\cdot\mathbf{b} - iak \times \mathbf{b}] \tag{5.75}$$

where the quantity a is given by

$$a = \frac{\omega_L}{\omega}\frac{\omega^2 - k^2 c^2}{\omega^2 - \omega_p^2 - k^2 c^2}$$

Finally, substituting eq. (5.75) into the first of eqs. (5.67), we obtain the dispersion formula

$$\omega^2(\omega^2 - \omega_p^2)(\omega^2 - \omega_p^2 - k^2 c^2)^2$$
$$= \omega_L^2(\omega^2 - k^2 c^2)[\omega^2(\omega^2 - \omega_p^2 - k^2 c^2) + \omega_p^2 c^2 (\mathbf{k} \cdot \mathbf{b})^2] \quad (5.76)$$

which for the special case $\omega_L = 0$ reduces to eqs. (5.70) and (5.71) for $s^2 = 0$. We see therefore that eq. (5.76) implies the existence of four values of ω^2 for which there will be waves, and the physical significance of these waves can be obtained by use of eqs. (5.73) through (5.75). In particular for the case that $\mathbf{k}$ is perpendicular to $\mathbf{B}_0$, we find easily that there are three nonzero roots of eq. (5.76) and one of these is given by eq. (5.70) while the other two are the solutions of the quadratic equation,

$$(\omega^2 - \omega_p^2)(\omega^2 - \omega_p^2 - k^2 c^2) = \omega_L^2(\omega^2 - k^2 c^2)$$

Similarly, for the case $\mathbf{k}$ parallel to $\mathbf{B}_0$, it is easy to see that one of the roots is given directly by the plasma frequency while the remaining ones are obtained by the solution of a cubic equation. However, rather than pursue this application of the two fluid equations further here, let us refer the interested reader to the problems and references at the end of this chapter and in particular to the article by Wyld which contains a complete discussion of the case $\mathbf{k} \cdot \mathbf{B}_0 = 0$.

PLASMA OSCILLATIONS
WITHOUT AN EQUATION OF STATE

As a final application of the two-fluid equations, let us again examine this same problem of the electron oscillations in a plasma but this time in place of an equation of state, let us assume that the heat flow tensor Q_{ijk} is negligible and that the pressure tensor therefore satisfies the equation

$$\frac{\partial}{\partial t} p_{ij} + \nabla \cdot (\mathbf{u} p_{ij}) + \sum_{k=1}^{3} \left\{ p_{ik} \frac{\partial}{\partial x_k} u_j + p_{jk} \frac{\partial}{\partial x_k} u_i \right\}$$
$$= \sum_{e,m=1}^{3} B_m \{ \varepsilon_{emj} p_{ie} + \varepsilon_{emi} p_{je} \} \quad (5.77)$$

The statement of the conservation of the number of electrons in the first of eqs. (5.54) is, of course, still valid; on the other hand in place of eq. (5.55), we now have

$$mn \left\{ \frac{\partial}{\partial t} u_i + (\mathbf{u} \cdot \nabla) u_i \right\} = -qn E_i - qn (\mathbf{u} \times \mathbf{B})_i - \sum_{j=1}^{3} \frac{\partial}{\partial x_j} p_{ij} \quad (5.78)$$

As before, we shall neglect completely the motions of the ions and therefore eqs. (5.77) and (5.78), the first of eqs. (5.54), plus Maxwell's equations constitute a complete description. It is to be noted that even though this set of equations is not precisely identical to what we have been calling the two-fluid model, nevertheless this analysis is made in the spirit of this model and is but slightly more general in that it is based on eq. (5.77) rather than on equation of state.

As in the previous example, let us assume that the plasma is infinitely large and is characterized in its original, equilibrium state by a uniform density n_0, by a vanishing fluid velocity, and by a spatially uniform and scalar pressure tensor $p_0 \delta_{ij}$. Let n, $\mathbf{u}$, and p_{ij} be the perturbations associated with these variables so that the charge and current densities are still given by eqs. (5.63) while the linearized equations for n, $\mathbf{u}$, and p_{ij} are given by

$$\frac{\partial}{\partial t} n + n_0 \nabla \cdot \mathbf{u} = 0 \tag{5.79}$$

$$\frac{\partial}{\partial t} u_i = -\frac{q}{m} E_i - \frac{1}{mn_0} \sum_{j=1}^{3} \frac{\partial}{\partial x_j} p_{ij} \tag{5.80}$$

$$\frac{\partial}{\partial t} p_{ij} + p_0 \delta_{ij} \nabla \cdot \mathbf{u} + p_0 \left\{ \frac{\partial u_i}{\partial x_j} + \frac{\partial u_j}{\partial x_i} \right\} = 0 \tag{5.81}$$

The first of these equations is, of course, identical to eq. (5.64) and thus requires no discussion; while in obtaining the second of these from eq. (5.78) we make use of the fact that the magnetic field term vanishes since both $\mathbf{u}$ and $\mathbf{B}$ are of first order in the perturbation. We have assumed here that there are no external fields present. Finally, in deriving eq. (5.81) from eq. (5.77) we have made use of the fact that the right-hand side of this latter equation vanishes for the part of the pressure tensor proportional to δ_{ij}; thus the right-hand side is of second order. The applicable form of Maxwell's equations are, of course, still given by eqs. (5.66).

We now Fourier analyze eqs. (5.79)–(5.81) and obtain thus

$$n = \frac{n_0}{\omega} \mathbf{k} \cdot \mathbf{u}$$

$$\omega u_i = \frac{1}{mn_0} \sum_{j=1}^{3} k_j p_{ij} - \frac{iq}{m} E_i^1$$

$$\omega p_{ij} - p_0 \delta_{ij} \mathbf{k} \cdot \mathbf{u} - p_0 [k_i u_j + k_j u_i] = 0 \tag{5.82}$$

and these equations when combined with the last four of eqs. (5.67), constitute the set that is now to be analyzed. On solving the last of eqs.

(5.82) for p_{ij} and substituting this into the second of these equations, the result may be expressed in the form

$$\mathbf{u} = \frac{\omega}{\omega^2 - p_0 k^2/mn_0}\left[-\frac{iq}{m}\mathbf{E} + 2\frac{p_0\mathbf{k}\cdot\mathbf{u}}{mn_0\omega}\mathbf{k}\right]$$

This formula may be directly combined with eq. (5.68) to yield two dispersion relations. For the longitudinal modes we obtain in this way

$$\omega^2 = \omega_p^2 + 3\frac{p_0}{mn_0}k^2 \tag{5.83}$$

while the transverse modes satisfy the dispersion relation

$$\omega^2 - k^2 c^2 - \frac{\omega^2\omega_p^2}{\omega^2 - (p_0 k^2/mn_0)} = 0 \tag{5.84}$$

The result for the longitudinal mode in eq. (5.83) is essentially the same as that obtained previously in eq. (5.71) since we expect that the quantity p_0/mn_0 is of the order of the square of the thermal velocity and in turn this is proportional to s^2. On the other hand, for the transverse modes, eq. (5.84) now predicts two distinct frequencies whereas our previous calculation in eq. (5.70) only yielded a single one. However, on making use of the fact that we expect the inequality $(p_0/mn_0)k^2 \ll \omega_p^2$ to be valid, one of the roots of eq. (5.84) is approximately given by

$$\omega^2 \cong \omega_p^2 + k^2 c^2 \tag{5.85}$$

and this is, of course, identical to eq. (5.70). In addition to this root, however, there is a second one which is approximately given by

$$\omega^2 \cong \frac{p_0}{mn_0}c^2 k^4 \tag{5.86}$$

However, since the present discussion is only valid for long wavelengths (compare eqs. (4.29) and (5.71)) or equivalently only small values for k, the root in eq. (5.86) is very small compared to ω_p and should actually be compared to the lower frequencies associated with the ions. Since these ionic waves have already been neglected, it follows that for reasons of consistency the root in eq. (5.86) must also be discarded.

Thus, we see that in the derivation of plasma oscillations via the two-fluid model the substitution of eq. (5.77) for an equation of state yields essentially nothing new. And this suggests an alternate interpretation for the assumed existence of an equation of state and that is that the heat flow tensor Q_{ijk} is negligible.

THE ONE-FLUID EQUATIONS
FOR A MULTICOMPONENT PLASMA

In carrying out the above derivation of the one-fluid equations by use of the two-fluid model, it was found necessary to make various restrictive assumptions, for example, those in eq. (5.60). It would seem to be evident that additional assumptions would be required in order to obtain, in a similar way, the one-fluid equations for a multicomponent plasma. Actually, it is possible, in general, to derive the one-fluid equations without any of these assumptions and the purpose of the present section is to examine such a derivation in detail. As one would expect, the resultant equations are essentially given by eqs. (4.62), (4.65), (4.75).

Our starting point is again the BV equations for the various charged species comprising the plasma, and the equation for the αth of these is given by

$$\frac{\partial}{\partial t} f^{(\alpha)} + \mathbf{v} \cdot \frac{\partial}{\partial \mathbf{r}} f^{(\alpha)} + \frac{q_\alpha}{m_\alpha} (\mathbf{E} + \mathbf{v} \times \mathbf{B}) \cdot \frac{\partial}{\partial \mathbf{v}} f^{(\alpha)} = 0 \qquad (5.87)$$

where q_a and m_a are the respective charge and mass of a particle of the species under consideration. The particle density $n^{(\alpha)}(\mathbf{r}, t)$ and the mean velocity $\mathbf{u}^{(\alpha)}(\mathbf{r}, t)$ associated with this component of the plasma are defined by the relations

$$n^{(\alpha)}(\mathbf{r},t) = N^{(\alpha)} \int d\mathbf{v}\, f^{(\alpha)}(\mathbf{r},\mathbf{v},t) \qquad (5.88)$$

and

$$\mathbf{u}^{(\alpha)}(\mathbf{r},t) = \frac{N^{(\alpha)}}{n^{(\alpha)}} \int d\mathbf{v}\, \mathbf{v} f^{(\alpha)}(\mathbf{r},\mathbf{v},t) \qquad (5.89)$$

where $N^{(\alpha)}$ is the total number of particles of type α, and we have assumed that each of the $f^{(\alpha)}$'s is normalized to unity. The macroscopic quantities that serve to characterize the entire plasma are the mass density ρ, the mean velocity of the center of mass $\mathbf{u}$, the charge density ρ_q and the current density $\mathbf{j}$ and these are given by the relations

$$\rho = \sum_\alpha m_\alpha n^{(\alpha)} \qquad (5.90)$$

$$\mathbf{u} = \frac{1}{\rho} \sum_\alpha m_\alpha n^{(\alpha)} \mathbf{u}^{(\alpha)} \qquad (5.91)$$

$$\rho_q = \sum_\alpha q_\alpha n^{(\alpha)} \qquad (5.92)$$

$$\mathbf{j} = \sum_\alpha q_\alpha n^{(\alpha)} \mathbf{u}^{(\alpha)} \qquad (5.93)$$

where the summations are to be carried out over all species. Unlike the considerations of the single-species plasma in the last chapter, the pressure tensor and the heat-flow tensor are now defined in terms of the velocity relative to the center of mass $\mathbf{u}$ and not with respect to the mean velocity $\mathbf{u}^{(a)}$. More specifically we now define $p_{ij}^{(\alpha)}$ $Q_{ijk}^{(\alpha)}$ by the relations

$$p_{ij}^{(\alpha)} = N^{(\alpha)} m_\alpha \int d\mathbf{w} \; w_i w_j f^{(\alpha)}(\mathbf{r},\mathbf{w},t) \tag{5.94}$$

and

$$Q_{ijk}^{(\alpha)} = N^{(\alpha)} m_\alpha \int d\mathbf{w} \; w_i w_j w_k f^{(\alpha)}(\mathbf{r},\mathbf{w},t) \tag{5.95}$$

where $\mathbf{w}$ is defined in terms of the variable $\mathbf{v}$ in the BV equation by

$$\mathbf{w} = \mathbf{v} - \mathbf{u}(\mathbf{r},t) \tag{5.96}$$

This latter relation is formally identical to eq. (4.51) but in the present context, $\mathbf{u}$ is the velocity of the center of mass of the entire plasma. The total pressure tensor p_{ij} and the total heat-flow tensor Q_{ijk} are given by the additive relations

$$p_{ij} = \sum_\alpha p_{ij}^{(\alpha)} \tag{5.97}$$

and

$$Q_{ijk} = \sum_\alpha Q_{ijk}^{(\alpha)} \tag{5.98}$$

where the sums are again over-all species in the plasma.

In order to obtain the equations of motion of the macroscopic variables associated with the entire plasma, it is again convenient to change variables in the BV equation for each species from $\mathbf{r}$, $\mathbf{v}$, t to $\mathbf{r}$, $\mathbf{w}$, t with $\mathbf{w}$ as defined in eq. (5.96). With the understanding that $\mathbf{u}$ is now defined by eq. (5.91), the partial derivatives again transform as in eq. (4.54), and thus eq. (5.87) may be written

$$\frac{\partial}{\partial t} f^{(\alpha)}(\mathbf{r},\mathbf{w},t) + \frac{\partial}{\partial \mathbf{r}} \cdot \{(\mathbf{w}+\mathbf{u})f^{(\alpha)}\} + \frac{\partial}{\partial \mathbf{w}} \cdot \{\mathbf{a}^{(\alpha)} f^{(\alpha)}\} = 0 \tag{5.99}$$

where $\mathbf{a}^{(\alpha)}$ is given by

$$\mathbf{a}^{(\alpha)} = \frac{q_\alpha}{m_\alpha}(\mathbf{E}+\mathbf{u}\times\mathbf{B}) - \frac{d}{dt}\mathbf{u} - \left(\mathbf{w}\cdot\frac{\partial}{\partial\mathbf{r}}\right)\mathbf{u} + \frac{q_\alpha}{m_\alpha}\mathbf{w}\times\mathbf{B} \tag{5.100}$$

and the symbol d/dt is to be interpreted here and in the following formulas by the relation

$$\frac{d}{dt} = \frac{\partial}{\partial t} + \mathbf{u} \cdot \frac{\partial}{\partial \mathbf{r}} \tag{5.101}$$

On comparing eqs. (5.99) and (5.100) with eqs. (4.55) and (4.56) we observe that their structure is almost identical and thus can expect that a calculation of the various moments of eq. (5.99) will be very similar to that carried out in the last chapter. As a matter of fact, the only difference between the present derivation and the previous one is that now eq. (4.60) is no longer valid. Instead of that relation, we now have

$$\frac{N^{(\alpha)}}{n^{(\alpha)}} \int d\mathbf{w} \ \mathbf{w} f^{(\alpha)}(\mathbf{r},\mathbf{w},t) = \frac{N^{(\alpha)}}{n^{(\alpha)}} \int d\mathbf{v} \ (\mathbf{v} - \mathbf{u}) f^{(\alpha)}(\mathbf{r},\mathbf{v},t) \tag{5.102}$$

$$= \mathbf{u}^{(\alpha)} - \mathbf{u}$$

$$\equiv \mathbf{v}^{(\alpha)}$$

Thus the first moment of $f^{(\alpha)}$ no longer vanishes as for the case of a single-species plasma, but instead is the velocity of species α relative to that of the center-of-mass, and this quantity has been designated by the symbol $\mathbf{v}^{(\alpha)}$.

Bearing in mind the result in eq. (5.102), the taking of the moments of eq. (5.99) involves essentially the same techniques as were used in the analogous derivation in the previous chapter. On multiplying eq. (5.99) by $N^{(\alpha)}$ and integrating over-all values of $\mathbf{w}$, we thus obtain

$$\frac{\partial}{\partial t} n^{(\alpha)} + \nabla \cdot (\mathbf{u}^{(\alpha)} n^{(\alpha)}) = 0 \tag{5.103}$$

where use has been made of the definitions in eqs. (5.88) and (5.89). In a similar way, by multiplying eq. (5.99) by $m_\alpha w_i$ and integrating over-all values of $\mathbf{w}$ we obtain

$$m_\alpha n^{(\alpha)} \frac{d}{dt} u_i + \sum_{j=1}^{3} \frac{\partial}{\partial x_j} p_{ij}^{(\alpha)} - q_\alpha n^{(\alpha)} [\mathbf{E} + \mathbf{u} \times \mathbf{B}]_i$$

$$= -\sum_{j=1}^{3} \frac{\partial}{\partial x_j} [m_\alpha n^{(\alpha)} u_i v_j^{(\alpha)}] - \frac{\partial}{\partial t} (m_\alpha n^{(\alpha)} v_i^{(\alpha)}) - m_\alpha n^{(\alpha)} \left(\mathbf{v}^{(\alpha)} \cdot \frac{\partial}{\partial \mathbf{r}} \right) u_i \tag{5.104}$$

The left-hand side of this equation has all the terms present in eq. (4.65) but in addition to these, the right-hand side of eq. (5.104) now contains several terms that are linear functions of $\mathbf{v}^{(\alpha)}$. Finally, by multiplying eq. (5.99) by $m_\alpha w_i w_j$ and integrating over-all values of $\mathbf{w}$, there results

$$\frac{\partial}{\partial t} p_{ij}^{(\alpha)} + \nabla \cdot (\mathbf{u} p_{ij}^{(\alpha)}) + \sum_{k=1}^{3} \left[\frac{\partial}{\partial x_k} Q_{ijk}^{(\alpha)} + p_{ik}^{(\alpha)} \frac{\partial}{\partial x_k} u_j + p_{jk}^{(\alpha)} \frac{\partial}{\partial x_k} u_i \right]$$

$$- \frac{q_\alpha}{m_\alpha} \sum_{e,m=1}^{3} B_m \left[\varepsilon_{emj} p_{ie}^{(\alpha)} + \varepsilon_{emi} p_{je}^{(\alpha)} \right]$$

$$= q_\alpha n^{(\alpha)} \{ [\mathbf{E} + \mathbf{u} \times \mathbf{B}]_i v_j^{(\alpha)} + v_i^{(\alpha)} [\mathbf{E} + \mathbf{u} \times \mathbf{B}]_j \}$$

$$- m_\alpha n^{(\alpha)} \left\{ \left(\frac{d}{dt} u_i \right) v_j^{(\alpha)} + v_i^{(\alpha)} \frac{d}{dt} u_j \right\} \tag{5.105}$$

where use has been made of eqs. (5.94) and (5.95). By virtue of eqs. (5.102), the moment eqs. (5.103) through (5.105) are more complicated than those obtained for a single-species plasma in that now terms containing $\mathbf{v}^{(\alpha)}$ are present.

The one-fluid equations, which are considerably simpler and consequently considerably less informative, can be obtained by summing each of eqs. (5.103) through (5.105) over all species. On multiplying eq. (5.103) by m_α and carrying out this summation over the index α, we find on making use of eqs. (5.90) and (5.91) the result

$$\frac{\partial}{\partial t} \rho + \nabla \cdot (\mathbf{u} \rho) = 0 \tag{5.106}$$

which is, of course, nothing more than the statement of the conservation of mass for the entire fluid. In a similar way, one obtains the equation of motion for the fluid by carrying out the sum over all species in eq. (5.104) with the result

$$\rho \left\{ \frac{\partial}{\partial t} u_i + \left(\mathbf{u} \cdot \frac{\partial}{\partial \mathbf{r}} \right) u_i \right\} = - \sum_{j=1}^{3} \frac{\partial}{\partial x_j} P_{ij} + \rho_q E_i + (\mathbf{j} \times \mathbf{B})_i \tag{5.107}$$

where use has been made of the defining relations in eqs. (5.90) through (5.93). Also, in carrying out the sum over α in eq. (5.104), the right-hand side of this equation vanished by virtue of the relations

$$\sum_\alpha m_\alpha n^{(\alpha)} \mathbf{v}^{(\alpha)} = \sum_\alpha m_\alpha n^{(\alpha)} [\mathbf{u}^{(\alpha)} - \mathbf{u}] = \rho \mathbf{u} - \rho \mathbf{u} = 0 \tag{5.108}$$

which follow by a direct application of eqs. (5.90), (5.91) and (5.102). It is to be noted that both of eqs. (5.106) and (5.107) are formally identical to those obtained previously for a single species, but now, of course, all macroscopic quantities are defined by eqs. (5.90) through (5.93) and refer to properties of the entire fluid. Needless to say, eqs. (5.106) and (5.107) plus Maxwell's equations do not comprise a complete set. For, in addition to requiring an equation for p_{ij} we also need to obtain equations for ρ_q and $\mathbf{j}$ and, as in our previous discussions of the one-fluid equations, this requires some further assumptions.

Unfortunately, on carrying out the sum over α in eq. (5.105) we do not obtain an equation involving only dynamical quantities that refer to the plasma in its entirety; that is, we cannot obtain a formula as simple as eq. (4.75). In order to see this feature in detail let us actually carry out the sum over α in eq. (5.105). Making note of the fact that the second term on the right-hand side of this equation vanishes, we obtain on making use of eqs. (5.97) and (5.98), the result

$$\frac{\partial}{\partial t}p_{ij} + \nabla \cdot (\mathbf{u}p_{ij}) + \sum_{k=1}^{3}\left\{\frac{\partial}{\partial x_k}Q_{ijk} + p_{ik}\frac{\partial}{\partial x_k}u_j + p_{jk}\frac{\partial}{\partial x_k}u_i\right\}$$

$$- \{(\mathbf{E} + \mathbf{u} \times \mathbf{B})_i(\mathbf{j} - \mathbf{u}\rho_q)_j + (\mathbf{j} - \mathbf{u}\rho_q)_i(\mathbf{E} + \mathbf{u} \times \mathbf{B})_j\}$$

$$= \sum_{\alpha}\frac{q_\alpha}{m_\alpha}\sum_{e,m=1}^{3}B_m\{\varepsilon_{emj}p_{ie}^{(\alpha)} + \varepsilon_{emi}p_{je}^{(\alpha)}\} \tag{5.109}$$

where use has also been made of the relations

$$\sum_{\alpha}q_\alpha n^{(\alpha)}\mathbf{v}^{(\alpha)} = \sum_{\alpha}q_\alpha n^{(\alpha)}(\mathbf{u}^{(\alpha)} - \mathbf{u}) = \mathbf{j} - \mathbf{u}\rho_q \tag{5.110}$$

The second equality follows by use of the definitions in eqs. (5.92) and (5.93). We see, therefore, that except for its right-hand side, eq. (5.109) is essentially identical to eq. (4.75) which in turn was derived only for a single-species plasma. With the possible exception of this anomalous term, eqs. (5.106), (5.107), and (5.109) are identical to the equations for a single-species plasma, and may there be thought as a generalized form of the one-fluid equations. Of course, further relations and assumptions are required to convert these to a complete, and thus closed, set of equations.

THE CHEW, GOLDBERGER, LOW APPROXIMATION

As a final note to the present introduction to the equations of magnetohydrodynamics, let us make a study of a method that has been developed by Chew, Goldberger, and Low* and which may be used for purposes of

---

* G. F. Chew, M. L. Goldberger, and F. E. Low, "The Boltzmann Equation and the One Fluid Hydromagnetic Equations in the Absence of Particle Collisions," *Proc. Roy., Soc. (London)* A, 236, 112 (1956).

obtaining a very neat and closed set of one-fluid equations. These authors start directly with the BV equation and eq. (5.13) and make a systematic expansion of the solution of this equation in inverse powers of the magnetic field. Of course, the actual expansion parameter must be dimensionless and in more precise language, we can say that this approximation may be presumed to be valid provided that the ion Larmor frequency is very large compared to all other relevant frequencies. The electronic plasma frequency, of course, is not to be included in such a comparison, since in the spirit of the one-fluid model this latter frequency must be taken to be infinite.

Rather than repeat here in detail the analysis of the above-mentioned authors, however, we shall make direct use of the arguments of Bernstein and Trehan and start with eqs. (5.106), (5.107), (5.109), plus, of course, Maxwell's equations. The three basic assumptions that will be required in our discussion are as follows:

(1) The term involving the heat-flow tensor in eq. (5.109) is negligible.
(2) The conductivity of the plasma is very large so that Ohm's law in the form of eq. (5.13) is valid.
(3) The magnetic field in the plasma is sufficiently great so that the ion Larmor frequency is much larger than any other frequency.

For purposes of obtaining a closed set of equations, the first of these assumptions is, of course, mandatory and it may be presumed to be valid provided that the thermal velocities of the particles are sufficiently small. Similarly, the second assumption which assumes the validity of a form of Ohm's law is also required in order to produce a closed system of one-fluid equations. Indeed eqs. (5.106), (5.107), (5.109) plus Maxwell's equations in the one-fluid form—that is, eqs. (5.4) through (5.7)—when supplemented by the first two of the above assumptions constitute a complete system of equations. Nevertheless, we shall, in addition, make use of the third of the above assumptions; for not only does this lead to mathematical simplifications in the equation for the pressure tensor, but it also permits a simple physical interpretation to the resulting equations.

On making use of the second assumption, which is given by the relation

$$\mathbf{E} + \mathbf{u} \times \mathbf{B} = 0 \tag{5.111}$$

eq. (5.109) for the pressure tensor takes on the simpler form

$$\frac{\partial}{\partial t} p_{ij} + \nabla \cdot (\mathbf{u} p_{ij}) + \sum_{k=1}^{3} \left\{ p_{ik} \frac{\partial}{\partial x_k} u_j + p_{jk} \frac{\partial}{\partial x_k} u_i \right\}$$

$$= \sum_{\alpha} \frac{q_\alpha}{m_\alpha} \sum_{e,m=1}^{3} B_m \{ \varepsilon_{emj} p_{ie}^{(\alpha)} + \varepsilon_{emi} p_{je}^{(\alpha)} \} \tag{5.112}$$

where according to the first assumption the heat-flow tensor has also been neglected. Now, since each of the pressure tensors, $p_{ij}^{(\alpha)}$ is symmetric in its two indices, it follows that we can always find a local coordinate system in which these tensors are all diagonal. In this local coordinate system we have

$$p_{ij}^{(\alpha)} = p_{ii}^{(\alpha)} \delta_{ij}$$

and for this form of the pressure tensors, the right-hand side of eq. (5.112) vanishes and thus we obtain

$$\frac{\partial}{\partial t} p_{ij} + \nabla \cdot (\mathbf{u} p_{ij}) + \sum_{k=1}^{3} \left\{ p_{ik} \frac{\partial}{\partial x_k} u_j + p_{jk} \frac{\partial}{\partial x_k} u_i \right\} = 0 \qquad (5.113)$$

At first glance, it would seem that the electromagnetic fields do not appear at all in this question. However, it is physically plausible to expect that on the basis of the third assumption, one of the axes of the local system in which the pressure tensor is diagonal must lie along the direction of the magnetic field and this direction, which can vary in both space and time, is implicitly contained in eq. (5.113). In particular, the derivatives of the unit vector along this direction do not vanish. However, it is easy to see that the derivatives of $\mathbf{B}/B$ are of order $1/B$ and therefore, in view of the third assumption, these derivatives will be consistently neglected in all of the following considerations.

Furthermore, because of eq. (5.97), the total pressure tensor is also diagonal in the local system one of whose axes is along $\mathbf{B}$, and thus we may write

$$p_{ij} = \begin{pmatrix} p_s & 0 & 0 \\ 0 & p_s & 0 \\ 0 & 0 & p_n \end{pmatrix} \qquad (5.114)$$

where we have arbitrarily taken the z axis to be the direction of $\mathbf{B}$ and have again made use of the third assumption which implies rotational symmetry about the direction of the magnetic field.* Thus we see that the above three basic assumptions enable us to express the equation for the pressure tensor by the two relations

$$\frac{\partial}{\partial t} p_n + \nabla \cdot (\mathbf{u} p_n) + 2 p_n \frac{\partial}{\partial x_3} u_3 = 0$$

$$\frac{\partial}{\partial t} \left(p_s + \frac{1}{2} p_n \right) + \nabla \cdot \left\{ \mathbf{u} \left(p_s + \frac{1}{2} p_n \right) \right\} + p_s \nabla \cdot \mathbf{u} + (p_n - p_s) \frac{\partial}{\partial x_3} u_3 = 0 \quad (5.115)$$

where the first equation is the (3.3) component of eq. (5.113) and the second

---

* That is, the magnetic field is so strong it produces the only preferred direction in the plasma.

is one half the trace of this same equation. Making use of the definition of the operator d/dt as given in eq. (5.101), these two eqs. (5.115) may be combined to yield the two relations

$$\frac{d}{dt}\left(\frac{1}{2}p_n\right) + \frac{1}{2}p_n\nabla\cdot\mathbf{u} + p_n\frac{\partial}{\partial x_3}u_3 = 0 \tag{5.116}$$

and

$$\frac{d}{dt}p_s + 2p_s\nabla\cdot\mathbf{u} - p_s\frac{\partial}{\partial x_3}u_3 = 0 \tag{5.117}$$

In order to simplify these equations further, we shall now eliminate the term $\partial u_3/\partial x_3$. On making use of Maxwell's equations and eq. (5.111), we may write

$$\frac{d}{dt}\mathbf{B} = \frac{\partial}{\partial t}\mathbf{B} + \left(\mathbf{u}\cdot\frac{\partial}{\partial\mathbf{r}}\right)\mathbf{B}$$

$$= \left(\mathbf{u}\cdot\frac{\partial}{\partial\mathbf{r}}\right)\mathbf{B} + \nabla\times(\mathbf{u}\times\mathbf{B})$$

$$= \left(\mathbf{B}\cdot\frac{\partial}{\partial\mathbf{r}}\right)\mathbf{u} - \mathbf{B}\nabla\cdot\mathbf{u} \tag{5.118}$$

and since $\mathbf{B}$ has a component only along the local z axis, this equation may be expressed in the form

$$\frac{1}{B}\frac{d}{dt}B = \frac{\partial}{\partial x_3}u_3 - \nabla\cdot\mathbf{u} \tag{5.119}$$

Furthermore, the term $\nabla\cdot\mathbf{u}$ may be expressed in terms of ρ by the relation

$$\nabla\cdot\mathbf{u} = -\frac{1}{\rho}\frac{d}{dt}\rho \tag{5.120}$$

which is, of course, nothing more than the equation for the conservation of mass. If we now combine eqs. (5.119) and (5.120) there follows the relation

$$\frac{\partial}{\partial x_3}u_3 = \frac{1}{B}\frac{d}{dt}B - \frac{1}{\rho}\frac{d}{dt}\rho \tag{5.121}$$

which may be directly substituted into eqs. (5.116) and (5.117) in order to yield after slight regroupings the results

$$\frac{d}{dt}\left\{\frac{p_nB^2}{\rho^3}\right\} = 0 \tag{5.122}$$

and

$$\frac{d}{dt}\left\{\frac{p_s}{\rho B}\right\} = 0 \tag{5.123}$$

Taking note of the definition of the pressure tensor in eq. (5.94), the second of these relations is seen to be the statement of the fact that in the local rest frame of the plasma, the transverse kinetic energy of a particle divided by the magnetic field is a constant of the motion. This is a simple restatement of the constancy of the magnetic moment of a particle and has been independently derived in Chapter 2 in the adiabatic approximation. In a similar way, eq. (5.122) may be interpreted as saying that the quantity $p_n B^2/\rho^3$ is a constant of the motion and is also known as the longitudinal invariant.

To summarize this discussion then, we see that in the Chew, Goldberger, and Low approximation, the following equations constitute a closed system:

$$\frac{\partial}{\partial t}\rho + \nabla\cdot(\mathbf{u}\rho) = 0$$

$$\rho\frac{d}{dt}u_i = -\sum_{j=1}^{3}\frac{\partial}{\partial x_j}p_{ij} + \{(\mathbf{j}-\mathbf{u}\rho_q)\times\mathbf{B}\}_i$$

$$p_{ij} = \begin{pmatrix} p_s & 0 & 0 \\ 0 & p_s & 0 \\ 0 & 0 & p_n \end{pmatrix}$$

$$\frac{d}{dt}\left\{\frac{p_n B^2}{\rho^3}\right\} = 0$$

$$\frac{d}{dt}\left\{\frac{p_s}{\rho B}\right\} = 0$$

$$\mathbf{j} = \frac{1}{\mu_0}\nabla\times\mathbf{B}$$

$$\rho_q = -\varepsilon_0\nabla\cdot(\mathbf{u}\times\mathbf{B})$$

$$\frac{\partial}{\partial t}\mathbf{B} = \nabla\times(\mathbf{u}\times\mathbf{B})$$

where the last three equations are essentially Maxwell's equations after use is made of eq. (5.111). In writing down the second of these equations, eq. (5.111) has also been used to eliminate the electric field.

Suggested Reading and References

1. General

I. B. Bernstein and S. K. Trehan, "Plasma Oscillations (I)," *Nuclear Fusion* 1, 3, 6–12 (1960).

T. G. Cowling, *Magnetohydrodynamics*. New York: Interscience Publishers, Inc., 1957.

A. R. Kantrowitz and H. E. Petscheck, "An Introductory Discussion of Magnetohydrodynamics," contained in *Magnetohydrodynamics*, R. K. M. Landshoff (editor). Stanford, Cal.: Stanford University Press, 1957.

R. L. Liboff, "Long-Wavelength Phenomena in a Plasma," *Phys. of Fluids*, **5**, 963 (1962).

L. Spitzer, Jr., *Physics of Fully Ionized Gases*. New York: Interscience Publishers, Inc., 1956.

Y. A. Yoler, "A Review of Magnetohydrodynamics," contained in *Plasma Physics*, J. E. Drummond (editor). New York: McGraw Hill Book Company, Inc., 1961.

2. Applications of the MHD Equations

J. G. Linhart, *Plasma Physics*, Chap. 4. Amsterdam: North Holland Publishing Co., 1960.

J. D. Jackson, *Classical Electrodynamics*, Chapter 10. New York: John Wiley & Sons, Inc., 1962.

L. Oster, "Linearized Theory of Plasma Oscillations," *Rev. Mod. Phys.* **32**, 141 (1960).

Shih-I Pai, *Magnetogasdynamics and Plasma Dynamics*, Chap. 6. Vienna: Springer-Verlag, 1961.

Problems

1. Consider the flow of a plasma between two infinite planes in the presence of uniform external electric and magnetic fields as in Figure 5.1. Assuming now that the upper plane has the velocity v_0 as in this figure, and in addition that the lower plane has a velocity v_1 (also along the x axis), calculate $u(z)$ and $B(z)$. Also, obtain an explicit formula for the pressure. What is the significance of the arbitrary constant in your formula for $p(z)$? Make a plot of the velocity profiles across the channel for very small and for very large values for the Hartmann number.

2. (a) Calculate the relativistic form of the single-fluid magneto-hydrodynamic equations by taking the first three moments of eq. (4.89). Interpret the various terms physically and compare your results to the non-relativistic forms in eqs. (4.62), (4.65), (4.75).

(b) Make use of these equations to calculate the longitudinal plasma oscillations assuming that the heat-flow tensor is negligible, and that the electrons are originally characterized by a uniform pressure tensor $p_0 \delta_{ij}$, a uniform mass density ρ_0, and a uniform mean velocity $\mathbf{u}_0$. Neglect ionic motions.

(c) Is the assumption that the heat-flow tensor may be neglected necessarily inconsistent with relativistic treatment?

(d) Repeat (b) for the transverse oscillations.

3. Generalize the one-fluid model analysis of magnetohydrodynamic waves in the text.

(a) Write down the modified forms of eqs. (5.39) for the case that σ and η are both finite.

(b) Obtain the dispersion relations for the particular cases discussed in the text and show that now damping of the waves is possible.

(c) Calculate explicit forms for the frequencies and damping constants correct to first order in η and $1/\sigma$.

4. Starting with eqs. (5.54) through (5.58) calculate the dispersion relation for the longitudinal waves by use of the two-fluid model. Assume that initially the electrons as well as the ions have an equilibrium density n_0, that an equation of state for each species exists, that the mean velocities of both fluids vanish, and that there are no external electromagnetic fields present. Evaluate the results to first order in m/M.

5. Repeat Problem (4) if an external uniform magnetic field $\mathbf{B}_0$ is present. Obtain explicit forms for the cases $\mathbf{k}$ at right angles to and parallel to $\mathbf{B}_0$.

6. Repeat Problem (4) for the case that the electrons have a mean velocity $\mathbf{u}_0$ relative to the stationary ions. Discuss the physical significance and origins of any roots that have imaginary parts.

7. (a) Set up the linearized equations for an electron gas that is characterized in its equilibrium state by a mass density ρ_0, a scalar pressure p_0, and a mean velocity $\mathbf{u}_0 (=0)$. You may assume that the ions are immobile, that an equation of state for the electron gas exists and that there are no external electromagnetic fields present.

(b) Calculate the dispersion relation for the transverse modes of oscillation.

(c) Find explicit formulas for the frequencies and possible damping constants for the special cases that $\mathbf{k}$ and $\mathbf{u}_0$ are either parallel or at right angles to each other. Assume, for this purpose, that the wavelength of the disturbance is sufficiently large so that $k^2 u_0^2$ as well as $k^2 s^2$ are small compared to ω_p^2 and thus retain only first order terms in $k^2 u_0^2$, and $k^2 s^2$.

8. Repeat Problem (7), but this time, assume in addition the existence of an external magnetic field $\mathbf{B}_0$. For the sake of simplicity, assume that $\mathbf{k}$, $\mathbf{B}_0$, and $\mathbf{u}_0$ form an orthogonal set.

9. (a) Obtain the dispersion relation for the longitudinal electronic oscillations in the presence of a uniform external magnetic field $\mathbf{B}_0$ by assuming that the heat-flow tensor is negligible and that the ions serve only to produce a uniform background of positive charge. The electrons are characterized in their original equilibrium state by a mass density ρ_0, a pressure tensor $p_0 \delta_{ij}$, and a vanishing mean velocity.

(b) Repeat the calculation in part (a) for the transverse oscillations.

(c) Calculate explicit forms for these frequencies in the long wavelength limit.

10. Repeat Problem (9) for the case that the electrons have a mean velocity $\mathbf{u}_0$. Assume for the sake of simplicity that $\mathbf{u}_0$ and $\mathbf{B}_0$ are either perpendicular or parallel.

11. Make use of eqs. (5.106), (5.107), (5.109) in order to obtain the dispersion relation for magnetohydrodynamic waves by assuming that the heat-flow tensor is negligible, that the plasma has a finite conductivity σ, and that there are no external fields present. Initially, the plasma has a mass density ρ_0, a vanishing mean velocity, and a scalar pressure tensor $p_0 \delta_{ij}$. The equilibrium form of the pressure tensor for each of the plasma components also has a similar form.

12. Repeat Problem (11), but this time assume in addition that the plasma has a finite mean velocity $\mathbf{u}_0$.

13. (a) Calculate the dispersion relation for magnetohydrodynamic waves in the Chew, Goldberger, Low approximation and show that it is given by

$$\rho_0 \omega^2 + k \cos \theta \left(p_n - p_s - \frac{B^2}{\mu_0} \right) - k^2 \sin^2 \theta \left(2p_s + \frac{B^2}{\mu_0} \right)$$
$$= \frac{p_s^2 k^4 \sin^2 \theta \cos^2 \theta}{\rho_0 \omega^2 - 3p_n k^2 \cos^2 \theta}$$

where ρ_0, p_s, p_n, B stand for the unperturbed values for these quantities and θ is the angle between $\mathbf{k}$ and $\mathbf{B}$. The equilibrium mean velocity has been taken to be zero.

(b) Show further that for all values of θ less than a critical angle θ_c, which is the solution of the equation

$$\frac{B^2}{\mu_0} + p_s(1 + \sin^2 \theta_c) = \frac{p_s^2}{3p_n} \sin^2 \theta_c + 2p_n \cos^2 \theta_c$$

these waves are unstable.

(c) Examine the detailed properties of these waves for the special case $p_s = p_n$.

6

Plasma Oscillations

INTRODUCTION

In the previous two chapters we briefly examined the phenomenon of the electronic oscillations of a plasma from several points of view. On the one hand, by making use of the two-fluid equations in their simplest form we were able to derive a dispersion relation by assuming the validity of an electronic equation of state. Furthermore, the replacement of this latter assumption with the requirement that the heat-flow tensor be negligible, yielded essentially the same result; namely, that the dispersion relation had only one real root which was approximately equal to ω_p. On the other hand, the very simplified analysis of this phenomenon that was made by use of the BV equation gave rise to a dispersion relation that had a complex root, and whose imaginary part gave rise to the damping of the initial disturbance. Thus it is apparent that as far as the analysis of plasma oscillations is concerned, the BV equation is a much more reliable starting point, and furthermore, for purposes of studying one subject in some "depth" the problem will be examined from this viewpoint in the present chapter.

Besides the plasma frequency ω_p, the quantity that is of the greatest physical importance is the damping constant associated with a plasma characterized by a specified density and temperature. The very existence of this damping shows that the BV equation, even without the inclusion of two-particle collisions, yields results that agree with the fact that a plasma returns to equilibrium subsequent to the introduction of a small disturbance. In contrast to this, we discovered previously that the two-fluid model only predicts oscillatory behaviour under the same conditions. With regard to the physical basis for this damping there is considerable controversy in the literature and all heretofore proposed mechanisms are subject to some criticism. One of the more appealing of these is based on the notion of the trapping of electrons in the moving potential troughs of the wave associated with any given disturbance. In this picture we think of an energy exchange between the thermal energy of the electrons and the electric energy of the collective oscillations. Thus, if the disturbance is damped, then the thermal energy must increase at the expense of the electric energy and vice versa for growing waves. If there is an initial velocity spread in the electrons (it follows from eq. (4.127) that if $f_0(\mathbf{v})$ is a delta function, there exists only a real root and consequently there is no damping), then there will be a certain group of electrons that are in step with the traveling wave and consequently will be captured in the associated potential trough. In other words in a coordinate system with respect to which the phase of the wave is stationary, these electrons will be approximately at rest and will be captured by the wave with an increase (decrease) of their energy for the case that the disturbance is damped (exponentially growing). This interpretation has been discussed semiquantitatively by Jackson who showed in detail that the power fed into the electrons was equal to the loss of energy in the electric field. Of course, the difficulty with even this argument is that the electric energy is a quadratic function of the perturbation and thus is not suitable for inclusion in a linear theory. Nevertheless, the physical picture provided by this mechanism offers a very convenient approach to this phenomenon in an intuitive way.

An alternate physical interpretation of this phenomenon will be found in the problems. In particular, it is shown that for those values of ω which satisfy the dispersion relation in eq. (4.127) the dielectric constant of the plasma vanishes. Thus at these frequencies, the plasma becomes a very good reflector of electromagnetic waves and, for example, this is the reason that radio waves are reflected from the various layers of the ionosphere.

In this chapter after giving a general derivation of the dispersion relation in the absence of an external magnetic field, we shall discuss in detail the longitudinal modes of oscillation. Subsequently, the modifications required in this analysis by virtue of the presence of an external magnetic field will be examined.

THE DISPERSION RELATIONS
IN THE ABSENCE
OF A MAGNETIC FIELD

Because of the fact that the plasma frequency is so much greater than all other frequencies, it is reasonable to assume, as in our previous considerations, that the ions have a density n_0, and do not participate in any motions but serve only to provide a uniform background of positive charge, Initially, the entire system is in equilibrium and in particular the electrons also are of constant density n_0 and have the equilibrium distribution function (normalized to the total number of particles N)

$$f(\mathbf{r},\mathbf{v}) = n_0 f_0(\mathbf{v}) \tag{6.1}$$

where the detailed structure of $f_0(\mathbf{v})$ need not be specified at this point but frequently will be assumed to be a Maxwellian distribution. Following the familiar procedure we assume that the distribution function consists of the unperturbed terms in eq. (6.1) plus a small perturbation $g(\mathbf{r}, \mathbf{v}, t)$ that vanishes for negative times. Correspondingly, the electric and magnetic fields consist of their unperturbed values plus the small corrections $\mathbf{E}$ and $\mathbf{B}$, respectively. Substituting this form of the distribution function into the BV equation for the electrons, we find on neglecting terms of second order in the perturbations the result

$$\frac{\partial}{\partial t}g\,(\mathbf{r},\mathbf{v},t) + \mathbf{v}\cdot\frac{\partial}{\partial\mathbf{r}}g - \frac{qn_0}{m}[\mathbf{E}+\mathbf{v}\times\mathbf{B}]\cdot\frac{\partial}{\partial\mathbf{v}}f_0(\mathbf{v}) = 0 \tag{6.2}$$

where the perturbing fields $\mathbf{E}$ and $\mathbf{B}$ satisfy Maxwell's equations with charge and current densities given by

$$\rho(\mathbf{r},t) = -q\int d\mathbf{v}\,g\,(\mathbf{r},\mathbf{v},t)$$

$$\mathbf{j}(\mathbf{r},t) = -q\int \mathbf{v}\,d\mathbf{v}\,g\,(\mathbf{r},\mathbf{v},t) \tag{6.3}$$

As before, a simple way for solving eq. (6.2) and Maxwell's equations is to Fourier analyze these in both space and time by use of eqs. (1.29) and (1.46). After the usual manipulations we find the results

$$-g_0 + i(\mathbf{k}\cdot\mathbf{v}-\omega)g_\omega(\mathbf{k},\mathbf{v}) - \frac{qn_0}{m}[\mathbf{E}_\omega(\mathbf{k})+\mathbf{v}\times\mathbf{B}_\omega(\mathbf{k})]\cdot\frac{\partial}{\partial\mathbf{v}}f_0(\mathbf{v}) = 0 \tag{6.4}$$

where $\mathbf{E}_\omega$ and $\mathbf{B}_\omega$ are determined by Maxwell's equations:

$$\mathbf{k}\cdot\mathbf{B}_\omega = 0$$

$$\mathbf{k}\cdot\mathbf{E}_\omega = -\frac{i}{\varepsilon_0}\rho_\omega$$

$$\mathbf{k}\times\mathbf{E}_\omega = \omega\mathbf{B}_\omega + \mathbf{b}_0(\mathbf{k})$$

$$\mathbf{k}\times\mathbf{B}_\omega = +i\mu_0\mathbf{j}_\omega - \frac{\omega}{c^2}\mathbf{E}_\omega + \frac{i}{c^2}\mathbf{e}_0(\mathbf{k}) \tag{6.5}$$

where $g_0(\mathbf{k}, \mathbf{v})$, $\mathbf{e}_0(\mathbf{k})$, $\mathbf{b}_0(\mathbf{k})$ are the initial values for the spatial transforms of g, $\mathbf{E}$, and $\mathbf{B}$, respectively, and where $\rho_\omega(\mathbf{k})$ and $\mathbf{j}_\omega(\mathbf{k})$ are given by

$$\rho_\omega(k) = -q \int d\mathbf{v}\, g_\omega(\mathbf{k}, \mathbf{v})$$

$$\mathbf{j}_\omega(k) = -q \int \mathbf{v}\, d\mathbf{v}\, g_\omega(\mathbf{k}, \mathbf{v}) \qquad (6.6)$$

We note that the term $\mathbf{v} \times \mathbf{B}_\omega$ is of order v/c compared to $\mathbf{E}_\omega$ and in the present nonrelativistic limit may therefore be dropped. Furthermore, if $f_0(\mathbf{v})$ is an isotropic function of $\mathbf{v}$, then this term vanishes even in the relativistic case.

In order to complete the solution of eqs. (6.4) and (6.5), we first solve eq. (6.4) for $g_\omega(\mathbf{k}, \mathbf{v})$ and obtain

$$g_\omega(\mathbf{k}, \mathbf{v}) = \frac{1}{i(\mathbf{k} \cdot \mathbf{v} - \omega)}\left[g_0 + \frac{qn_0}{m}\mathbf{E}_\omega(\mathbf{k}) \cdot \frac{\partial}{\partial \mathbf{v}} f_0(\mathbf{v})\right] \qquad (6.7)$$

We then solve Maxwell's equation for $\mathbf{j}_\omega(\mathbf{k})$ in terms of $\mathbf{E}_\omega$ to yield

$$\mathbf{j}_\omega(\mathbf{k}) = \frac{i}{\omega\mu_0}\left[\mathbf{E}_\omega\left(\frac{\omega^2}{c^2} - k^2\right) + \mathbf{k}\mathbf{k} \cdot \mathbf{E}_\omega\right] + \mathbf{a}_0 \qquad (6.8)$$

where all terms involving the initial conditions have been lumped into the vector $\mathbf{a}_0$. On the other hand, $\mathbf{j}_\omega(\mathbf{k})$ may also be expressed in terms of $\mathbf{E}_\omega(\mathbf{k})$ by use of the second of eqs. (6.6) and (6.7). Thus equating these two expressions we find

$$(\omega^2 - k^2 c^2)\mathbf{E}_\omega + c^2\mathbf{k}\mathbf{k} \cdot \mathbf{E}_\omega + \mathbf{a}_0$$

$$= \omega \int \mathbf{v}\, d\mathbf{v} \frac{g_0}{\mathbf{k} \cdot \mathbf{v} - \omega} + \frac{\omega q^2 n_0}{m\varepsilon_0}\int \frac{\mathbf{v}\, d\mathbf{v}}{\mathbf{k} \cdot \mathbf{v} - \omega}\frac{\partial}{\partial \mathbf{v}}f_0 \cdot \mathbf{E}_\omega \qquad (6.9)$$

In order to simplify the second integral on the right-hand side of this equation, we express $\mathbf{E}_\omega$ in terms of its longitudinal and transverse components by the formula

$$\mathbf{E}_\omega = \mathbf{E}_{\omega t} + \frac{\mathbf{k}}{k^2}\mathbf{k} \cdot \mathbf{E}_\omega \qquad (6.10)$$

with $\mathbf{k} \cdot \mathbf{E}_{\omega t} = 0$. Thus eq. (6.9) may be written

$$(\omega^2 - k^2 c^2)\mathbf{E}_\omega + c^2\mathbf{k}\mathbf{k} \cdot \mathbf{E}_\omega - \omega\omega_p^2\frac{\mathbf{k} \cdot \mathbf{E}_\omega}{k^2}\int \frac{\mathbf{v}d\mathbf{v}}{\mathbf{k} \cdot \mathbf{v} - \omega}\mathbf{k} \cdot \frac{\partial}{\partial \mathbf{v}}f_0(\mathbf{v})$$

$$- \omega\omega_p^2\int \frac{\mathbf{v}\, d\mathbf{v}}{\mathbf{k} \cdot \mathbf{v} - \omega}\mathbf{E}_{\omega t} \cdot \frac{\partial}{\partial \mathbf{v}}f_0 = \mathbf{c}_0 \qquad (6.11)$$

where again $\mathbf{c}_0$ is a vector involving the initial perturbations.

The longitudinal modes of oscillation may be obtained from this equation by dotting through with $\mathbf{k}$ to yield

$$\mathbf{k} \cdot \mathbf{E}_\omega \left\{ \omega^2 - \frac{\omega \omega_p^2}{k^2} \int \frac{d\mathbf{v} \, \mathbf{k} \cdot \mathbf{v}}{\mathbf{k} \cdot \mathbf{v} - \omega} \mathbf{k} \cdot \frac{\partial}{\partial \mathbf{v}} f_0 \right\} = \mathbf{k} \cdot \mathbf{c}_0 \tag{6.12}$$

where use has been made of the fact that the second integral in eq. (6.11) vanishes by virtue of the relations

$$\int d\mathbf{v} \, \mathbf{E}_{\omega t} \cdot \frac{\partial}{\partial \mathbf{v}} f_0 \frac{\mathbf{k} \cdot \mathbf{v} - \omega + \omega}{\mathbf{k} \cdot \mathbf{v} - \omega} = 0 + \omega \int \frac{d\mathbf{v}}{\mathbf{k} \cdot \mathbf{v} - \omega} \mathbf{E}_{\omega t} \cdot \frac{\partial}{\partial \mathbf{v}} f_0 = 0$$

The second equality is valid for an unperturbed distribution function that depends only on $|\mathbf{v}|$ and then the result follows since $\mathbf{E}_{\omega t}$ has components only at right angles to $\mathbf{k}$. By adding and subtracting ω from the numerator in the integrand in eq. (6.12), this integral may be simplified slightly. The result may finally be expressed by the formula

$$\mathbf{k} \cdot \mathbf{E}_\omega = \frac{\dfrac{1}{\omega^2} \mathbf{k} \cdot \mathbf{c}_0}{1 - \dfrac{\omega_p^2}{k^2} \displaystyle\int \frac{d\mathbf{v}}{\mathbf{k} \cdot \mathbf{v} - \omega} \mathbf{k} \cdot \frac{\partial}{\partial \mathbf{v}} f_0} \tag{6.13}$$

where it is to be noted that the denominator is proportional to the corresponding one in eq. (4.125), and thus we have agreement with our previous derivation of the longitudinal modes.

In a similar way the transverse modes may be obtained by taking the cross product of eq. (6.11) with $\mathbf{k}$. This time the second and third terms vanish exactly (the latter because of the assumed spherical symmetry of $f_0(\mathbf{v})$) and the integral in the fourth term may be transformed by an integration by parts into the form

$$\int \frac{d\mathbf{v}}{\mathbf{k} \cdot \mathbf{v} - \omega} (\mathbf{k} \times \mathbf{v}) \mathbf{E}_{\omega t} \cdot \frac{\partial}{\partial \mathbf{v}} f_0 = - \int d\mathbf{v} \, f_0 \mathbf{E}_{\omega t} \cdot \frac{\partial}{\partial \mathbf{v}} \left[\frac{\mathbf{k} \times \mathbf{v}}{\mathbf{k} \cdot \mathbf{v} - \omega} \right]$$

$$= - \mathbf{k} \times \mathbf{E}_\omega \int d\mathbf{v} \, \frac{f_0(\mathbf{v})}{\mathbf{k} \cdot \mathbf{v} - \omega}$$

where the derivative of the factor $(\mathbf{k} \cdot \mathbf{v} - \omega)^{-1}$ makes no contribution to the integral because of the transverse character of $\mathbf{E}_{\omega t}$. The subscript t has been dropped in the final equality since the cross-product of $\mathbf{k}$ with the longitudinal electric field vanishes. Making use of these facts, the formula for $\mathbf{k} \times \mathbf{E}_\omega$ becomes

$$\mathbf{k} \times \mathbf{E}_\omega = \frac{\mathbf{k} \times \mathbf{c}_0}{\omega^2 - k^2 c^2 + \omega \omega_p^2 \displaystyle\int \frac{d\mathbf{v}}{\mathbf{k} \cdot \mathbf{v} - \omega} f_0(\mathbf{v})} \tag{6.14}$$

The denominator in this expression is to be compared with the result in Problem 7, Chapter 4.

Equations (6.13) and (6.14) represent the formal solutions for the longitudinal and transverse components of the electric field and give rise to dispersion relations. These in turn enable us to obtain the oscillatory behaviour of an electronic plasma that is subject to some initial disturbance.

THE ROOTS
OF THE DISPERSION RELATION
FOR THE LONGITUDINAL MODES

We shall now make a detailed study of the implications of eq. (6.13); a corresponding analysis for the transverse modes can be easily carried out in a similar way by use of eq. (6.14) but will not be considered here.

For the present purpose, it is convenient to cast eq. (6.13) into the form

$$\mathbf{k} \cdot \mathbf{E}_\omega = \frac{a_0(\mathbf{k}, \omega)}{H(k, \omega/k)} \tag{6.15}$$

where the scalar function $a_0(\mathbf{k}, \omega)$ is determined by the initial conditions and where the function $H(k, \omega/k)$ is defined by

$$H\left(k, \frac{\omega}{k}\right) = \frac{k^2}{\omega_p^2} - \int_{-\infty}^{\infty} \frac{G(v)\, dv}{v - \omega/k} \tag{6.16}$$

The quantity $G(v)$ is obtained by integrating $f_0(\mathbf{v})$ over the two components of $\mathbf{v}$ at right angles to $\mathbf{k}$ and then differentiating the result with respect to the component of velocity along $\mathbf{k}$. For example, for the case that $f_0(\mathbf{v})$ is a Maxwellian distribution, $G(v)$ is given by

$$G(v) = -(2\pi u^2)^{-\frac{1}{2}} \frac{v}{u^2} \exp\left\{-\frac{v^2}{2u^2}\right\} \tag{6.17}$$

where u is the thermal velocity of the electrons. It should be clear from this discussion that the problem of the electronic plasma oscillations is essentially one dimensional in nature and we would have obtained an identical result had we assumed this at the start. Indeed, many authors choose to start with a one-dimensional model for this very reason. However, the present discussion which does not require this restriction is to be preferred since it is more easily generalized to the cases that are truly three dimensional. These will arise whenever there is an anisotropy in space such as an external electric or magnetic field or when a plasma is confined to a finite geometry.

The time dependence of the longitudinal electric field is obtained by taking the inverse Fourier transform of the solution in eq. (6.15). Making use of eq. (1.30), we obtain

$$\mathbf{k} \cdot \mathbf{E}(\mathbf{k},t) = \int d\omega \, e^{-i\omega t} \frac{a_0(\mathbf{k},\omega)}{H(k,\omega/k)} \tag{6.18}$$

where the integration over ω is along a line parallel to the real ω axis but above all singularities in $\mathbf{k} \cdot \mathbf{E}_\omega(\mathbf{k})$ (Figure 6.1). The reason we must carry out the ω integral along a line above any poles is the same as the corresponding argument used to give the path of integration in the p plane for taking

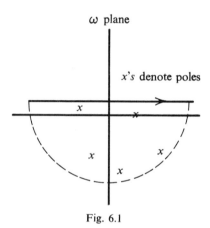

Fig. 6.1

inverse Laplace transforms. Of course, if there are no poles in the upper half plane, then the integration can be carried out essentially along the real ω axis—but just infinitesimally above it in order to insure the convergence of integrals such as in eq. (1.29). It is to be recalled in this connection that $g(\mathbf{k}, \mathbf{v}, t)$ vanishes for negative times.

Since we are concerned only with positive times, the negative sign in the exponential of eq. (6.18) suggests that we attempt to evaluate this integral by closing the contour in the lower half plane (dashed line in Figure 6.1). Assuming that the integral along the semicircle vanishes, it follows by Cauchy's theorem that eq. (6.18) may be written

$$\mathbf{k} \cdot \mathbf{E}(\mathbf{k},t) = 2\pi i \sum_j \exp\{-i\omega_j t\} \, \text{residue} \left[\frac{a_0(k,\omega)}{H(k,\omega/k)} \right]_{\omega = \omega_j} \tag{6.10}$$

where the ω_j's represent those values of ω for which the integrand in eq. (6.18) has poles. It follows that if there are poles in the upper half plane, then there will be exponentially growing waves that will dominate the situation completely after the elapse of sufficient time; in this case we describe the system as being in a state of unstable equilibrium. That is to say, $f_0(\mathbf{v})$ does not represent a true equilibrium state of the system in this case in that any initial small perturbation grows ever larger and eventually the system finds itself in another more stable state. Indeed, for this situation in which there are exponentially growing waves, the analysis breaks down since the linear approximation upon which most of the present discussion is based ceases to be valid. On the other hand if there are only poles along the real ω axis, then the system is in a steady state at such frequencies. Finally, if there are poles only in the lower half plane, then the longitudinal electric field as well as $g(\mathbf{k}, \mathbf{v}, t)$ are both exponentially damped and the system will return to its original unperturbed state in a time that is a characteristic property of the system. In this case, we say that the plasma is in stable equilibrium. It is clear from these considerations that if we are interested in questions relating to the stability of the plasma, we must first determine if the integrand in eq. (6.18) has any poles in the upper half plane. If it does, then the plasma will have only a transitory existence and further details can only be obtained by use of a more complicated and nonlinear analysis. Only where there are no poles in the upper half plane do we become interested in obtaining the frequencies and the damping constants associated with the remaining poles.

According to eq. (6.18) poles will appear either because $H(k, \omega/k)$ has zeros for certain values of ω or because the numerator, which is a given functional of the initial conditions, has a singularity. We shall ignore the latter possibility since poles that arise in this way do not represent intrinsic properties of the plasma but instead may be interpreted as certain mathematical initial conditions that could make any plasma unstable. It is beyond the scope of the present analysis, however, to treat such pathological initial conditions and presumably under these circumstances the system will return to equilibrium after having started out in such a state and gone through various other states whose details can only be calculated by use of a nonlinear theory. Therefore, leaving such possibilities out of our considerations, the poles are obtained by finding those values of ω that satisfy the equation

$$H(k, \omega/k) = 0 \tag{6.20}$$

According to eq. (6.16) this is then the same dispersion relation as was obtained in eq. (4.127). Of course, some effects of the initial conditions are felt here also, by virtue of the fact that the only values of $\mathbf{k}$ that are of interest are those present in the original disturbance.

Let us now turn to the problem of explicitly finding some of the roots of the dispersion relations in eqs. (6.16) and (6.20). First, we must ask if there are any roots in the upper half plane. This question is partially answered by the following theorem:

A one-dimensional velocity distribution $f_0(v)$ with a single maximum cannot support growing oscillations.

This does not mean, for example, that a double-peaked velocity distribution is of necessity unstable, but only that all velocity distributions with a single peak represent a plasma in either a steady state or one that is exponentially damped to small perturbations. In order to prove this assertion let us define two real numbers x and y by the formula

$$\frac{\omega}{k} = x + iy \tag{6.21}$$

and rewrite the real and imaginary parts of eq. (6.16) in the form

$$Re\{H(k, x + iy)\} = \frac{k^2}{\omega_p^2} - \int_{-\infty}^{\infty} \frac{(v - x)G(v)\, dv}{(v - x)^2 + y^2} \tag{6.22}$$

and

$$Im\{H(k, x + iy)\} = -y \int_{-\infty}^{\infty} \frac{G(v)\, dv}{(v - x)^2 + y^2} \tag{6.23}$$

We must now show that there exists no real number x and no *positive* number y for which both the real and imaginary part of H vanish simultaneously. Suppose, therefore, that for some fixed positive value of y we have obtained a corresponding value for x such that the imaginary part of H vanishes. We will now show that for this same pair of numbers (x, y) the real part of H must be positive definite and therefore cannot vanish. Since $Im\{H\} = 0$, we may subtract the quantity

$$\frac{x}{y} Im\{H\}$$

from the right hand side of eq. (6.22) to obtain

$$Re\{H(k, x + iy)\} = \frac{k^2}{\omega_p^2} - \int_{-\infty}^{\infty} \frac{v\, dv\, G(v)}{(v - x)^2 + y^2} \tag{6.24}$$

By hypothesis, $f_0(v)$ has only a single maximum and consequently $G(v)$ has a single zero (besides those at $\pm\infty$) which, without loss of generality, may be chosen to be at the origin. Further, by using the fact that $G(v)$ is positive for negative v and negative for positive v, eq. (6.24) may be written equivalently in the form

$$Re\{H(k, x + iy)\} = \frac{k^2}{\omega_p^2} + \int_{-\infty}^{\infty} dv \frac{|vG(v)|}{(v - x)^2 + y^2} \tag{6.25}$$

Since both terms on the right-hand side are positive, the real part of H cannot vanish and thus the theorem is proved.

At this point we might well ask where it was necessary in this proof to specify the condition $y > 0$. It would seem that the above discussion could go through without essential alteration for the case $y > 0$. It seems, therefore, as if we might be able to prove that if there are any roots at all, they could only lie along the real ω axis. The point is that the function H as defined in eq. (6.16) is meaningful only for values of ω in the upper half plane. For values of ω with negative imaginary parts, the integral in eq. (1.29) would in general diverge, and thus eq. (6.16) is a valid definition only for values of ω in the upper half plane. The above proof, which was based on this formula, does not work for values of ω with a negative imaginary part.

In order to obtain a formula for $H(k, \omega/k)$ in the lower half plane, it is necessary to make an analytic continuation of eq. (6.16) into this region. This analytic continuation is accomplished by the following definition:

$$H(\omega) = \begin{cases} \dfrac{k^2}{\omega_p^2} - \displaystyle\int_{-\infty}^{\infty} \dfrac{G(v)\, dv}{v - \omega/k} & ; Im(\omega) > 0 \\[4mm] \dfrac{k^2}{\omega_p^2} - \displaystyle\int_{-\infty}^{\infty} \dfrac{G(v)\, dv}{v - \omega/k} - 2\pi i G\left(\dfrac{\omega}{k}\right); Im(\omega) < 0 \end{cases} \tag{6.26}$$

This equation specifies a function $H(\omega)$ in the entire complex ω plane, and it coincides with the previously defined function $H(k, \omega/k)$ for positive values of $Im(\omega)$, and, finally, it is continuous across the real ω axis. Let us verify the fact that $H(\omega)$ as defined in eq. (6.26) is indeed continuous across the real ω axis.

To this end we shall consider a function $f(x)$ that is continuous, etc., and construct the quantity

$$I_{\pm} = \lim_{\varepsilon \to 0+} \int_{a}^{b} \frac{f(x)\, dx}{x - x_0 \pm i\varepsilon} \tag{6.27}$$

where $b > x_0 > a$. We shall first show that $I_\pm$ may be written in the form

$$I_\pm = P \int_a^b \frac{f(x)\,dx}{x - x_0} \mp \pi i f(x_0) \tag{6.28}$$

where the integral is to be interpreted in the principal value sense—that is,

$$P \int_a^b \frac{f(x)\,dx}{x - x_0} = \lim_{\varepsilon \to 0+} \left\{ \int_a^{x_0 - \varepsilon} \frac{f(x)\,dx}{x - x_0} + \int_{x_0 + \varepsilon}^b \frac{f(x)\,dx}{x - x_0} \right\} \tag{6.29}$$

Now starting with eq. (6.27) we may express it in the form

$$I_\pm = \lim_{\varepsilon \to 0+} \int_a^a \frac{f(x) - f(x_0)}{x - x_0 \pm i\varepsilon}\,dx + f(x_0) \lim_{\varepsilon \to 0+} \int_a^b \frac{dx}{x - x_0 \pm i\varepsilon}$$

$$= \int_a^b \frac{f(x) - f(x_0)}{x - x_0}\,dx + f(x_0) \lim_{\varepsilon \to 0+} \ln \frac{b - x_0 \pm i\varepsilon}{a - x_0 \pm i\varepsilon}$$

$$= \int_a^b \frac{f(x) - f(x_0)}{x - x_0}\,dx + f(x_0) \ln \frac{b - x_0}{x_0 - a} \mp \pi i f(x_0) \tag{6.30}$$

where the second equality follows by virtue of the fact that in this form the integrand is well behaved and the limit may be taken explicitly under the integral. If we show that the first two terms in the third equality in eq. (6.30) comprise the principal value integral, the identity in eq. (6.28) will then be established. But from eq. (6.29) we have

$$P \int_a^b \frac{f(x)\,dx}{x - x_0} = \int_a^b \frac{f(x) - f(x_0)}{x - x_0}\,dx + f(x_0) P \int_a^b \frac{dx}{x - x_0}$$

$$= \int_a^b \frac{f(x) - f(x_0)}{x - x_0}\,dx$$

$$+ f(x_0) \lim_{\varepsilon \to 0+} \left\{ \int_a^{x_0 - \varepsilon} \frac{dx}{x - x_0} + \int_{x_0 + \varepsilon}^b \frac{dx}{x - x_0} \right\}$$

$$= \int_a^b \frac{f(x) - f(x_0)}{x - x_0}\,dx + f(x_0) \ln \frac{b - x_0}{x_0 - a}$$

and therefore the validity of eq. (6.28) is established.

Let us now examine $H(\omega)$ as given in eq. (6.26) in the limits as ω approaches the real axis from above and below. We obtain for $\omega=\omega_r\pm i\varepsilon$, $\varepsilon>0$

$$\lim_{\varepsilon\to 0+} \{H(\omega_r + i\varepsilon) - H(\omega_r - i\varepsilon)\}$$

$$= \lim_{\varepsilon\to 0+} \left\{ \frac{k^2}{\omega_p^2} - \int_{-\infty}^{\infty} \frac{G(v)\,dv}{v - (\omega_r/k) - i\varepsilon} - \frac{k^2}{\omega_p^2} \right.$$

$$\left. + \int_{-\infty}^{\infty} \frac{G(v)\,dv}{v - (\omega_r/k) + i\varepsilon} + 2\pi i G\left(\frac{\omega_r - i\varepsilon}{k}\right) \right\}$$

$$= -P\int_{-\infty}^{\infty} \frac{G(v)\,dv}{v - \omega_r/k} - \pi i G\left(\frac{\omega_r}{k}\right)$$

$$+ P\int_{-\infty}^{\infty} \frac{G(v)\,dv}{v - \omega_r/k} - \pi i G\left(\frac{\omega_r}{k}\right) + 2\pi i G\left(\frac{\omega_r}{k}\right)$$

$$= 0$$

where eq. (6.28) has been used twice. Thus it follows that $H(\omega)$ is continuous across the real ω axis, and the function defined in eq. (6.26) is the proper analytic continuation of $H(k, \omega/k)$ into the lower half plane. Consequently, for the cases of interest, where there are no poles in the upper half plane, we must make use of eq. (6.26) in order to study the properties of the equilibrium configurations of the plasma if any such exist.

In general, it is not possible to find an analytic form for the roots of $H(\omega)$ in eq. (6.26). In the two limits of large and small wave numbers, however, approximate roots can be obtained and it is of interest to display these in some detail. Our present interests are confined to stable systems and thus we shall assume that $G(v)$ is associated with a single maximum distribution such as a Maxwellian.

For the case of small wave numbers, we shall further restrict our attention to obtaining the root that is so close to the real ω axis it is possible to expand $H(\omega)$ in a power series in $Im(\omega)$ and to keep only the lowest order terms. Since $y=Im(\omega/k)$ is negative, we must solve the equation

$$0 = H(x + iy) = \frac{k^2}{\omega_p^2} - \int_{-\infty}^{\infty} \frac{G(v)\,dv}{v - x - iy} - 2\pi i\, G(x + iy) \quad (6.31)$$

The expansion in a power series in y of the first and third term is routine and is given by

$$\frac{k^2}{\omega_p^2} - 2\pi i G(x) + 2\pi y\, G'(x) + 0(y^2) \quad (6.32)$$

While a little more delicacy is required in order to expand the integral in eq. (6.31). Let us for the moment call this term $I(x+iy)$. By use of Taylor's theorem we may write

$$I(x + iy) = I(x - i\varepsilon) + i(y - \varepsilon)I'(x - i\varepsilon) + 0(y^2) \qquad (6.33)$$

where ε, as before, is a positive infinitesimal that is always to approach zero. From the definition of I, we obtain the result

$$I(x - i\varepsilon) = -\int_{-\infty}^{\infty} \frac{G(v)\, dv}{v - x + i\varepsilon}$$

$$= P\int_{-\infty}^{\infty} \frac{G(v)\, dv}{v - x} + \pi i\, G(x) \qquad (6.34)$$

and in a similar way we find

$$I'(x - i\varepsilon) = -\int_{-\infty}^{\infty} \frac{G(v)\, dv}{(v - x + i\varepsilon)^2}$$

$$= -\int_{-\infty}^{\infty} \frac{G'(v)\, dv}{v - x + i\varepsilon}$$

$$= -P\int_{-\infty}^{\infty} \frac{G'(v)\, dv}{v - x} + \pi i\, G'(x) \qquad (6.35)$$

where use has been made of eq. (6.28) as well as an integration by parts. Substituting now eqs. (6.32) through (6.35) into eq. (6.31) there results

$$H(x + iy) \cong \frac{k^2}{\omega_p^2} + 2\pi y G'(x) - P\int_{-\infty}^{\infty} \frac{G(v)\, dv}{v - x} - \pi y G'(x)$$

$$+ i\left\{ -2\pi G(x) + \pi G(x) - yP\int_{-\infty}^{\infty} \frac{G'(v)\, dv}{v - x} \right\} \qquad (6.36)$$

Hence, equating the real and imaginary separately to zero we obtain, correct to lowest order in y, the results

$$\frac{k^2}{\omega_p^2} = P\int_{-\infty}^{\infty} \frac{G(v)\, dv}{v - \omega/k}$$

$$\omega_i = \frac{-\pi k G(\omega/k)}{P\int_{-\infty}^{\infty} \frac{G'(v)\, dv}{v - \omega/k}} \qquad (6.37)$$

where ω_i is the presumed small, imaginary part of ω and the symbol ω without a subscript refers to its real part.

As in our previous discussion in Chapter 4, an approximate evaluation of the first of eqs. (6.37) may be made by considering wave numbers sufficiently small so that the wave velocity ω/k is much larger than the mean thermal velocity in the plasma. In this situation the singularity in the integrand occurs for values of v, for which $G(v)$ is negligible. Thus expanding the denominator in a power series in $k(v/\omega)$ we obtain

$$\omega^2 \cong \omega_p^2 + 3k^2u^2 \tag{6.38}$$

where u is the thermal velocity. In a similar way the denominator in the second of eqs. (6.37) may be evaluated and we find for the imaginary part of ω the result

$$\omega_i = \frac{\pi k}{2}\left(\frac{\omega_p}{k}\right)^3 G\left(\frac{\omega_p}{k}\right) \tag{6.39}$$

For the special case that the one-dimensional distribution function associated with $G(v)$ is Maxwellian, this formula reduces to the familiar Landau result

$$\omega_i = -\left(\frac{\pi}{8}\right)^{\frac{1}{2}} \omega_p \left(\frac{\omega_p}{ku}\right)^3 \exp\left\{-\frac{\omega_p^2}{k^2u^2}\right\} \tag{6.40}$$

It is to be emphasized that the approximate root given in eqs. (6.38)–(6.39) is valid only for small k; in addition we have obtained only that root which is very near the real axis. There will be other roots further away but in general these are associated with oscillations that are damped in a much shorter time than the one associated with the root in eqs. (6.38) and (6.39). Finally, it should be noted that the result in eq. (6.40) has an essential singularity in the neighborhood of $k = 0$, and thus the assumption that k was an effective expansion parameter is open to serious question. At best, we can say that the above formulas represent an *asymptotic form* of the root valid for sufficiently small k. Evaluation of the dispersion relation by use of numerical tables will substantiate this point.

At the other extreme—that is, in the region of very large wave numbers— it is again possible to obtain an approximate evaluation of a root of eq. (6.31). It must be borne in mind, however, that in this limit of very short wavelengths, the validity of the BV equation itself is in doubt. The reason for this is that for sufficiently short wavelengths we are not justified in making use of a smoothed-out macroscopic electric field. The initial disturbance for this case will involve only a very small number of particles and consequently the effective field will, in general, vary over distances comparable to the interparticle spacing. Nevertheless, since the case of large wave numbers is amenable to simple analysis, we shall consider it briefly.

Again, we start with eq. (6.31) but this time let us assume that the imaginary part of ω/k is very large compared to the real part and also large compared to the thermal velocity u. As we noted above, the consistency of these assumptions can always be substantiated afterwards. On expanding the integrand in eq. (6.31) in a power series in $1/y$ there results

$$0 = \frac{k^2}{\omega_p^2} + \frac{1}{iy}\int_{-\infty}^{\infty} dv G(v)\left[1 + \frac{v-x}{iy} + \left(\frac{v-x}{iy}\right)^2 + \cdots\right] - 2\pi i G(x+iy)$$

(6.41)

Hence, equating the real and imaginary parts separately to zero we find in lowest order

$$\frac{k^2}{\omega_p^2} + 2\pi ImG(x+iy) = 0 \tag{6.42}$$

$$ReG(x+iy) = 0$$

In order to proceed further, let us assume that the distribution function associated with $G(v)$ is Maxwellian, so that $G(v)$ has the form

$$G(v) = -(2\pi u^2)^{-\frac{1}{2}}\frac{v}{u^2}\exp\left\{-\frac{v^2}{2u^2}\right\}$$

In this case, the second of eqs. (6.42) may be expressed in the form

$$\frac{u^2}{y^2} = -\frac{u^2}{xy}\tan\frac{xy}{u^2} \tag{6.43}$$

with approximate solution

$$xy \cong \pi u^2 \tag{6.44}$$

since we have assumed $u^2 \ll y^2$. On making use of this result, the first of eqs. (6.42) may now be written

$$\frac{y}{u^3}\exp\left\{\frac{y^2}{2u^2}\right\} \cong (2\pi)^{-\frac{1}{2}}\left(\frac{k}{\omega_p}\right)^2 \tag{6.45}$$

which yields the approximate root

$$x \cong \pi u\left[\ln\frac{k^4 u^4}{2\pi\omega_p^4}\right]^{-\frac{1}{2}}$$

$$y \cong -u\left[\ln\frac{k^4 u^4}{2\pi\omega_p^4}\right]^{\frac{1}{2}} \tag{6.46}$$

An examination of these formulas shows that for values of $k \gg \lambda_D^{-1} = \omega_p/u$, all of the above assumptions are internally consistent. Also we note that the damping constant is so large that any disturbance in the plasma is damped long before the system can carry out even a single collective oscillation.

The analysis for the transverse oscillations can be carried out in a similar way and will be left for the problems. Suffice it to say that for this case we must first analytically continue the function

$$H(\omega) = \omega^2 - k^2 c^2 + \frac{\omega \omega_p^2}{k} \int_{-\infty}^{\infty} dv \, \frac{f_0(v)}{v - \omega/k} \tag{6.47}$$

into the lower half plane and then proceed as above.

THE EFFECTS OF AN EXTERNAL
MAGNETIC FIELD

Let us now examine the modifications required in the above analysis when an external magnetic field is impressed on the electronic plasma. Again, it is convenient to carry out the discussion for an infinite plasma; thus the results will be applicable to regions far removed from the bounding surface and for times short compared to the time required for a small disturbance to propagate to the surface. Bearing this physical limitation in mind, the subject is nevertheless of considerable interest since associated with most plasmas there is a magnetic field produced by the motions of the particles themselves. Frequently it is possible to simulate the effects of such an internally generated magnetic field by use of an external one.

Assuming at the outset, this time, that the unperturbed electronic distribution function is Maxwellian, it follows that in the linearized equation the first-order correction to the magnetic field is again absent and consequently the linearized BV equation involves only the uniform external field $\mathbf{B}_0$. The Fourier transform in space and time of the perturbation in the distribution function $g_\omega(\mathbf{k}, \mathbf{v})$ therefore satisfies a slight modification of eq. (6.4) and is given by

$$- g_0 + i(\mathbf{k} \cdot \mathbf{v} - \omega) g_\omega(\mathbf{k}, \mathbf{v}) - \frac{q n_0}{m} \mathbf{E}_\omega \cdot \frac{\partial}{\partial \mathbf{v}} f_0(\mathbf{v}) + \frac{q}{m} \mathbf{B}_0 \cdot \left(\mathbf{v} \times \frac{\partial}{\partial \mathbf{v}} \right) g_\omega(\mathbf{k}, \mathbf{v}) = 0 \tag{6.48}$$

where $\mathbf{E}_\omega(\mathbf{k})$ again satisfies eq. (6.8)—that is

$$\mathbf{j}_\omega(\mathbf{k}) = \frac{i}{\omega \mu_0} \left[\left(\frac{\omega^2}{c^2} - k^2 \right) \mathbf{E}_\omega + \mathbf{k}\mathbf{k} \cdot \mathbf{E}_\omega \right] + \mathbf{a}_0 \tag{6.8}$$

with $\mathbf{j}_\omega(\mathbf{k})$ expressed in terms of $g_\omega(\mathbf{k}, \mathbf{v})$ by the formula

$$\mathbf{j}_\omega(\mathbf{k}) = -q \int \mathbf{v} \, d\mathbf{v} \, g_\omega(\mathbf{k}, \mathbf{v}) \tag{6.49}$$

The quantities $\mathbf{a}_0$, g_0 are again uniquely specified by the initial conditions.

For the present case, eq. (6.48) involves derivatives with respect to $\mathbf{v}$ and therefore is no longer a simple algebraic equation for $g_\omega(\mathbf{k}, \mathbf{v})$. Thus it is necessary to modify the above procedure and now we must first solve the partial differential eq. (6.48) in order to obtain the solution that will be a functional of $\mathbf{E}_\omega(\mathbf{k})$. On substituting this solution back into eqs. (6.8) and (6.49), the ultimate result will be the dispersion relation.

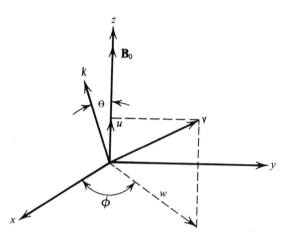

Fig. 6.2

In order to solve eq. (6.48), it is convenient to select a coordinate system in velocity space with $\mathbf{B}_0$ along the z direction and the x axis selected so that the vector $\mathbf{k}$ lies in the x-z plane and makes an angle θ with the z axis (Figure 6.2). It turns out to be simplest to express the velocity vector $\mathbf{v}$ in cylindrical coordinates w, ϕ, u; that is, we have

$$\mathbf{v} = (w \cos \phi, w \sin \phi, u) \tag{6.50}$$

With these definitions eq. (6.48) may be expressed simply as

$$\frac{\partial}{\partial \phi} g_\omega(\mathbf{k}, \mathbf{v}) + \frac{ik}{\Omega}\left[w \cos \phi \sin \theta + u \cos \theta - \frac{\omega}{k} \right] g_\omega(\mathbf{k}, \mathbf{v})$$

$$= \frac{1}{\Omega} g_0(\mathbf{k}, \mathbf{v}) + \frac{q n_0}{m\Omega} \mathbf{E}_\omega(\mathbf{k}) \cdot \frac{\partial}{\partial \mathbf{v}} f_0(\mathbf{v}) \tag{6.51}$$

where Ω is the electronic Larmor frequency and given by $q B_0/m$. Thus in the present case, the linearized BV equation instead of being algebraic is an ordinary, linear, first-order differential equation that can be integrated by elementary means. Making use of the facts that on physical grounds $g_\omega(\mathbf{k}, \mathbf{v})$ must be periodic in ϕ with period 2π and that the imaginary part of

ω must be positive for the same reasons as for the case of no magnetic field, the solution of eq. (6.51) is unique and is given by

$$g_\omega(\mathbf{k},\mathbf{v}) = \frac{1}{\Omega} h(-\phi) \int_{-\infty}^{\phi} h(\phi') \, d\phi' \left\{ g_0(\mathbf{k},\mathbf{v}') + \frac{q n_0}{m} \mathbf{E}_\omega \cdot \frac{\partial}{\partial \mathbf{v}'} f_0(\mathbf{v}') \right\} \quad (6.52)$$

where the function $h(\phi)$ is

$$h(\phi) = \exp\left\{ \frac{ik}{\Omega} \left[\phi \left(u \cos\theta - \frac{\omega}{k} \right) + w \sin\theta \sin\phi \right] \right\} \quad (6.53)$$

and where $\mathbf{v}'$ is a vector identical to $\mathbf{v}$ except that the angle ϕ has been replaced by ϕ'; that is, we have by definition

$$\mathbf{v}' = (w \cos\phi', w \sin\phi', u) \quad (6.54)$$

Before proceeding with the derivation of the dispersion relation, let us briefly examine the solution in eq. (6.52) in order to verify that in the limit of vanishing magnetic field—that is, $\Omega \to 0$—it approaches the expected result in eq. (6.7). The expansion of $g_\omega(\mathbf{k}, \mathbf{v})$ in a power series in Ω is simplified by noting that the function $h(\phi)$ may be expressed in the form

$$h(\phi) = \exp\left\{ \frac{i}{\Omega} \int_0^\phi d\phi' (\mathbf{k} \cdot \mathbf{v}' - \omega) \right\} \quad (6.55)$$

by use of which there follows the useful identity

$$h(\phi) = \frac{\Omega}{i(\mathbf{k} \cdot \mathbf{v} - \omega)} \frac{\partial}{\partial\phi} h(\phi) \quad (6.56)$$

Now the solution for $g_\omega(\mathbf{k}, \mathbf{v})$ in eq. (6.52) involves integrals of the form

$$I = \frac{1}{\Omega} \int_{-\infty}^{\phi} d\phi' \, h(\phi') f(\phi')$$

which by repeated use of eq. (6.56) and successive integrations by parts may be written

$$\begin{aligned}
I &= \int_{-\infty}^{\phi} d\phi' \frac{f(\phi')}{i(\mathbf{k} \cdot \mathbf{v}' - \omega)} \frac{\partial}{\partial\phi'} h(\phi') \\
&= \frac{f(\phi')h(\phi')}{i(\mathbf{k} \cdot \mathbf{v}' - \omega)} \Big|_{-\infty}^{\phi} - \int_{-\infty}^{\phi} d\phi' \, h(\phi') \frac{\partial}{\partial\phi'} \left[\frac{f(\phi')}{i(\mathbf{k} \cdot \mathbf{v}' - \omega)} \right] \\
&= \frac{f(\phi)h(\phi)}{i(\mathbf{k} \cdot \mathbf{v} - \omega)} + \Omega \int_{-\infty}^{\phi} \frac{d\phi'}{\mathbf{k} \cdot \mathbf{v}' - \omega} \frac{\partial h}{\partial\phi'} \left(\frac{\partial}{\partial\phi'} \frac{f(\phi')}{\mathbf{k} \cdot \mathbf{v}' - \omega} \right) \\
&= \frac{f(\phi)h(\phi)}{i(\mathbf{k} \cdot \mathbf{v} - \omega)} + \frac{\Omega h(\phi)}{\mathbf{k} \cdot \mathbf{v} - \omega} \frac{\partial}{\partial\phi} \left(\frac{f(\phi)}{\mathbf{k} \cdot \mathbf{v} - \omega} \right) + O(\Omega^2)
\end{aligned}$$

where use has been made of the fact that ω has a positive imaginary part and that therefore $h(-\infty)$ vanishes. Furthermore, making use of the fact that according to eq. (6.53) we have

$$h(\phi)h(-\phi) = 1$$

it follows that in the limit $\Omega \to 0$, the solution in eq.(6.52) is identical to the previous one in eq. (6.7).

Proceeding now with the derivation of the dispersion relation, we multiply eq. (6.52) by $-q\mathbf{v}$, integrate the result over all velocity space in order to obtain $\mathbf{j}_\omega(\mathbf{k})$, and on substituting this result into eq. (6.8) obtain

$$(\omega^2 - k^2 c^2)\mathbf{E}_\omega + c^2\mathbf{kk} \cdot \mathbf{E}_\omega$$

$$- \frac{i\omega\omega_p^2}{\Omega k^2} \int \mathbf{v} \, d\mathbf{v} \int_{-\infty}^{\phi} d\phi' h(-\phi)h(\phi')\mathbf{k} \cdot \frac{\partial}{\partial \mathbf{v}'} f_0(\mathbf{v}')\mathbf{k} \cdot \mathbf{E}_\omega$$

$$- \frac{i\omega\omega_p^2}{\Omega} \int \mathbf{v} \, d\mathbf{v} \int_{-\infty}^{\phi} d\phi' h(-\phi)h(\phi')\mathbf{E}_{\omega t} \cdot \frac{\partial}{\partial \mathbf{v}'} f_0(\mathbf{v}') = \mathbf{a} \quad (6.57)$$

where under the integral we have split $\mathbf{E}_\omega(\mathbf{k})$ into its longitudinal and transverse components and where $\mathbf{a}$ is again an integral involving the initial distribution function. Unlike the case of vanishing magnetic field, in general if we take the dot or cross product of this equation with $\mathbf{k}$, the longitudinal and transverse parts of the electric field do not separate. In this event these two modes of oscillation are said to be *coupled*.

Because of the mathematical complexity that arises by virtue of this coupling, let us first examine the situation $\theta = 0$—that is, $\mathbf{k}$ parallel to $\mathbf{B}_0$. In this case the function $h(\phi)$ has the simpler form

$$h(\phi) = \exp\left\{\frac{i\phi}{\Omega}(ku - \omega)\right\} \quad (6.58)$$

and on dotting eq. (6.57) with $\mathbf{k}$, the second integral on the right-hand side vanishes and thus we obtain

$$\mathbf{k} \cdot \mathbf{E}_\omega\left\{\omega^2 - \frac{i\omega\omega_p^2}{\Omega k^2} \int \mathbf{k} \cdot \mathbf{v} \, d\mathbf{v} \int_{-\infty}^{\phi} d\phi' h(-\phi)h(\phi')\mathbf{k} \cdot \frac{\partial}{\partial \mathbf{v}'} f_0(\mathbf{v}')\right\} = \mathbf{k} \cdot \mathbf{a}$$

$$(6.59)$$

Furthermore, since $\mathbf{k}$ is along the z axis, the factor $\mathbf{k} \cdot \dfrac{\partial f_0(\mathbf{v}')}{\partial \mathbf{v}'}$ does not involve the angle ϕ', and therefore the integral over ϕ' is elementary and may be easily carried out thus enabling us to rewrite eq. (6.59) as

$$\mathbf{k} \cdot \mathbf{E}_\omega\left\{\omega^2 - \frac{\omega\omega_p^2}{k^2} \int d\mathbf{v} \frac{\mathbf{k} \cdot \mathbf{v}}{\mathbf{k} \cdot \mathbf{v} - \omega} \mathbf{k} \cdot \frac{\partial}{\partial \mathbf{v}} f_0(\mathbf{v})\right\} = \mathbf{k} \cdot \mathbf{a} \quad (6.60)$$

This is, of course, identical to eq. (6.12) and thus we conclude that for disturbances that have a propogation vector along $\mathbf{B}_0$, the longitudinal modes of oscillation are identical to those produced in the absence of a magnetic field.

In a similar way, by taking the cross product of eq. (6.57) with $\mathbf{k}$, for this special case $\theta = 0$, the longitudinal components of the electric field will cancel, and we readily obtain a dispersion relation for the transverse components of the field. An examination of this result (the details of this derivation are left to the problems) shows that the effects of the magnetic field do *not* cancel in this case. Physically, the reason for this is easy to see. For the case of the longitudinal modes, the motions of the particles are disturbed only along $\mathbf{B}_0$, and since the entire effect is due to a variation in the charge density, the disturbed particles are unaware of the magnetic field. On the other hand, the transverse oscillations are produced by currents associated with the motions of particles at right angles to $\mathbf{B}_0$ and thus the magnetic field modifies the dispersion relations for this case.

In order to simplify the obtaining of the longitudinal dispersion relation for the general case—that is, the one for which $\mathbf{k}$ is not parallel to $\mathbf{B}_0$—let us assume that the coupling between the longitudinal and transverse oscillations is small. Thus, on dotting eq. (6.57) with $\mathbf{k}$ and neglecting the integral involving $\mathbf{E}_{\omega t}$, there results for the longitudinal modes the dispersion relation

$$1 - \frac{i\omega_p^2}{k^2 \omega \Omega} \int d\mathbf{v} \, \mathbf{k} \cdot \mathbf{v} \, h(-\phi) \int_{-\infty}^{\phi} d\phi' \, h(\phi') \mathbf{k} \cdot \frac{\partial}{\partial \mathbf{v}'} f_0(\mathbf{v}') = 0 \quad (6.61)$$

In order to proceed further, it is now necessary to make a particular choice for the equilibrium distribution function $f_0(\mathbf{v}')$. Let us assume that $f_0(\mathbf{v})$ is a Maxwellian distribution with thermal velocity u. For this case it is shown in the references (for example, in the article by Bernstein) that three of the four integrals in eq. (6.61) may be carried out explicitly and therefore this dispersion relation may be expressed in the equivalent form

$$1 + \frac{v}{\omega_p^2} = -i\omega \int_0^\infty dt \, \exp\left\{ i\omega t - \frac{1}{2} v t^2 \cos^2 \theta \right.$$
$$\left. - \frac{v}{\Omega^2} (1 - \cos \Omega t) \sin^2 \theta \right\} \quad (6.62)$$

where the parameter v is defined in terms of the thermal velocity u by

$$v = k^2 u^2$$

and where, of course, θ is the angle between $\mathbf{k}$ and $\mathbf{B}_0$. It is to be noted that in either of the limits, $\theta \to 0$ or $\Omega \to 0$, this result reduces to the one in Problem 6, Chapter 4.

An examination of the integral in eq. (6.61) shows that this dispersion relation which was derived for values of ω in the upper half plane is equally valid in the entire complex ω plane, provided only $\theta \neq \pi/2$ and, of course, $k \neq 0$. The reason for this is that for $v \cos^2 \theta > 0$, the t^2 dependence in the exponential dominates the integral and insures its convergence. Furthermore, for the case $\theta = \pi/2$—that is, $\mathbf{k}$ perpendicular to $\mathbf{B_0}$—eq. (6.61) may be cast into the equivalent forms

$$1 + \frac{v}{\omega_p^2} = -i\omega \sum_{n=0}^{\infty} \int_{(2n\pi)/\Omega}^{(2n+1)(\pi/\Omega)} dt \, \exp\left\{i\omega t - \frac{v}{\Omega^2}(1 - \cos \Omega t)\right\}$$

$$= -i\omega \sum_{n=0}^{\infty} \exp\left\{\frac{2n\pi i\omega}{\Omega}\right\} \int_0^{(2\pi)/\Omega} dt \, \exp\left\{i\omega t\right.$$
$$\left. -\frac{v}{\Omega^2}(1 - \cos \Omega t)\right\}$$

$$= \frac{-i\omega}{1 - \exp\{(2\pi i\omega)/\Omega\}} \int_0^{(2\pi)/\Omega} dt \, \exp\left\{i\omega t\right.$$
$$\left. -\frac{v}{\Omega^2}(1 - \cos \Omega t)\right\} \quad (6.63)$$

which is again valid in the entire complex ω plane. That is, for the case $\theta = \pi/2$, the term after the last equality in eq. (6.63) represents a function analytic in the entire complex ω plane except for simple poles at the points $\omega = \pm\Omega, \pm 2\Omega \cdots$. Therefore, the roots of eq. (6.62) or of eq. (6.63) (if it applies) will yield the characteristic frequencies and decay constants for the plasma in a magnetic field for all values of θ.

In the problems it is shown, by using methods very similar to those employed for the case of no magnetic field, that there are no roots of this dispersion relation in the upper half plane. Thus, the remaining problem confronting us deals with obtaining the roots of this dispersion relation on the real axis and in the lower half plane.

Let us first examine again the special case $\theta = \pi/2$. By means of a simple change of dummy variable, the dispersion relation in eq. (6.63) may be written

$$1 + \frac{v}{\omega_p^2} = \frac{i\frac{\omega}{\Omega} \exp\{-(v/\Omega^2)\}}{\exp\{(2\pi i\omega)/\Omega\} - 1} \int_0^{2\pi} dt \, \exp\left\{\frac{i\omega}{\Omega}t + \frac{v}{\Omega^2} \cos t\right\} (6.64)$$

On making use of the well-known result*

---

* See, for example, E. T. Whittaker and G. N. Watson, *A Course of Modern Analysis*, New York: Cambridge University Press, 1950 p. 372.

$$\exp\left\{\frac{v}{\Omega^2}\cos t\right\} = \sum_{n=-\infty}^{\infty} I_n\left(\frac{v}{\Omega^2}\right) e^{int} \tag{6.65}$$

where $I_n(x)$ is the Bessel function of imaginary argument and has the series expansion

$$I_n(x) = \sum_{l=0}^{\infty} \frac{(x/2)^{2l+|n|}}{l!(|n|+l)!} \tag{6.66}$$

eq. (6.64) may be cast into the forms

$$1 + \frac{v}{\omega_p^2} = \frac{i(\omega/\Omega)\exp\{-(v/\Omega^2)\}}{\exp\{(2\pi i\omega)/\Omega\}-1} \sum_{n=-\infty}^{\infty} I_n\left(\frac{v}{\Omega^2}\right)\int_0^{2\pi} dt\, e^{it(\omega/\Omega+n)}$$

$$= \frac{\omega}{\Omega}\exp\left\{-\frac{v}{\Omega^2}\right\} \sum_{n=-\infty}^{\infty} I_n\left(\frac{v}{\Omega^2}\right)\frac{1}{n+\omega/\Omega}$$

$$= I_0\left(\frac{v}{\Omega^2}\right)\exp\left\{-\frac{v}{\Omega^2}\right\}$$

$$+ 2\exp\left\{-\frac{v}{\Omega^2}\right\}\sum_{n=1}^{\infty} \frac{(\omega/\Omega)^2 I_n(v/\Omega^2)}{(\omega/\Omega)^2 - n^2} \tag{6.67}$$

The last equality shows that the right-hand side is an even function of ω and therefore the real part of the right-hand side is also an even function of $Im(\omega)$ while the imaginary part is an odd function of $Im(\omega)$. Furthermore, since we know that there are no roots in the upper half of the ω plane, it follows that there will be none in the lower half plane either and thus for the case $\theta = \pi/2$ all roots must be on the real ω axis.

For a fixed value of v/Ω^2, the real roots of eq. (6.64) may be obtained numerically in the following way. A plot is made of the terms after the last equality in eq. (6.67) as a function of ω/Ω. The intersections of this plot with a straight horizontal line a distance $1+v/\omega_p^2$ above the axis will produce these roots. An approximate plot for the case $v = \Omega^2$ is given in Figure 6.3. It is to be noted from this graph that there are no roots for values of ω/Ω less than one, but above this value there are an infinite number of such roots, which for large values of ω/Ω are separated by integers. Thus we see that for the two extreme cases—namely, $\theta = 0$ and $\theta = \pi/2$—the modes of oscillation can be either reduced to the case of no magnetic field or else can be analyzed in a straightforward way. Let us finally then briefly examine the case for a general value of θ.

We shall consider first the situation for which the magnetic field is weak

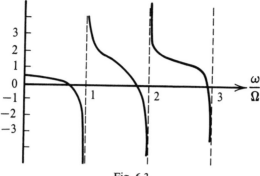

Fig. 6.3

and assume that we are interested in the long wavelength limit. Expanding the exponential in eq. (6.63) in a power series in Ω and v, there results

$$1 + \frac{v}{\omega_p^2} \cong - i\omega \int_0^\infty dt\, e^{i\omega t} \exp\left\{ -\frac{v}{2}t^2 \cos^2 \theta \right.$$

$$\left. - \frac{v}{\Omega^2}\left(\frac{1}{2}\Omega^2 t^2 - \frac{1}{24}\Omega^4 t^4 \right) \sin^2 \theta \right\}$$

$$\cong - i\omega \int_0^\infty dt\, e^{i\omega t} \left[1 - \frac{v}{2}t^2 + \frac{\Omega^2}{24}vt^4 \sin^2 \theta + \frac{1}{8}vt^4 \right]$$

$$= 1 + \frac{v}{\omega^2} + \frac{1}{\omega^4}(3v^2 + v\Omega^2 \sin^2 \theta) \tag{6.68}$$

where the last equality follows if we assume that ω has a small positive imaginary part. To lowest order in v and Ω the solution of eq. (6.68) is easily found to be given by

$$\omega^2 \cong \omega_p^2 + 3v + \Omega^2 \sin^2 \theta \tag{6.69}$$

And for the special cases $\theta = 0$, or $\Omega = 0$, this reduces to the previously obtained result in eq. (6.38). In an analogous way, the presumed small and negative imaginary part of ω can also be obtained from eq. (6.68). This time, unfortunately, we cannot simply expand the t^2-dependent exponential completely, for in this event the integral will not converge. Nevertheless, this integral may be evaluated to lowest order in v and Ω and for the imaginary part of ω we would obtain the result

$$\omega_i = -\left(\frac{\pi}{8}\right)^{1/2} \omega_p \left(\frac{\omega_p}{ku}\right)^3 \exp\left\{ -\frac{\omega_p^2}{2v} \right\}\left[1 + \frac{1}{24}\sin^2 \theta \frac{\omega_p^4 \Omega^2}{v^3} \right] \tag{6.70}$$

which for the special cases of vanishing magnetic field and $\theta = 0$ reproduces the Landau result. We know that for $\mathbf{k}$ perpendicular to $\mathbf{B}_0$ the damping should vanish, however, and this feature is not borne out by eq. (6.70). Thus as noted in the vanishing magnetic-field case, the assumption that k or v is an effective expansion parameter is seriously to be questioned and here we see a case for which this assumption leads to an incorrect result.

Similarly, for the case of small wave number but very large Ω, an approximate evaluation of eq. (6.62) can be carried out. This time we approximate the factor $\cos \Omega t$ in the integrand by its average value of zero and then proceed as in eq. (6.68). The results may be expressed by the formulas:

$$\omega^2 \cong \omega_p^2 \cos^2 \theta \left[1 + \frac{3v}{\omega_p^2} - \frac{\omega_p^2}{\Omega^2} \sin^2 \theta \right]$$

$$\omega_i \cong -\left(\frac{\pi}{8}\right)^{\frac{1}{2}} \omega_p \left(\frac{\omega_p}{ku}\right)^3 \exp\left\{ -\frac{\omega_p^2}{2v} \right\} \cos \theta \tag{6.71}$$

which for the special cases $\theta = 0$ and $\pi/2$ now reduce to the expected results.

Suggested Readings and References

I. B. Bernstein, "Waves in a Plasma in a Magnetic Field," *Phys. Rev.*, **109** 10 (1950).

J. D. Jackson, "Plasma Oscillations," *J. Nuclear Energy*, Part C. 1, 141 (1960).

A. Simon, "Collisionless Boltzmann Equation", contained in "International Summer Course in Plasma Physics, 1960" *Risö Report N*, 18 (Danish Atomic Energy Commission at Risö), November, 1960.

T. H. Stix, *The Theory of Plasma Waves*. New York: McGraw-Hill Book Co., Inc., 1962.

Problems

1. Make use of eq. (4.143) in order to calculate the quantity

$$\sum_{i,j} k_i \kappa_{\omega ij} k_j$$

and show that if ω satisfies the dispersion relation in eq. (4.127), then this quantity vanishes. Give a physical interpretation of this result.

2. Repeat Problem 1 for the case that a uniform magnetic field $\mathbf{B}_0$ exists in the plasma.

3. The result in eq. (6.19) is valid only for the case that the zeroes in $H(\omega)$ are simple. If the unperturbed distribution function is a

Gaussian, show in detail that the roots are simple. *Hint:* Use the representation of Problem 6, Chapter 4 and show that if $H'(\omega_0)$ vanishes, then $H(\omega_0)$ does not.

4. Show that the transverse oscillations satisfy the dispersion relation $H(\omega)=0$ where $H(\omega)$ is given by

$$
H(\omega) =
\begin{cases}
\omega^2 - k^2c^2 + \dfrac{\omega\omega_p^2}{k} \displaystyle\int_{-\infty}^{\infty} \dfrac{dv f_0(v)}{v - \omega/k} & ; \ Im(\omega) > 0 \\[3ex]
\omega^2 - k^2c^2 + \dfrac{\omega\omega_p^2}{k} \displaystyle\int_{-\infty}^{\infty} \dfrac{dv f_0(v)}{v - \omega/k} - \dfrac{2\pi i \omega\omega_p^2}{k} f_0\!\left(\dfrac{\omega}{k}\right); \\[2ex]
\hspace{8cm} Im(\omega) < 0
\end{cases}
$$

5. Use the result in Problem 4 to calculate the real and imaginary parts of the transverse dispersion relation in the long-wavelength limit.

6. Show for the case that $f_0(v)$ is Maxwellian, that for $k \neq 0$, $H(\omega)$ in Problem 4 may be cast into the form

$$
H(\omega) = \omega^2 - k^2c^2 - i\omega\omega_p^2 \int_0^{\infty} dt\, e^{i\omega t} \exp\left\{ -\tfrac{1}{2}k^2u^2t^2 \right\}
$$

where u is the thermal velocity. Verify this formula for both positive and negative values for the imaginary part of ω.

7. Verify the fact that for a Maxwellian distribution the result in eq. (6.26) is identical to that in Problem 6, Chapter 4.

8. Show that for $k = 0$, all values of ω satisfy the dispersion relation for the longitudinal modes of oscillation. What is the physical significance of zero wave number? Interpret the above result in the light of your explanation.

9. Show that $g_\omega(\mathbf{k}, \mathbf{v})$ as given by eq. (6.52) satisfies eq. (6.51) and is periodic in the variable ϕ with a period of 2π.

10. For the case $\theta = 0$, take the cross product of eq. (6.57) with $\mathbf{k}$ and thus derive the dispersion relation for the transverse oscillations in a magnetic field. Assuming that the unperturbed distribution function is Maxwellian, carry out three of the four integrals in this dispersion relation.

11. Starting with eq. (6.61) carry out the integrals for the case that $f_0(v)$ is Maxwellian and thus derive the equivalent form in eq. (6.62).

12. Assuming that

$$f_0(\mathbf{v}) = \delta(\mathbf{v} - \mathbf{v}_0)$$

carry out all integrals in the dispersion relation in eq. (6.61) and thus reduce it to an algebraic one. Find explicit formulas for the roots in the long-wavelength limit for the special cases that $\mathbf{v}_0$ is parallel to and perpendicular to the magnetic field.

13. Work out the detailed derivations of eqs. (6.69), (6.70) and (6.71).

14. (a) For the case that the equilibrium distribution function is Maxwellian, show that if there is no magnetic field present, then the dispersion relation for the longitudinal modes of oscillation may be written

$$1 + \frac{v}{\omega_p^2} = -i\omega A(\omega)$$

where $v = k^2 u^2$ and $A(\omega)$ satisfies the differential equation

$$\frac{dA}{d\omega} + \frac{\omega}{v} A = \frac{i}{v}$$

(b) Show that $A(0) = \left(\dfrac{\pi}{2v}\right)^{1/2}$

(c) Solve this differential equation and thus show that this dispersion relation may be written

$$1 + \frac{v}{\omega_p^2} = -i\omega \left(\frac{\pi}{2v}\right)^{1/2} \exp\left\{-\frac{\omega^2}{2v}\right\}\left[1 + i\left(\frac{2}{\pi v}\right)^{1/2}\int_0^\omega dx \exp\left\{\frac{x^2}{2v}\right\}\right]$$

Note: The integral appearing in this equation is known as an error function of complex argument and can be evaluated by existing tables. See, for example, V. N. Faddeyeva and M. N. Terentor, *Tables of Values of the Function*

$$w(z) = 1 + \frac{2i}{\pi^{1/2}}e^{-z^2}\int_0^z dt \exp\{t^2\}$$

New York: Pergamon Press, Inc., 1961.

15. In analogy to the method in Problem 12, show that the transverse oscillations satisfy the dispersion relation

$$\omega^2 - k^2 c^2 = -i\omega\omega_p^2\left(\frac{\pi}{2v}\right)^{1/2}\exp\left\{-\frac{\omega^2}{2v}\right\}\left[1 + i\left(\frac{2}{\pi v}\right)^{1/2}\int_0^\omega dx \exp\left\{\frac{x^2}{2v}\right\}\right]$$

INDEX